UCI

UNIVERSITY OF CALIFORNIA, IRVINE

FUNCTIONAL ANALYSIS

Proceedings of a Conference held at the University of California, Irvine

Edited by

BERNARD R. GELBAUM

Department of Mathematics
University of California, Irvine

1967

Thompson Book Company
Washington, D.C.

Academic Press
London

THOMPSON BOOK COMPANY
383 National Press Building
Washington, D.C. 20004

Library of Congress Catalog Number: 67-31437

Printed in the United States of America

Introduction

This volume contains sixteen papers presented during the period March 28 through April 1, 1966 at the Conference on Functional Analysis at the University of California, Irvine. The Conference was sponsored by the Air Force Office of Scientific Research under Contract No. AF-AFOSR-998-66. Acknowledgement is made and gratitude is expressed to Dr. Robert Pohrer and to the sponsor for the support and encouragement that were essential to the success of this Conference.

The papers have been grouped into three sections:

I Linear Spaces
II Operators
III Banach Algebras

Unfortunately and regrettably, two of the papers presented at the Conference are not included here because the authors were unable to submit the manuscripts in time for publication. The papers in question are:

- Singular Measures on Locally Compact Abelian Groups by Edwin Hewitt
- Probabilistic Methods in Functional Analysis by Shizuo Kakutani

It is hoped that the publication of this research will serve to orient an interested fraction of the mathematical community with respect to a significant part of the work presently being pursued in the domain of Functional Analysis.

BERNARD R. GELBAUM
Department of Mathematics
University of California, Irvine

Contents

PART I Linear Spaces

PART II Operators

PART III Banach Algebras

I

LINEAR SPACES

Integral Representations of Continuous Linear Mappings on BV

GREGERS KRABBE

Let u be a linear mapping on the space BV (consisting of all left-continuous functions of bounded variation on an interval $[a, b]$): we shall describe several equivalent conditions implying that the mapping u has a natural representation in terms of a Stieltjes integral (that is, there exists a function F such that ug is the Stieltjes integral of g with respect to F, for all g in BV). Although such a natural representation is not possible if it is required only that u be continuous on the Banach space BV (cf. the comments on p. 393 of [**5**]), it can be achieved by requiring, for example, that u be continuous on a certain topologization of BV (see 1.6).

Let G denote the family of all functions g in BV such that $|g(a)| + \operatorname{var} g \leq 1$ (where var = total variation on the interval $[a, b]$). Definition: a G_0-net is a generalized sequence in G that converges pointwise to the constant zero. Theorem: any linear mapping on BV has the form

$$g \to \int g dF \tag{1}$$

if (and only if) it transforms G_0-nets into bounded nets that converge to $\mathbf{o}$. Let $\mathfrak{F}$ be the space of all right-continuous, simply discontinuous functions F such that $F(a) = \mathbf{o} = F(a+)$ and $F(b-) = F(b)$; if $F \in \mathfrak{F}$, then the mapping (1) is Helly-type (i.e., it transforms G_0-nets into bounded nets that converge to $\mathbf{o}$). Conversely, if u is a Helly-type mapping on BV, then there exists a function F in $\mathfrak{F}$ such that

$$ug = \int g dF \qquad \text{(for all } g \text{ in BV).}$$

T. H. Hildebrandt, in a paper [8] to appear soon in the Proceedings, has proved an analogous result. The σ (BV,$\mathfrak{F}$) topology makes BV into a locally convex Hausdorff space on which the most general continuous linear functional has the form (1) for some F in $\mathfrak{F}$: more generally, a linear mapping on the locally convex space BV is continuous if (and only

This research was supported by National Science Foundation grant GP-1665.

if) it is Helly-type. A Helly-type linear functional necessarily belongs to the norm-dual of the Banach space **BV**, but the converse is false.

The chief aim of this paper is a continuous-extension property for mappings on polynomials (see 1.11): in contrast with the case where **BV** is considered as a Banach space, polynomials are dense in the locally convex Hausdorff space **BV**. Instead of limiting ourselves to functionals, we shall consider mappings of **BV** into an arbitrary quasi-complete locally convex Hausdorff space; for example, the Fourier transformation is a Helly-type mapping into the space l_p (see 8.3). For a classical example involving a range space that is not a Banach space, see 8.7. The case where the mappings are into a C*-algebra of operators is of special importance for applications to spectral analysis; as I plan to show in a subsequent paper, all homomorphisms of the locally convex algebra **BV** are Helly-type.

1. INTRODUCTION

Throughout, $\mathfrak{A}$ is a quasicomplete locally convex Hausdorff space (i.e., every bounded Cauchy net in $\mathfrak{A}$ converges in $\mathfrak{A}$); also, we fix an interval $[a, b]$ such that $-\infty \leq a < b \leq \infty$.

1.1 DEFINITION. Let $\mathfrak{F}$ be the family of all mappings F of the interval $[a, b]$ into $\mathfrak{A}$ that satisfy the following four conditions:

$$F(a) = F(a+) = \mathbf{o} \qquad (= \text{the zero-element of } \mathfrak{A})$$
$$F(b-) = F(b)$$
$$F(t) = F(t+) \qquad (\text{for } a < t < b)$$
$$F(t-) \text{ exists} \qquad (\text{for } a < t < b).$$

1.2 Let **BV** be the family of all left-continuous functions of bounded variation on the interval $[a, b]$. We shall define in 7.7 a topologization V_b of **BV** with the following property: a net $\{g_s, s\}$ in **BV** converges in V_b if (and only if)

$$\int g\,dF = \lim_s \int g_s\,dF \qquad (\text{all } F \text{ in } \mathfrak{F}).$$

The space V_b is locally convex and Hausdorff—if we disregard the values of the functions at the end-points a, b. Furthermore, if u is a continuous linear mapping of V_b into $\mathfrak{A}$, then there exists one—and only one—function F in $\mathfrak{F}$ such that the refinement integral exists and equals ug:

$$ug = \int g\,dF \qquad (\text{for all } g \text{ in } \mathbf{BV}).$$

1.3. Suppose that $F \in \mathfrak{F}$. The refinement integral $\int g dF$ exists for all g in BV, and

$$F(\theta) = \int \chi(a, \theta] dF \qquad (\text{for } a \leq \theta \leq b),$$

where $\chi(a, \theta]$ is the characteristic function of the interval $(a, \theta] \cap (a, b)$. Moreover, the mapping u^F:

$$g \rightarrow \int g dF$$

that maps BV into $\mathcal{A}$ and belongs to $\mathcal{L}[V_b:\mathcal{A}]$ (= that of all continuous linear mappings of V_b into $\mathcal{A}$). Finally, the transformation $F \rightarrow u^F$ is a bijection (one-to-one) of $\mathfrak{F}$ onto $\mathcal{L}[V_b:\mathcal{A}]$ (see 7.6).

1.4 Let V_0 be the Banach space obtained by endowing BV with the topology determined by the norm

$$g \rightarrow \| g \|_0 = | g(a) | + \operatorname{var} g,$$

where var = total variation on the interval $[a, b]$; we have

$$\mathcal{L}[V_b:\mathcal{A}] \subset \mathcal{L}[V_0:\mathcal{A}].$$

1.5. A net $\{g_s, s\}$ is called a "G_0-net" if $\|g_s\|_0 \leq 1$ and

$$0 = \lim_s g_s(\tau) \qquad (\text{for all } \tau \text{ in } (a, b)).$$

Let $\mathcal{H}$ be the family of all linear mappings of BV into $\mathcal{A}$ that transform G_0-nets into bounded nets which converge to zero. Thus, $u \in \mathcal{H}$ if (and only if) the net $\{ug_s, s\}$ is bounded in $\mathcal{A}$ and converges to $\mathbf{o}$ whenever $\{g_s, s\}$ is a G_0-net. The family $\mathcal{H}$ consists of all the continuous linear mappings of the Banach space V_0 (into $\mathcal{A}$) such that

$$\mathbf{o} = \lim_s ug_s \qquad (\mathcal{A}\text{-convergence})$$

whenever $\{g_s, s\}$ is a G_0-net (see 7.3).

1.6. THEOREM (7.3 + 7.14): is precisely the family of all continuous linear mappings of the topological space V_b into $\mathcal{A}$:

$$\mathcal{H} = \mathcal{L}[V_b:\mathcal{A}].$$

1.7. EXAMPLE. Let M be a Hausdorff barreled space, and let $\mathcal{L}[M:\mathfrak{N}]$ be the family of all continuous linear mappings of M into a complete locally convex Hausdorff space $\mathfrak{N}$: if $\mathcal{A}$ denotes the result of endowing $\mathcal{L}[M:\mathfrak{N}]$ with the topology of pointwise convergence (on M), then $\mathcal{A}$ is a quasicomplete locally convex Hausdorff space (see 2.10). In case $M = \mathfrak{N}$ is a Hilbert space, any self-adjoint operator in M gives rise to a family $\{E_\lambda: \lambda\}$ of orthogonal projections: it follows from [14, pp. 345–

349] the existence of an interval $[a, b]$ such that the function

$$[a, b] \ni \lambda \to E_\lambda$$

belongs to $\mathfrak{F}$.

1.8. Let Z be the family of all subdivisions of the interval $[a, b]$. When $z = \{z_k: 0 \leq k \leq N + 1\}$ belongs to Z, denote by $\bar{z}_k$ the midpoint of the interval $[z_k, z_{k+1}]$. When $g \in$ BV and $F \in \mathfrak{F}$ we set

$$\langle g, F\rangle_z = \sum_{k=0}^{N} g(\bar{z}_k)\{F(\bar{z}_{k+1}) - F(z_k)\}.$$

1.9. THEOREM (7.5). If $g \in$ BV and $F \in \mathfrak{F}$, then the net

$$\{\langle g, F\rangle_z, \quad z \in Z, \quad \supset\}$$

is bounded in $\mathfrak{A}$ and converges to $\int g dF$.

1.10. The symbol $\supset$ is used above to indicate the refinement relation: a subdivision z is a refinement of a subdivision $w \Longleftrightarrow z \supset w \Longleftrightarrow$ all the points of w belong to z. Henceforth, the interval $[a, b]$ is supposed to be finite. The family P (= the set of all polynomials) is a dense subset of the topological space V_b: let P_b be the result of endowing P with the topology of V_b.

1.11. EXTENSION THEOREM (9.3). If $u \in \mathfrak{L}\,[P_b: \mathfrak{A}]$ there is one—and only one—element $\bar{u}$ of $\mathfrak{L}\,[V_b: \mathfrak{A}]$ such that $\bar{u}p = up$ for all p in P.

1.12. UNIQUENESS THEOREM (9.2). If u_1 and u_2 belong to $\mathfrak{L}\,[V_b: \mathfrak{A}]$, then $u_1 = u_2$ whenever $u_1 p = u_2 p$ for all p in P.

1.13. These two theorems are the main motivation for topologizing BV; note that the range space need not be complete. The above results are all found in Part II. Part I contains preparatory material on locally convex spaces (§2), two fairly routine approximation theorems for BV (§3); the easy half of the representation theorem is given in §4 ("Helly-type mappings"), the space of integrators is studied in §5, and the existence of the integral is finally established in §6. Part II consists of §7 ("The topological space V_b"), §8 ("Applications), and §9 ("Approximation by polynomials").

PART I

2. THE RANGE SPACE

2.1. NOTATION. A locally convex space is a linear topological space whose family of convex neighborhoods of zero forms a local base.

If E is a locally convex space, there exists a family E^* of seminorms determining the topology of E. A net $\{e_s, s \in S, \succ\}$ in E is *bounded* if (and only if)

$$\infty \neq \sup_{s \in S} e^*[e_s] \qquad \text{(for all } e^* \text{ in } E^*\text{)}.$$

Suppose that $e \in E$, as in [10, pp. 66–68], we say that the net $\{e_s, s \in S, \succ\}$ *converges* to e if (and only if)

$$0 = \lim \{e^*[e_s - e], s \in S, \succ\} \qquad \text{(all } e^* \text{ in } E^*\text{)}. \tag{2}$$

If E is a Hausdorff space, we write

$$e = \lim\{e_s, s \in S, \succ\} \qquad (E\text{-convergence}) \tag{3}$$

if (and only if) relation (2) obtains. Both (2) and (3) are often abbreviated as follows:

(i)
$$0 = \lim_s e^*[e_s - e] \qquad \text{(all } e^* \in E^*\text{)},$$

and

$$e = \lim_s e_s \qquad (E\text{-convergence}).$$

The net $\{e_s, s\}$ is said to *converge in E* if relation (i) is satisfied for some e in E.

2.3. Let E be a locally convex space: a sequence that converges in E is necessarily a bounded net. Indeed, let S be the directed set of all positive integers, and observe that (i) implies the existence of a number $n \in S$ such that $e^*[e_s - e] \leq 1$ for all $s > n$, whence

$$\sup_s e^*[e_s] \leq 1 + e^*[e] + \max_{1 \leq s \leq n} e^*[e_s] \qquad \text{(all } e^* \in E^*\text{)}.$$

2.4 Let X and $\mathfrak{A}$ be locally convex spaces, and let X^* (respectively, $\mathfrak{A}^*$) be a family of seminorms determining the topology of X (respectively, $\mathfrak{A}$). Further let $[X^*]$ denote the family of all positive multiples of finite sums of elements of X^*; thus, $p \in [X^*]$ if (and only if) there is a number $C > 0$ and a finite subset $\{x_i^* : i\}$ of X^* such that

$$p[x] = C \sum_i x_i^*[x] \qquad \text{(all } x \in X\text{)}.$$

Let u be a mapping $x \to ux$ of X into $\mathfrak{A}$; if $K = \{K_r : r \in \mathfrak{A}^*\}$ is a subfamily of $[X^*]$ such that

(ii$_1$)
$$r[ux] \leq K_r[x] \qquad \text{(all } r \in \mathfrak{A}^*, x \in X\text{)},$$

then we call K a *majorant* of u. Let us verify the following fact: if u is a linear mapping of X into $\mathfrak{A}$, then *u is continuous if (and only if) it has a* *majorant*. To that effect, we begin by supposing that u belongs to the family $\mathcal{L}\,[X:\mathfrak{A}]$ of all continuous linear mappings of X into $\mathfrak{A}$: the existence of a majorant follows easily from [4, p. 6]; next, (ii_1) implies that

$$(\mathbf{ii}_2) \qquad 0 = \lim_s r[ux_s] \qquad (\text{all } r \in \mathfrak{A}^*)$$

for any net $\{x_s, s\}$ in X which converges to $\mathbf{o}$: therefore, the net $\{ux_s, s\}$ converges to $\mathbf{o}$ for every such net. The verification is now completed by noting that (ii_2) implies $u \in \mathcal{L}\,[X:\mathfrak{A}]$ (see [10, p. 86] and [11, p. 37]). Thus, u has a majorant if (and only if)

$$(\mathbf{ii}_3) \qquad u \in \mathcal{L}\,[X:\mathfrak{A}].$$

2.5. LEMMA. Let $\{x_s: s\}$ be a bounded subset of X; if (ii_3), then $\{ux_s: s\}$ is a bounded subset of $\mathfrak{A}$.

Proof. Almost immediate. See also Corollaire 2 in [3, p. 7].

2.6. In particular, if $\{x_s, s\}$ is a bounded net in X and if $u \in \mathcal{L}\,[X:\mathfrak{A}]$, then u transforms the net $\{x_s, s\}$ into the bounded net $\{ux_s, s\}$.

2.7. DEFINITION. A locally convex space is called a *QC*-space if it is a Hausdorff space such that every bounded Cauchy net converges in it.

2.8. EXTENSION THEOREM A. Let D be a linear subset of a locally convex space X, and suppose that every x in X is the limit of a bounded net in D. If $\mu \in \mathcal{L}[D:\mathfrak{A}]$ and if $\mathfrak{A}$ is a *QC*-space, then there is an extension $\bar{\mu}$ of μ such that $\bar{\mu} \in \mathcal{L}[X:\mathfrak{A}]$; further, if K is a majorant of μ, then

$$r[\bar{\mu}x] \leq K_r[x] \qquad (\text{all } r \in \mathfrak{A}^*, x \in X). \tag{4}$$

Proof. Again, $\mathfrak{A}^*$ is a family of seminorms determining the topology of $\mathfrak{A}$. It is understood that D is endowed with the topology induced on it by X. By hypothesis, every x in X is the limit of a bounded net $\{d_s, s\}$ in D; therefore, $\{d_s, s\}$ is a Cauchy net [11, p. 56], whence the continuity of μ implies that the net $\{\mu d_s, s\}$ is also a Cauchy net [11, p. 56]: since $\{d_s, s\}$ is a bounded net, the net $\{\mu d_s, s\}$ is a bounded Cauchy net in $\mathfrak{A}$ (from 2.6). The *QC*-property now implies that the bounded Cauchy net $\{\mu d_s, s\}$ converges in $\mathfrak{A}$; that is, there exists some element $\bar{\mu}(x)$ of $\mathfrak{A}$ such that

$$\bar{\mu}(x) = \lim_s \mu d_s \qquad (\mathfrak{A}\text{-convergence}). \tag{5}$$

Let $E(\mu, x)$ be the family of all such elements $\bar{\mu}(x)$ of $\mathfrak{A}$; that is, $E(\mu, x)$ consists of all $A \in \mathfrak{A}$ such that $A = \lim_s \mu x_s$ for some bounded net $\{x_s, s\}$ in D which converges to x. From the linearity of μ it is easily seen that the family $E(\mu, x)$ contains only one element, again denoted by $\bar{\mu}(x)$. Let $\bar{\mu}$ be the mapping

$$X \ni x \to \bar{\mu}(x);$$

since $\bar{\mu}(d) = \mu d$ when $d \in D$, the mapping $\bar{\mu}$ is an extension of μ which maps X into $\mathcal{Q}$. It is easily verified that $\bar{\mu}$ is linear; we shall now verify (4) (in view of 2.4, this will establish the fact that $\bar{\mu} \in \mathcal{L}[X:\mathcal{Q}]$). By hypothesis, K is a subfamily $\{K_r: r \in \mathcal{Q}^*\}$ of $[X^*]$ such that

$$r[\mu d] \leq K_r[d] \qquad (\text{all } r \in \mathcal{Q}^*, d \in D). \tag{6}$$

Take any $r \in \mathcal{Q}^*$ and any $x \in X$; there exists a bounded net $\{d_s, s\}$ converging to x. Since $K_r \in [X^*]$, we have

$$0 = \lim_s K_r[x - d_s]. \tag{7}$$

On the other hand, $\bar{\mu}(d_s) = \mu d_s$ (since $d_s \in D$), whence

$$r[\bar{\mu}x] \leq r[\bar{\mu}(x) - \mu d_s] + r[\mu d_s]. \tag{8}$$

Combining (8) with (6), we get

$$r[\bar{\mu}x] \leq r[\bar{\mu}(x) - \mu d_s] + K_r[d_s - x] + K_r[x]; \tag{9}$$

but $0 = \lim_s r[\bar{\mu}(x) - \mu d_s]$ (this comes from (5)), whence the conclusion (4) can now be obtained by taking limits of both sides of (9) and using (7).

2.9. THEOREM B. Let M be a Hausdorff barreled space, and let $\mathfrak{N}$ be a QC-space: if $\mathcal{Q}$ is the result of endowing $\mathcal{L}[M:\mathfrak{N}]$ with the topology of simple convergence, then $\mathcal{Q}$ is a QC-space.

2.10. In particular, $\mathcal{Q}$ is a QC-space when $\mathfrak{N}$ is a complete locally convex Hausdorff space. Theorem B can be derived from Corollary 2 in [3, p. 31]; it can also be obtained in the manner described in 2.11. Let $\mathfrak{N}^*$ be a family of seminorms determining the topology of $\mathfrak{N}$; the space $\mathcal{Q} = \mathcal{L}[M:\mathfrak{N}]$ is endowed with the topology determined by the seminorms

$$\mathcal{Q} \ni A \to N^*[\mathrm{A}m],$$

where $N^* \in \mathfrak{N}^*$ and $m \in M$. The following two statements are equivalent:

$$B = \lim_s A_s \qquad (\mathcal{Q}\text{-convergence}) \tag{10}$$

$$Bm = \lim_s A_s m \qquad (\mathfrak{N}\text{-convergence, all } m \in M). \tag{11}$$

2.11. *Proof of 2.9.* Let $\{A_s, s\}$ be a bounded Cauchy net in $\mathcal{Q}$: we must prove that it converges in $\mathcal{Q}$. To that effect, take any m in M: it follows from 2.10 that the net $\{A_s m, s\}$ is a Cauchy net in $\mathfrak{N}$ such that

$$\infty \neq \sup_s N^*[A_s m] \qquad (\text{all } N^* \in \mathfrak{N}^*). \tag{12}$$

Thus, $\{A_s m, s\}$ is a bounded Cauchy net in the QC-space $\mathfrak{N}$, whence definition 2.7 implies the existence of an element $B(m)$ of $\mathfrak{N}$ such that

$$B(m) = \lim_s A_s m \qquad (\mathfrak{N}\text{-convergence}). \tag{13}$$

This holds for all $m \in M$, whence the mapping B defined by

$$M \ni m \to \lim_s A_s m$$

belongs to $\mathfrak{L}\,[M:\mathfrak{N}\,]$ because of what is called the Banach-Steinhaus theorem in [3, p. 27]. Thus, $B \in \mathfrak{A}$; since (13) holds for all m in M, it follows from (10)-(11) that the bounded net $\{A_s, s\}$ converges to the element B of $\mathfrak{A}$. This concludes the proof.

3. THE SPACE OF INTEGRANDS

3.1. Let BV be the family of all left-continuous functions of bounded variation on an interval $[a, b]$ such that $-\infty \le a < b \le \infty$. Thus, if $g \in$ BV, then

$$g(\tau) = g(\tau-) \qquad (\text{for } a < \tau < b). \tag{1}$$

We write

$$\|g\|_0 = |g(a)| + \operatorname{var} g, \tag{2}$$

where var = total variation on $[a, b]$. Note that

$$|g(\lambda)| \le \|g\|_0 \qquad (\text{if } a \le \lambda \le b). \tag{3}$$

To verify (3), observe that

$$|g(\lambda)| \le |g(\lambda) - g(a)| + |g(a)|,$$

whence conclusion (3) now comes from the fact that

$$|g(\lambda) - g(a)| \le |g(\lambda) - g(a)| + |g(b) - g(a)|.$$

3.2. SUBDIVISIONS. Let Z be the family of all finite sets $z = \{z_k: 0 \le k \le N + 1\}$ such that

$$a = z_0 < z_1 < z_2 < \cdots < z_N < z_{N+1} = b,$$

and let $X(z)$ be the family of all sets $x = \{x_k: 0 \le k \le N\}$ such that

$$z_k \le x_k \le z_{k+1} \qquad (\text{all } k = 0, 1, \ldots, N). \tag{4}$$

When $w = \{w_i: 0 \le i \le I + 1\}$ belongs to Z, then $z \supset w$ if (and only if) every interval $[z_k, z_{k+1}]$ is contained in some interval $[w_i, w_{i+1}]$. The relation $\supset$ directs the set Z.

Further, let π be the family of all pairs (x, z) such that $z \in Z$ and $x \in X(z)$; thus, $(x, z) \in \pi$ whenever

$$a = z_0 \leq x_0 \leq z_1 \leq \cdots \leq z_N \leq x_N \leq z_{N+1} = b.$$

The set π is directed by the "refinement" relation $\gg$, which is defined as follows:

$$(x, z) \gg (y, w) \quad \text{if and only if} \quad z \supset w.$$

3.3. THE INTEGRAL. Suppose that $g \in \mathrm{BV}$. If F is a mapping of $[a, b]$ into some topological space, the refinement integral is defined as follows:

$$\int g dF = \lim\{g^F(x, z), (x, z) \in \pi, \gg\}, \tag{5}$$

where

$$g^F(x, z) = \sum_{k=0}^{N} g(x_k)\{F(z_{k+1}) - F(z_k)\}. \tag{6}$$

Thus, the integral (5) is a limit in the sense of successive subdivisions (or refinements)—such integrals are called σ-integrals in [8, 9]; it appears [6, p. 5] that they were first studied by S. O. Shatunovskiĭ.

3.4. ORIENTATION. The rest of this section deals with approximation by step-functions. If $g \in \mathrm{BV}$ and $(x, z) \in \pi$, let $g(x, z)$ be the function defined on $[a, b]$ by

$$g(x, z)(\tau) = \begin{cases} 0 & \text{if } \tau = a \\ g(x_k) & \text{if } z_k < \tau \leq z_{k+1} \quad (\text{for } 0 \leq k \leq N). \end{cases} \tag{7}$$

3.5. LEMMA. If $g \in \mathrm{BV}$ then

$$g(\tau) = \lim_{(x, z)} g(x, z)(\tau) \qquad (\text{all } \tau \in (a, b)), \tag{8}$$

where (x, z) runs over the directed set $(\pi, \gg)$ which was defined in 3.2.

Proof. Take any τ in the open interval (a, b) and $\epsilon > 0$: it is a question of finding an element w of Z such that

$$|g(\tau) - g(x, z)(\tau)| \leq \epsilon \qquad (\text{all } (x, z) \in \pi \text{ with } z \supset w). \tag{9}$$

From (1) it follows the existence of a $\delta > 0$ such that

$$|g(\tau) - g(\theta)| \leq \epsilon \qquad (\text{when } \tau - \delta \leq \theta \leq \tau). \tag{10}$$

Suppose that $(x, z) \in \pi$ and $z \supset \{a, \tau - \delta, \tau, b\} = w$; consequently, there exist two integers m and n such that

$$\tau - \delta = z_m \quad \text{and} \quad \tau = z_{n+1}. \tag{11}$$

Clearly, $z_m \leq z_n$ (otherwise $z_m \geq z_{n+1}$, whence (11) implies the contradiction $\tau - \delta \geq \tau$). Consequently,

$$\tau - \delta \leq z_n \leq x_n \leq z_{n+1} = \tau;$$

the last three inequalities are from (4). But (10) now implies that $|g(\tau) - g(x_n)| \leq \epsilon$, whence the conclusion (9) comes from definition (7) and $z_n < \tau = z_{n+1}$.

3.6. LEMMA. If $g \in \mathrm{BV}$ and $(x, z) \in \pi$, then

$$\| g(x, z) \|_0 \leq 2 \| g \|_0. \tag{12}$$

Proof. Set $h = g(x, z)$, and let var $h[\alpha, \beta]$ denote the total variation of h on the closed interval $[\alpha, \beta]$; thus, $\| h \|_0 =$ var $h[a, b]$. It is known [13, p. 220] that

$$\operatorname{var} h \leq \sum_{k=0}^{N} \operatorname{var} h[z_k, z_{k+1}]. \tag{13}$$

From definition (7) we see that $h(a) = 0$ and $h(\tau) = g(x_0)$ when $\tau \in (z_0, z_1]$; therefore,

$$\operatorname{var} h[z_0, z_1] \leq |g(x_0)| \leq \| g \|_0; \tag{14}$$

the second inequality is from 3.1(3). When $2 \leq n \leq N$, then (7) shows that $h(\tau) = g(x_{n-1})$ if $\tau = z_n$, while $h(\tau) = g(x_n)$ otherwise; consequently,

$$\operatorname{var} h[z_n, z_{n+1}] \leq |g(x_{n-1}) - g(x_n)| \qquad (\text{for } 2 \leq n \leq N),$$

whence the conclusion $\| h \|_0 \leq 2 \| g \|_0$ is now immediate from (13), (14), definition 3.1(2), and $h(a) = 0$.

4. HELLY-TYPE MAPPINGS

Throughout, $\mathfrak{A}$ is a QC-space (as in 2.7) and $\mathfrak{A}^*$ is a family of seminorms determining the topology of $\mathfrak{A}$.

4.1. Let V_0 be the Banach space obtained by adjoining to BV the norm $\| \cdot \|_0$ that was defined in 3.1. A subset $\{g_s: s\}$ of BV is *V_0-bounded* if (and only if) $\infty \neq \sup_s \| g_s \|_0$.

4.2. DEFINITIONS. A net in BV is called "*zero-approaching*" if it converges pointwise to the constant zero on the open interval (a, b); thus, a net $\{h_s, s\}$ is zero-approaching if (and only if)

$$0 = \lim_s h_s(\tau) \qquad (\text{for } a < \tau < b).$$

If $A_0 \in \mathcal{A}$ and if $\{A_s, s\}$ is a bounded net in $\mathcal{A}$ that converges (in $\mathcal{A}$) to A_0, then we write

$$A_0 = \lim_s A_s \qquad \text{(bounded } \mathcal{A}\text{-convergence)}, \tag{1}$$

and say that the net $\{A_s, s\}$ converges *boundedly* to A_0. A *Helly-type* mapping is a linear mapping of BV into $\mathcal{A}$ that transforms V_0-bounded zero-approaching nets into nets that converge boundedly to $\mathbf{o}$.

4.3. LEMMA. A linear mapping u of BV into $\mathcal{A}$ is Helly-type if (and only if)

$$ug_0 = \lim_s ug_s \qquad \text{(bounded } \mathcal{A}\text{-convergence)} \tag{2}$$

whenever $g_0 \in$ BV and $\{g_s, s\}$ is a V_0-bounded net in BV such that

$$g_0(\tau) = \lim_s g_s(\tau) \qquad (\text{all } \tau \in (a, b)). \tag{3}$$

Proof. Relation (2) is the conjunction of the following two properties:

$$\infty \neq \sup_s r[ug_s] \qquad (\text{all } r \in \mathcal{A}^*), \tag{4}$$

and

$$ug_0 = \lim_s ug_s \qquad (\mathcal{A}\text{-convergence}). \tag{5}$$

If (3) implies (2), the Helly-type property is immediate from definition 4.2. Conversely, let u be Helly-type, and let $\{g_s, s\}$ be an arbitrary V_0-bounded net satisfying (3): it is a question of proving (2). To that effect, set $h_s = g_0 - g_s$ and note that $\{h_s, s\}$ is a V_0-bounded zero-approaching net; since u is Helly-type, definition 4.2 implies that

$$\infty \neq \sup_s r[u(g_0 - g_s)] \qquad (\text{all } r \in \mathcal{A}^*)$$

and

$$\mathbf{o} = \lim_s u(g_0 - g_s) \qquad (\mathcal{A}\text{-convergence}).$$

Conclusion (2) now comes from the fact that u is a linear mapping.

4.4. NOTATION. If $S \subset [a, b]$, we denote by χS the characteristic function of the set $S \cap (a, b)$; thus,

$$\chi S(t) = \begin{cases} 1 & \text{if } t \in S \text{ and } a < t < b \\ 0 & \text{otherwise.} \end{cases}$$

In particular, if $a \leq \lambda < b$, then

$$\chi(\lambda, b] = \chi(\lambda, b). \tag{6}$$

4.5. THEOREM C. If u is Helly-type, there exists a right-continuous, simply discontinuous mapping F of $[a, b]$ into $\mathfrak{A}$ such that

(iii$_1$) $$F(a) = F(a+) = \mathbf{o}\,(= \text{zero-element of } \mathfrak{A}),$$

(iii$_2$) $$F(b-) = F(b)$$

and

$$ug = \lim_{(x,z)} g^F(x, z) \qquad (\text{bounded } \mathfrak{A}\text{-convergence}), \tag{7}$$

where (x, z) runs over the directed set $(\pi, \gg)$, as in 3.5. In fact,

$$F(\theta) = u\chi(a, \theta] \qquad (\text{for } a \le \theta \le b). \tag{8}$$

Proof. From 3.5, 3.6 and 4.3 it follows that

$$ug = \lim_{(x,z)} ug(x, z) \qquad (\text{bounded } \mathfrak{A}\text{-convergence}). \tag{9}$$

In view of definitions 3.4 and 4.4, the step function $g(x, z)$ can be written

$$g(x, z) = g(x_0)\chi(z_0, z_1] + \cdots + g(x_N)\chi(z_N, b]; \tag{10}$$

further, note that

$$\chi(z_k, z_{k+1}] = \chi(a, z_{k+1}] - \chi(a, z_k] \qquad (\text{for } 0 \le k \le N). \tag{11}$$

Let F be defined by (8); combining (10) and (11), the linearity of u implies that

$$ug(x, z) = \sum_{k=0}^{N} g(x_k)\{F(z_{k+1}) - F(z_k)\} = g^F(x, z); \tag{12}$$

the last equality is from definition 3.3(6). Conclusion (7) now comes from (9) and (12).

Obviously, $F(a) = \mathbf{o}$; to complete the verification of (iii$_1$) it will suffice to show that $F(a+) = \mathbf{o}$. It is easily seen that

$$0 = \lim_{\lambda \to a+} \chi(a, \lambda](\tau) \qquad (\text{all } \tau \in (a, b));$$

on the other hand, $\| \chi(a, \lambda] \|_0 \le 2$, so that the net

$$\{\chi(a, \lambda], \lambda \in (a, b], \le\}$$

is V_0-bounded and zero-approaching; consequently, definition 4.2 implies that

$$\infty \ne \sup_{a<\lambda\le b} r[u\chi(a, \lambda]] \qquad (\text{all } r \in \mathfrak{A}^*) \tag{14}$$

and

$$0 = \lim_{\lambda \to a+} u\chi(a, \lambda] = \lim_{\lambda \to a+} F(\lambda) = F(a+);$$

the second equality is from definition (8). This concludes the verification of (iii_1).

4.6. There are still three properties of F that need to be verified; let us begin with (iii_2). Since

$$\chi(a,b)(\tau) = \lim_{\lambda \to b-} \chi(a,\lambda](\tau) \qquad (\text{all } \tau \in (a,b)),$$

it follows that the net

$$\{\chi(a,\lambda], \lambda \in (a,b), \geq\}$$

is V_0-bounded and converges pointwise to the function $\chi(a,b)$ (which equals $\chi(a,b]$ by definition (6)), whence the conclusion $F(b) = F(b-)$ now comes from 4.3 and definition (8).

4.7. We still have to verify

(iii_3) $\qquad F(t) = F(t+) \qquad (\text{for } a < t < b),$

(iii_4) $\qquad F(t-) \text{ exists} \qquad (\text{for } a < t < b).$

To deal with (iii_3), note that

$$\chi(a,t](\tau) = \lim_{\alpha \to t+} \chi(a,\alpha](\tau) \qquad (\text{all } \tau \in (a,b)). \tag{15}$$

Set $g_\alpha = \chi(a,\alpha]$; obviously, $\|g_\alpha\|_0 \leq 2$, whence (15) implies that the net

$$\{g_\alpha, \alpha \in (t,b), \leq\}$$

is V_0-bounded and satisfies 4.3(3) with $g_0 = \chi(a,t]$: from 4.3 it now follows

$$u\chi(a,t] = \lim_{\alpha \to t+} u\chi(a,\alpha].$$

Accordingly, conclusion (iii_3) now comes from definition (8).

4.8. Only condition (iii_4) remains. It is easily verified that

$$0 = \lim_{\alpha,\beta} \chi(a,\alpha](\tau) - \chi(a,\beta](\tau)$$

(for all τ in (a,b)), where $\alpha, \beta \to t-$: this implies that the net

$$\{\chi(a,\alpha] - \chi(a,\beta], (\alpha,\beta) \in (a,t) \times (a,t)\}$$

is zero-approaching; since it is obviously V_0-bounded, the Helly-type property implies

$$\mathbf{o} = \lim_{\alpha,\beta} u[\chi(a,\alpha] - \chi(a,\beta]] \tag{16}$$

see definition 4.2. Using the linearity of u, now we can infer from (16) and definition (8) that the net

$$\{F(\lambda), \lambda \in (a,t), \geq\}$$

is a Cauchy net; in fact, (14) implies that is is a bounded Cauchy net in $\mathfrak{A}$: therefore, its convergence comes from the QC-space assumption on $\mathfrak{A}$ (see 2.7). Thus, the limit

$$\lim_{\lambda \to t+} F(\lambda)$$

exists, which proves the last property (iii_4).

5. THE SPACE OF INTEGRATORS

Again, $\mathfrak{A}$ is a QC-space, $\mathfrak{A}^*$ is a family of seminorms determining the topology of $\mathfrak{A}$, and $[a, b]$ is a fixed interval. We denote by $\mathfrak{F}$ the family of all the right-continuous simply discontinuous mappings of $[a, b]$ into $\mathfrak{A}$ that are continuous at both end-points of $[a, b]$ and vanish at a.

5.1. Thus, $F \in \mathfrak{F}$ if (and only if) F maps the interval $[a, b]$ into $\mathfrak{A}$ while satisfying the following four conditions:

(iii_1) $$F(a) = F(a+) = \mathbf{o},$$

(iii_2) $$F(b-) = F(b),$$

(iii_3) $$F(t) = F(t+) \qquad (\text{for } a < t < b),$$

(iii_4) $$F(t-) \text{ exists} \qquad (\text{for } a < t < b).$$

5.2. ORIENTATION. This section deals with approximation by step-functions in $\mathfrak{F}$. Again, let Z be the family of all finite sets $z = \{z_k: 0 \leq k \leq N + 1\}$ such that $a = z_0 < z_1 < z_2 < \ldots < z_N < z_{N+1} = b$; if $k < N$ we denote by z^k the half-open interval $[z_k, z_{k+1})$ and set $z^N = [z_N, z_{N+1}]$. Note that $z_k \in z^k$ (for all values of k), and

$$[a, b] \subset \bigcup \{z^k: 0 \leq k \leq N\}. \tag{1}$$

The family Z is directed by the relation $\supset$: observe that $z \supset w$ if (and only if) every interval z^k is contained in some interval w^i.

5.3 Throughout, we suppose that $F \in \mathfrak{F}$ and $r \in \mathfrak{A}^*$. If $E \in \mathfrak{F}$ we set

$$\| E \|_r = \sup \{r[E(\lambda)]: a \leq \lambda \leq b\}. \tag{2}$$

If $z \in Z$, let F_z be the function defined on $[a, b]$ by

$$F_z(\lambda) = F(z_n) \qquad \text{when } \lambda \in z^n \text{ and } 0 \leq n \leq N. \tag{3}$$

We shall prove that

$$0 = \lim\{ \| F - F_z \|_r, z \in Z, \supset\}$$

To that effect, we need the following

5.4. LEMMA. To any $\epsilon > 0$ there corresponds a finite set $w = \{w_i: 0 \leq i \leq I + 1\}$ such that

$$r[F(\alpha) - F(\beta)] \leq \epsilon \qquad (\text{all } \alpha, \beta \text{ in } w^i, 0 \leq i \leq I). \tag{4}$$

Proof. See 5.7.

5.5. THEOREM D. If $F \in \mathfrak{F}$ and $r \in \mathfrak{A}^*$, then

$$0 = \lim_z \| F - F_z \|_r, \tag{5}$$

where z runs over the directed set $(Z, \supset)$.

Proof. Take any $\epsilon > 0$, let w be the element of Z that is mentioned in 5.4, and let $z \in Z$ be such that $z \supset w$. It is a question of verifying $\| F - F_z \|_r \leq \epsilon$, that is,

$$r[F(\lambda) - F_z(\lambda)] \leq \epsilon \qquad (\text{all } \lambda \text{ in } [a, b]). \tag{6}$$

Take λ in $[a, b]$: it follows from (1) that λ belongs to some interval z^n; but z^n is contained in some interval w^i (because of $z \supset w$): thus, both λ and z_n belong to the same interval w^i, whence the inequality

$$r[F(\lambda) - F(z_n)] \leq \epsilon \tag{7}$$

comes from (4). On the other hand, definition (3) (together with the fact that $\lambda \in z^n$) implies that $F_z(\lambda) = F(z_n)$, so that (6) now results from (7).

5.6. COROLLARY. $\| F \|_r \neq \infty$.

Proof. If $\lambda \in [a, b]$ then $\lambda \in w^i$ for some $i \leq I$; since $w_i \in w^i$, it now results from 5.4 that

$$r[F(\lambda) - F(w_i)] \leq \epsilon$$

whence

$$r[F(\lambda)] \leq \epsilon + \max_{0 \leq i \leq I} | F(w_i) |_r \tag{8}$$

for all λ in $[a, b]$. Calling c_r the right-hand side of (8), definition (2) implies that $\| F \|_r \leq c_r$.

5.7. *Proof of 5.4.* If $S \subset [a, b]$ we set

$$\Omega S = \sup \{r[F(\alpha) - F(\beta)]: \alpha, \beta \in S\};$$

it is a question of constructing a finite set $w = \{w_i: 0 \leq i \leq I + 1\}$ such that $w \in Z$ and

$$\Omega w^i \leq \epsilon \qquad (\text{for } 0 \leq i \leq I). \tag{9}$$

Since $F \in \mathfrak{F}$, we can apply conditions (iii_1) and (iii_2) in 5.1: they imply the existence of two numbers Ra and Lb in (a, b) such that

$$\Omega [a, Ra) \leq \epsilon/2 \quad \text{and} \quad \Omega [Lb, b] \leq \epsilon/2. \tag{10}$$

If $Lb \le Ra$, then $[a, b]$ is contained in the union of $[a, Ra]$ and $[Lb, b]$, whence $\Omega[a, b] \le \epsilon$: conclusion (9) is satisfied for $w = \{a, b\}$.

Next, consider the case $Ra < Lb$. If $\lambda \in [Ra, Lb]$, we infer from 5.1 (iii_3) the existence of a number $R\lambda$ in (a, b) such that

$$\Omega[\lambda, R\lambda] \le \epsilon/2,$$

and from (iii_4) the existence of a number $L\lambda$ in (a, b) such that $\Omega[L\lambda, \lambda) \le \epsilon/2$; consequently, the relation

$$\Omega[L\lambda, R\lambda] \le \epsilon$$

holds for two numbers $L\lambda$ and $R\lambda$ such that $a < L\lambda < \lambda < R\lambda < b$. The family of open intervals $(L\lambda, R\lambda)$ is an open cover of the compact set $[Ra, Lb]$; consequently, there is a finite subset S of $[Ra, Lb]$ such that

$$[Ra, Lb] \subset \bigcup \{(Ls, Rs): s \in S\} \subset (a, b) \tag{11}$$

and

$$\lambda[Ls, Rs] \le \epsilon \qquad (\text{all } s \in S). \tag{12}$$

Now set

$$E = \{Ls: s \in S\} \cup \{Rs: s \in S\} \tag{13}$$

and define $w_0 = a$, $w_1 = Ra$, and w_i recursively by

$$w_{i+1} = \min E_i \qquad (\text{all } i \ge 1), \tag{14}$$

where

$$E_i = \{e \in E: e > w_i\}. \tag{15}$$

Obviously,

$$Ra = w_1 \le w_i < w_{i+1} \qquad (\text{all } i \ge 1). \tag{16}$$

Also, set

$$j = \max \{i: w_i < Lb\}. \tag{17}$$

Thus, if we define $w_{j+1} = Lb$ and $w_{j+2} = b$, then the finite set $w = \{w_i; 0 \le i \le j + 2\}$ belongs to Z. The inequality

$$\Omega[w_i, w_{i+1}) \le \epsilon \tag{18}$$

holds for $i = 0$ (since $w_1 = Ra$ and by (10)) as well as for $i = j + 1$ (since $w_{j+1} = Lb$ and by (10)). It remains to verify (18) in the case $1 \le i \le j$. From $i \le j$ and definition (17) it follows that

$$Lb > w_i \ge Ra; \tag{19}$$

the last inequality is from (16) (since $i \geq 1$). From (19) and (11) it now follows the existence of some s in S such that

$$Rs > w_i > Ls; \tag{20}$$

therefore, $Rs > w_i$, whence $Rs \in E_i$ (since $Rs \in E$: see definition (15)). Having thus verified that $Rs \in E_i$, we may apply definition (14) to obtain $w_{i+1} \leq Rs$, whence

$$Rs \geq w_{i+1} \geq w_i > Ls; \tag{21}$$

the last two inequalities are from (16) and (20). Obviously, (21) implies that $w^i \subset [Ls, Rs]$: conclusion (9) now comes from (12).

6. EXISTENCE OF THE INTEGRAL

6.1. THEOREM C. If u is Helly-type, then

$$ug = \int g d\Gamma_u \qquad (\text{all } g \in BV),$$

where $\Gamma_u \in \mathfrak{F}$ and

$$\Gamma_u(\theta) = u\chi(a, \theta) \qquad (\text{for } a \leq \theta \leq b). \tag{1}$$

Proof. Immediate from theorem C(4.5), definition 3.3 and 5.1.

6.2. ORIENTATION. Our aim (achieved in 6.11) is to prove the converse: if $F \in \mathfrak{F}$ then the equation

$$ug = \int gdF \qquad (\text{all } g \in \text{BV}) \tag{2}$$

defines a Helly-type mapping u. Essentially, it is a question of establishing the existence of the integral. In this connection it might be appropriate to remark that, if the integral is interpreted as a norm integral (decreasing meshes), then it cannot exist for all g in BV unless F is continuous.

6.3. NOTATION. Suppose that $A \in \mathfrak{A}$ and $S \subset [a, b)$; we denote by AS the function

$$[a, b] \ni \lambda \rightarrow \begin{cases} \mathrm{A} & \text{if } \lambda \in S \\ \mathbf{o} & \text{if } \lambda \notin S. \end{cases}$$

In particular, if $a \leq \alpha < \beta \leq b$, then $A[\alpha, \beta)$ is the function defined on $[a, b]$ by

$$A[\alpha, \beta)(\lambda) = \begin{matrix} \mathrm{A} & \text{if } \alpha \leq \lambda < \beta \\ \mathbf{o} & \text{otherwise.} \end{matrix} \tag{3}$$

6.4. LEMMA. Suppose that $A \in \mathfrak{A}$ and $g \in \mathrm{BV}$. If $a < \tau < b$ $A[\tau, b] \in \mathfrak{F}$ and

$$g(\tau)A = \int g dA[\tau, b]. \tag{4}$$

Proof. Let b be the mapping defined on BV by

$$ug = g(\tau)A \qquad (\text{all } g \in \mathrm{BV}). \tag{5}$$

Note that

$$r[ug] = r[A]\,|\,g(\tau)\,| \leq r[A]\,\|\,g\,\|_0 \qquad (\text{all } r \in \mathfrak{A}^*);$$

where the inequality is from 3.1(3); consequently, u is Helly-type, whence Theorem C (6.1) shows that

$$g(\tau)A = \int g d\Gamma_u. \tag{6}$$

Take $a \leq \theta \leq b$; from (1), (5) and (3) we see that

$$\Gamma_u(\theta) = u\chi(a, \theta] = \chi(a, \theta](\tau)A = A[\tau, b](\theta).$$

Accordingly, $\Gamma_u = A[\tau, b]$; in view of (6), this concludes the proof.

6.5. REMARKS. Suppose that $F \in \mathfrak{F}$. If $z = \{z_k\colon 0 \leq k \leq N + 1\}$ belongs to Z, set $A_k = F(z_k)$; clearly,

$$F_z = \sum_{k=0}^{N-1} A_k[z_k, z_{k+1}) + A_N[z_N, b], \tag{7}$$

where F_z is the function that was defined in 5.3(3). Note that

$$A_k[z_k, z_{k+1}) = A_k[z_k, b] - A_k[z_{k+1}, b]$$

(for $0 \leq k \leq N-1$); consequently, if $g \in \mathrm{BV}$, then the equalities

$$\int g dA_k[z_k, z_{k+1}] = \{g(z_k) - (z_{k+1})\}A_k$$

and

$$\int g dA_N[z_N, b] = g(z_N)A_N$$

come from (4); it now results from (7) that

$$\int g dF_z = \sum_{k=1}^{N-1} \{g(z_k) - g(z_{k+1})\}F(z_k) + g(z_N)F(z_N). \tag{8}$$

6.6. LEMMA. If $\{h_s, s\}$ is a zero-approaching net, then

$$0 = \lim_s r[\int h_s dF_z] \qquad (\text{all } r \in \mathfrak{A}^*). \tag{9}$$

Proof. From (8) we see that

$$r[\int h_s dF_z] \leq \|\,F\,\|_r \left\{ \sum_{k=1}^{N-1} |\,h_s(z_k) - h_s(z_{k+1})\,| + |\,h_s(z_N)\,| \right\};$$

since $a < z_k \le z_{k+1} \le \cdots \le z_M < b$, conclusion (9) is immediate from definition 4.2.

6.7. REMARK. If $g \in$ BV, let $\bar{g}$ be the function defined on $[a, b]$ by

$$\bar{g}(\lambda) = \begin{cases} g(\lambda) & \text{if } a \le \lambda < b \\ 0 & \text{if } \lambda = b. \end{cases}$$

Thus, $\bar{g}(z_{N+1}) = \bar{g}(b) = 0$, and we may re-write (8) as follows:

$$\int g dF_z = \sum_{k=1}^{N} \{\bar{g}(z_k) - \bar{g}(z_{k+1})\} F(z_k). \tag{10}$$

6.8 LEMMA. Let X be the result of endowing $\mathfrak{F}$ with the topology of uniform convergence on the interval $[a, b]$. Suppose that $g \in$ BV, and let D be the family of all $F \in \mathfrak{F}$ such that the integral $\int g dF$ exists. The mapping μ defined on D by

$$\mu F = \int g dF \qquad (\text{all } F \text{ in } D) \tag{11}$$

has an extension $\bar{\mu} \in \mathfrak{L}[X:\mathfrak{A}]$ such that

$$r[\bar{\mu} F] \le 2 \| g \|_0 \| F \|_r \qquad (\text{all } F \in X, r \in \mathfrak{A}^*). \tag{12}$$

Proof. The topology of X is determined by the family $\{\| \cdot \|_r : r \in \mathfrak{A}^*\}$ of seminorms (defined in 5.3). From Theorem D (5.5) it follows that

$$F = \lim_z F_z \qquad (\text{bounded } X\text{-convergence}); \tag{13}$$

to verify that the net $\{F_z, z\}$ is bounded it suffices to note that the inequality $\| F_z \|_r \le \| F \|_r$ comes directly from definition 5.3(3). Let us assume for a moment that

$$r[\mu F] \le 2 \| g \|_0 \| F \|_r \qquad (\text{all } F \in D, r \in \mathfrak{A}^*). \tag{14}$$

Further, let K_r be defined on X by the relation

$$K_r[F] = 2 \| g \|_0 \| F \|_r \qquad (\text{all } F \in X);$$

from 2.4 and (14) it follows that K is a majorant of $\mu \in \mathfrak{L}[D:\mathfrak{A}]$. From (8) it follows that the net $\{F_z, z\}$ is in D, and from (13) it results that every F in X is the limit of a bounded net in D; obviously, D is a linear subspace of the locally convex space $X = \mathfrak{F}$, that is, Extension Theorem A(2.8) therefore implies that there is an extension $\bar{\mu}$ of μ such that $\bar{\mu} \in \mathfrak{L}[X:\mathfrak{A}]$ and

$$r[\bar{\mu} F] \le K_r[F] = 2 \| g \|_0 \| F \|_r \qquad (\text{all } F \in X):$$

this concludes the proof.

It remains to verify (14). By hypothesis, the integral in (11) exists, and from definition 3.3 we see that

$$0 = \lim_{(x,z)} r[\mu F - g^F(x, z)], \tag{15}$$

where (x, z) runs over the directed set $(\pi, \gg)$, and where

$$g^F(x, z) = \sum_{k=0}^{N} g(x_k)\{F(z_{k+1}) - F(z_k)\}.$$

Using the fact that $F(z_0) = F(a) = \mathbf{o}$, this can be written

$$g^F(x, z) = g(x_N)F(z_{N+1}) + \sum_{k=1}^{N} \{g(x_{k-1}) - g(x_k)\}F(z_k).$$

Consequently,

$$r[g^F(x, z)] \leq \|F\|_r\{|g(x_N)| + \sum_{k=1}^{N} |g(x_{k-1}) - g(x_k)|\};$$

using 3.1(3) and the fact that $a \leq x_0 \leq x_1 \leq \dots$, this yields

$$r[g^F(x, z)] \leq 2\|F\|_r\|g\|_0,$$

whence

$$r[\mu F] \leq r[\mu F - g^F(x, z)] + 2\|g\|_0\|F\|_r;$$

taking limits of both sides of this inequality, we now obtain (14) directly from (15).

6.9. COROLLARY. We write $\langle g, F\rangle = \bar{\mu}F$. Since $\bar{\mu}$ is an extension of μ, we have

$$\langle g, E\rangle = \bar{\mu}E = \mu E = \int g dE \qquad (\text{all } E \text{ in } D); \tag{16}$$

the last equality is from definition (11). Also, (12) becomes

$$r[\langle g, f\rangle] \leq 2\|g\|_0\|F\|_r \qquad (\text{all } r \in \mathfrak{A}^*, F \in \mathfrak{F}). \tag{17}$$

Since $\bar{\mu} \in \mathfrak{L}\,[X:\mathfrak{A}\,]$, it follows from (13) and (16) that

$$\langle g, F\rangle = \lim_{z} \int g dF_z \qquad (\text{all } g \in \mathbf{BV}, F \in \mathfrak{F}). \tag{18}$$

6.10. COROLLARY. If $F \in \mathfrak{F}$, then the mapping $g \to \langle g, F\rangle$ is Helly-type.

Proof. Let u be the mapping defined by

$$ug = \langle g, F\rangle \qquad (\text{all } g \in \mathbf{BV}). \tag{19}$$

First, note that u is a linear mapping of **BV** into $\mathfrak{A}$: in view of (18), this comes from the linearity of the mapping $g \to \int g dF_z$. Next, let $\{h_s, s\}$ be a zero-approaching net such that

$$\| h_s \|_0 \leq c_0 \qquad (\text{all } s) \tag{20}$$

for some $c_0 > 0$ independent of s. In view of definition 4.2, it will suffice to verify that

$$\mathbf{o} = \lim_s \langle h_s, F \rangle \qquad (\text{bounded}\,\mathfrak{A}\text{-convergence}). \tag{21}$$

On the other hand, (16) implies that

$$\langle h_s, F \rangle = \int h_s dF_z + \langle h_s, F - F_z \rangle,$$

whence, for an arbitrary $r \in \mathfrak{A}^*$,

$$r[\langle h_s, F \rangle] \leq r[\int h_s dF_z] + 2c_0 \| F - F_z \|_r \tag{22}$$

is a consequence of (17) and (20). Taking $\lim_s$ of both sides of (22), we can use 6.6 (9) to obtain

$$\lim_s r[\langle h_s, F \rangle] \leq 2c_0 \| F - F_z \|_r \tag{23}$$

recall that the net $\{h_x, s\}$ is zero-approaching by hypothesis. Taking limits of both sides of (23), conclusion (21) now comes from 6.8 (13). Finally, (17) and (20) imply that

$$r[\langle h_s, F \rangle] \leq 2 \| h_s \|_0 \| F \|_r \leq 2c_0 \| F \|_r,$$

whence the boundedness of the net in (21): this concludes the proof.

6.11. THEOREM E. If $F \in \mathfrak{F}$ then

$$\langle g, F \rangle = \int g dF \qquad (\text{all } g \in \mathbf{BV}), \tag{24}$$

and the mapping

$$\mathbf{BV} \ni g \to \int g dF \tag{25}$$

is Helly-type. Further,

$$\langle \chi(a, \theta], f \rangle = F(\theta) \qquad (\text{for } a \leq \theta \leq b). \tag{26}$$

Proof. Let u be the mapping defined by (19); since u is Helly-type (by 6.10), it follows from Theorem C(6.1) the existence of a function $\Gamma_u \in \mathfrak{F}$ such that

$$\langle g, F \rangle = \int g d\Gamma_u \qquad (\text{all } g \in \mathbf{BV}), \tag{27}$$

and from definition 6.1 (1) we see that

$$\Gamma_u(\theta) = \langle \chi(a, \theta], F \rangle \qquad (\text{for } a \leq \theta \leq b). \tag{28}$$

Let us assume for a moment that

$$\langle \chi(a, \tau], F \rangle = F(\tau) \qquad (\text{for } a < \tau < b); \tag{29}$$

from (28) it then follows that $\Gamma_u(\tau) = F(\tau)$ for all τ in (a, b); therefore, $\Gamma_u(a+) = F(a+)$ and $\Gamma_u(b-) = F(b-)$; since both Γ_u and F belong to $\mathfrak{F}$, we can use 5.1 (iii_1 and iii_2) to infer that $\Gamma_u(\theta) = F(\theta)$ for $\theta = a$ and $\theta = b$. Consequently, by assuming (29) we can conclude that $\Gamma_u = F$, whence (26) comes from (28), so that the mapping (25) is indeed equal to the Helly-type mapping u: the theorem is proved.

It remains to verify our assumption (29). From 6.7 (10) and (16) we see that

$$\langle g, F\rangle = \lim_{z} \sum_{k=1}^{N} \{\bar{g}(z_k) - \bar{g}(z_{k+1})\} F(z_k). \tag{30}$$

Set $g = \chi(a, \tau]$ and note that $g = \bar{g}$; the conclusion (29) will be obtained by verifying that the right-hand side of (30) equals $F(\tau)$. Take any $z \in Z$ with $z \supset \{a, \tau, b\}$: consequently, there exists some z_n such that

$$\tau = z_n < z_{N+1} = b;$$

recall that $\tau < b$. Since $g = \chi(a, \tau]$, we have $g(z_k) - g(z_{k+1}) = 1 - 1 = 0$ for $z_{k+1} \leq z_n = \tau$ (that is, for $k \leq n - 1$). On the other hand, $g(z_n) - g(z_{n+1}) = g(\tau) - 0 = 1$ and $g(z_k) - g(z_{k+1}) = 0$ when $k \geq n + 1$ (since $z_{n+1} \geq z_n = \tau$ and $g = \chi(a, \tau]$). Consequently,

$$\sum_{k=1}^{N} \{g(z_k) - g(z_{k+1})\} F(z_k) = F(z_n) = F_z(\tau); \tag{31}$$

the last equality is from definition 5.3 (3) and the fact that $\tau \in z^n = [z_n, z_{n+1})$ (or $[z_N, b]$ in case $n = N$). From (30) and (31) we see that

$$\langle g, F\rangle = \lim_{z} F_z(\lambda) = F(\lambda); \tag{32}$$

the second equality is from Theorem D (5.5) and

$$r[F(\lambda) - F_z(\lambda)] \leq \| F - F_z \|_r.$$

Since (32) implies our assumption (20), the proof is completed.

PART II

7. THE TOPOLOGICAL SPACE V_b

Throughout, BV is the family of all left-continuous functions on an interval $[a, b]$ such that $-\infty \leq a < b \leq \infty$. In this section we shall use the space $\mathfrak{F}$ (defined in 5.1) to endow BV with a topology which is weaker than the Banach space topology (defined in 4.1). As before, $\mathfrak{A}^*$ is a family of seminorms determining the topology of the QC-space $\mathfrak{A}$.

7.1. It follows from 6.11 the existence of a mapping $(g, E) \longrightarrow \langle g, E\rangle$ of the Cartesian product BV $\times\ \mathfrak{F}$ into $\mathfrak{A}$ such that

$$\langle g, E\rangle = \int g dE, \tag{1}$$

the integral being defined as in 3.3; further,

$$r[\langle g, E\rangle] \leq 2\|g\|_0\|E\|_r \qquad (\text{all } r \in \mathfrak{A}^*) \tag{2}$$

(see 6.8.) If $\chi(a, \theta]$ is the characteristic function of the interval $(a, \theta] \cap (a, b)$, then

$$\langle\chi(a, \theta], E\rangle = E(\theta) \qquad (\text{from } a \leq \theta \leq b) \tag{3}$$

see Theorem E (6.11).

7.2. Let $\mathfrak{H}$ be the family of all Helly-type mappings (defined in 4.2). If $u \in \mathfrak{H}$, Theorem C (6.1) yields

$$ug = \langle g, \Gamma_u\rangle \qquad (\text{all } g \in \text{BV}), \tag{4}$$

where $\Gamma_u \in \mathfrak{F}$: the inequality (2) now shows that the family $\mathfrak{H}$ is contained in the family $\mathfrak{L}[V_0:\mathfrak{A}]$ (of all continuous linear mappings of the Banach space V_0 into $\mathfrak{A}$).

7.3. THEOREM. If u is a linear mapping of BV into $\mathfrak{A}$, then $u \in \mathfrak{H}$ if (and only if) u belongs to $\mathfrak{L}[V_0:\mathfrak{A}]$ and transforms V_0-bounded zero-approaching nets into nets which converge to $\mathbf{o}$.

Proof. If $u \in \mathfrak{H}$, then $u \in \mathfrak{L}[V_0:\mathfrak{A}]$ (by 7.2) and u suitably transforms V_0-bounded zero-approaching nets (by definition 4.2). Conversely, assume that $u \in \mathfrak{L}[V_0:\mathfrak{A}]$ is such that

$$\mathbf{o} = \lim_s uh_s \qquad (\mathfrak{A}\text{-convergence}) \tag{5}$$

whenever $\{h_s, s\}$ is a V_0-bounded zero-approaching net. But $\{u_h, s\}$ is a bounded net in $\mathfrak{A}$ (because of the fact that $\{h_s, s\}$ is V_0-bounded and since $u \in \mathfrak{L}[V_0:\mathfrak{A}]$: see 2.6); thus, conclusion $u \in \mathfrak{H}$ is now immediate from definition 4.2.

7.4. THEOREM F. If $E \in \mathfrak{F}$ and $g \in$ BV, then

$$\int g dE = \langle g, E\rangle = \lim_{(x,z)} g^E(x, z) \qquad (\text{bounded } \mathfrak{A}\text{-convergence}), \tag{6}$$

where (x, z) runs over the directed set $(\pi, \gg)$ that was defined in 3.2.

Proof. If $z = \{z_k: 0 \leq k \leq N + 1\}$ belongs to Z, then

$$g^E(x, z) = \sum_{k=0}^{N} g(x_k)\{E(z_{k+1}) - E(z_k)\} \tag{7}$$

and $z_k \leq x_k \leq z_{k+1}$ (as in 3.2–3.3). Let u be the mapping defined by

$$ug = \langle g, E\rangle = \int g dE \qquad (\text{all } g \in \text{BV}): \tag{8}$$

it follows from Theorem E (6.11) that $u \in \mathcal{H}$, whence 4.5 (7) implies

$$\int g dE = \lim_{(x,z)} g^F(x,z) \qquad (\text{bounded } \mathcal{A}\text{-convergence}), \tag{9}$$

where

$$F(\theta) = u\chi(a,\theta] = \langle \chi(a,\theta], E\rangle = E(\theta) \tag{10}$$

(for $a \leq \theta \leq b$); these equalities are from 4.5(8), (8) and (3). Thus, $F = E$ and conclusion (6) is now immediate from (9).

7.5. REMARK. A weakened version of 7.4 (to be utilized in a subsequent paper) is stated in 1.9; in order to connect 7.4 with 1.9, let $\bar{z}_k$ denote the midpoint of the interval $[z_k, z_{k+1}]$ and set

$$\langle g, E\rangle_z = \sum_{k=0}^{N} g(\bar{z}_k)\{E(z_{k+1}) - E(z_k)\};$$

observe that $\langle g, E\rangle_z = g^E(\bar{z}, z)$, where $\bar{z}$ is the finite set $\{\bar{z}_k\colon 0 \leq k \leq N\}$. From definition 3.2 we see that $(\bar{z}, z) \in \pi$ and $(z,z) \gg (w,w)$ if (and only if) $z \supset w$. Therefore, (6) implies 1.9, namely,

$$\int g dE = \lim\{\langle g, E\rangle_z, z \in Z, \supset\} \qquad (\text{bounded } \mathcal{A}\text{-convergence}).$$

7.6. ORIENTATION. If $F \in \mathcal{F}$ and if we denote by $\langle\cdot\,, F\rangle$ the mapping

$$\text{BV} \ni g \to \langle g, F\rangle, \tag{11}$$

then we can express the main consequence of Theorem E (6.11) as follows: the linear transformation

$$\mathcal{F} \ni F \to \langle\cdot\,, F\rangle \tag{12}$$

is into the linear space $\mathcal{H}$. On the other hand, we know from 7.2 that the transformation

$$\mathcal{H} \ni u \to \Gamma_u \tag{13}$$

is into $\mathcal{F}$ and satisfies the relation

$$u = \langle\cdot\,, \Gamma_u\rangle. \tag{14}$$

Consequently, the linear transformation (12) is *onto* $\mathcal{H}$ and its inverse is the transformation (13); it identifies the linear spaces $\mathcal{H}$ and $\mathcal{F}$.

7.7. DEFINITION. If $F \in \mathcal{F}$ and $r \in \mathcal{A}^*$ then the function

$$\text{BV} \ni g \to r[\langle g, F\rangle]$$

is a seminorm which we shall denote by $r[\langle\cdot\,, F\rangle]$. Let V_b be the result of endowing BV with the topology determined by the family

$$\{r[\langle\cdot\,, F\rangle]: r \in \mathcal{A}^*, F \in \mathfrak{F}\}$$

of seminorms.

7.8. REMARKS. As we shall see, $\mathcal{H}$ is precisely the linear space of all continuous linear mappings of V_b into $\mathcal{A}$. Note that V_b is a locally convex space [4, p. 4]. If we discard the end-points a, b from the domain of our functions, then V_b becomes a Hausdorff space. Indeed, the Hausdorff property holds if the relation

$$r[\langle g, F\rangle] = 0 \qquad (\text{all } r \in \mathcal{A}^*, F \in \mathfrak{F}) \tag{15}$$

implies that $g(\tau) = 0$ for τ arbitrary in (a, b); this is precisely the case (take $F = A[\tau, b]$ with $A \in \mathcal{A}$, $A \neq \mathbf{o}$, and apply 6.4 in conjunction with (15) to obtain $g(\tau) = 0$).

7.9. Suppose that $g_0 \in$ BV, and let $\{g_s, s\}$ be a net in BV; we write

(**iv**$_1$) $$g_0 = \lim_s g_s \qquad (V_b\text{-convergence})$$

to indicate convergence in the topological space V_b. Note that (iv$_1$) obtains if (and only if)

(**iv**$_2$) $$\int g_0 dF = \lim_s \int g_s dF \qquad (\text{all } F \in \mathfrak{F}).$$

Indeed, definition 7.7 implies that (iv$_1$) is equivalent to

$$0 = \lim_s r[\langle g_0 - g_s, F\rangle] \qquad (\text{all } r \in \mathcal{A}^*, F \in \mathfrak{F});$$

by 2.1, this is equivalent to

(**iv**$_3$) $$\langle g_0, F\rangle = \lim_s \langle g_s, F\rangle \qquad (\mathcal{A}\text{-convergence, all F}),$$

and this is equivalent to (iv$_1$) (because of 7.1(1)).

7.10. Suppose that $g_0 \in$ BV, and let $\{g_s, s\}$ be a V_0-bounded net in BV such that

$$g_0(\tau) = \lim_s g_s(\tau) \qquad (\text{all } \tau \in (a, b)). \tag{16}$$

If $F \in \mathfrak{F}$, then $\langle\cdot\,, F\rangle \in \mathcal{H}$ (see 7.6), whence (iv$_3$) now follows from (16). Since (iv$_3$) implies (iv$_1$), we can say that *the pointwise convergence of V_0-bounded nets implies their convergence in the space V_b.*

7.11. Let u be a linear mapping of BV into $\mathcal{A}$; from 2.4 and definition 7.7 it follows that

(**v**$_1$) $$u \in \mathcal{L}[V_b:\mathcal{A}]$$

if (and only if) every r in $\mathfrak{A}^*$ gives rise to a number $C_r > 0$ and to a finite subset $\{(r_i, F_i): i\}$ of the Cartesian product $\mathfrak{A}^* \times \mathfrak{F}$ such that

$$(\text{v}_2) \qquad r[ug] \leq C_r \sum_i r_i[\langle g, F_i\rangle] \qquad (\text{all } g \in \mathbf{BV}).$$

7.12. THEOREM. $\mathfrak{L}[V_b:\mathfrak{A}] \subset \mathfrak{L}[V_0:\mathfrak{A}]$.

Proof. From (v_2) and 7.1(2) it follows that

$$r[ug] \leq 2C_r \|g\|_0 \sum_i \|F\|_{ri} \qquad (\text{all } g \in \mathbf{BV}),$$

where $ri = r_i$. Consequently, we have a number $K > 0$ such that $r[ug] \leq K\|g\|_0$ for all $g \in \mathbf{BV}$, whence $u \in \mathfrak{L}[V_0:\mathfrak{A}]$.

7.13. LEMMA. If $F \in \mathfrak{F}$ then the mapping $\langle \cdot, F\rangle$ belongs to $\mathfrak{L}[V_b:\mathfrak{A}]$.

Proof. Set $u = \langle \cdot, F\rangle$ and take $r \in \mathfrak{A}^*$; since $ug = \langle g, F\rangle$ we have

$$r[ug] \leq \sum_i r_i[\langle g, F_i\rangle] \qquad (\text{for } r_i = r, F_i = F);$$

the conclusion $\langle \cdot, F\rangle \in \mathfrak{L}[V_b:\mathfrak{A}]$ now comes from (v_2).

7.14. THEOREM G. A linear mapping of **BV** into $\mathfrak{A}$ is Helly-type if and only if) it is continuous on the topological space V_b; that is,

$$\mathfrak{H} = \mathfrak{L}[V_b:\mathfrak{A}].$$

Proof. From 7.2 we see that any $u \in \mathfrak{H}$ is of the form $u = \langle \cdot, F\rangle$, where $F \in \mathfrak{F}$; the conclusion $u \in \mathfrak{L}[V_b:\mathfrak{A}]$ now comes from 7.13. Conversely, assume (v_1), and let $\{h_s, s\}$ be a V_0-bounded zero-approaching net: to obtain $u \in \mathfrak{H}$ it will suffice to prove that

$$\mathbf{o} = \lim_s uh_s \qquad (\text{bounded } \mathfrak{A}\text{-convergence}). \tag{17}$$

Hypothesis (v_1) implies (v_2), whence

$$r[uh_s] \leq C_r \sum_i r_i[\langle h_s, F_i\rangle]. \tag{18}$$

On the other hand, the transformation $\langle \cdot, F\rangle$ belongs to $\mathfrak{H}$ (because of $F_i \in \mathfrak{F}$ and in view of 7.6); accordingly, definition 4.2 implies that

$$0 = \lim_s r_i[\langle h_s, F_i\rangle] \tag{19}$$

and

$$\infty \neq \sup_s r_i[\langle h_s, F_i\rangle]. \tag{20}$$

Taking limits of both sides of (18), the convergence in (17) comes immediately from (19)—recall that i ranges over a finite set. The boundedness of the net $\{uh_s, s\}$ is a consequence of (18)-(20): this completes the verification of (17).

8. APPLICATIONS

In this section we consider four types of QC-spaces $\mathfrak{A}$. To begin with the most common QC-space, let $\mathfrak{A}$ be the complex field; the family $\mathfrak{L}[V_b:\mathfrak{A}]$ is now the dual space V_b' of the locally convex Hausdorff space V_b. From 7.12 it follows that V_b' is included in the norm-dual of the Banach space V_0 (that was defined in 4.1); thus,

$$V_0' \supset V_b' \supset V_\infty',$$

where V_∞ is the result of endowing BV with the topology of pointwise convergence on (a, b): the right-hand inclusion is easily verified.

In view of 7.6, there is a one-to-one correspondence between V_b' and $\mathfrak{F}$ such that corresponding elements u and F satisfy the identity

$$ug = \int g\,dF \qquad (\text{all } g \in \text{BV}). \tag{1}$$

This representation property is comparable to some of the results obtained by Adams and Morse [**1**]: they made BV into a metric space (*not* a linear topological space) on which all continuous additive functionals are represented by Stieltjes integrals—as in (1), but their integrators F are continuous: our family $\mathfrak{F}$ is replaced by its subset $C[a, b]$.

8.1. FIRST APPLICATION. Let $\mathfrak{A}$ be the Banach space $L^p(\omega)$, where $1 < p < \infty$ and $\omega = \{0, \pm 1, \pm 2, \pm 3, \ldots\}$. If x is the sequence $\{n \to x_n\}$, then $x \in \mathfrak{A}$ if $\|x\|_p \neq \infty$, where

$$\|x\|_p = \left(\sum_{n\in\omega} |x_n|^p\right)^{1/p} \geq |x_i| \qquad (\text{all } i \in \omega). \tag{2}$$

The topology of $\mathfrak{A}$ is determined by the norm $\|\cdot\|_p$. If $-\infty < \lambda < \infty$ we set

$$F(\lambda)_n = \int_0^\lambda e^{-2\pi i n\theta}\,d\theta \qquad (\text{all } n \in \omega), \tag{3}$$

and let $F(\lambda)$ be the sequence $\{n \to F(\lambda)_n\}$; it is easily seen that $F(\lambda) \in L^p(\omega)$. We shall verify that the function F defined by

$$[0, 1] \ni \lambda \to F(\lambda) \tag{4}$$

belongs to $\mathfrak{F}$ (when $a = 0$, $b = 1$). Since $F(0)$ is the zero element $\{n \to 0\}$ of $\mathfrak{A}$, it will suffice to prove that

$$0 = \lim_{t \to \lambda} \| F(\lambda) - F(t) \|_p^p \tag{5}$$

for all λ in an open interval containing the interval [0, 1]. To that effect, note that

$$\| F(\lambda) - F(t) \|_p^p \leq | \lambda - t |^p + \sum_{n \neq 0} \left| \frac{h(\lambda, t, n)}{2\pi i n} \right|^p,$$

where

$$h(\lambda, t, n) = e^{-2\pi i n \lambda} - e^{-2\pi i n t};$$

this comes directly from (3). Since the infinite series is uniformly convergent (by the Weierstrass M-test), conclusion (5) is obtained by taking limits inside the summation sign.

8.2. INTEGRATION WITH RESPECT TO F. Having thus proved that $F \in \mathfrak{F}$, we can use Theorem F (7.4) to assert that

$$\int g dF = \langle g, F \rangle = \lim_{(x, z)} g^F(x, z) \qquad (\mathfrak{A}\text{-convergence}) \tag{6}$$

for $g \in$ BV, where

$$g^F(x, z) = \sum_{k=0}^{N} g(x_k)\{F(z_{k+1}) - F(z_k)\}$$

(See 7.4 (6) and (7). Note that $g^F(x, z)$ is a sequence $\{n \to g^F(x, z)_n\}$ such that

$$g^F(x, z)_n = \sum_{k=0}^{N} g(x_k)\{F(z_{k+1})_n - F(z_k)_n\}; \tag{7}$$

recall that $F(\lambda)_n$ is defined by (3). Since $\mathfrak{A}$-convergence implies pointwise convergence (on ω: see (2)), it follows from (6) that

$$\langle g, F \rangle_n = \lim_{(x, z)} g^F(x, z)_n,$$

and by (7):

$$\langle g, F \rangle_n = \int g(\lambda) dF(\lambda)_n = \int_0^1 e^{-2\pi i n \lambda} g(\lambda) d\lambda; \tag{8}$$

the second equality is an immediate consequence of definition (3).

8.3. THE FOURIER TRANSFORM. Our basic interval is $[a, b] = [0, 1]$;

if $g \in$ BV, let $g^\wedge$ be the sequence $\{n \to g_n^\wedge\}$ defined on ω by

$$g_n^\wedge = \int_0^1 e^{-2\pi i n\lambda} g(\lambda) d\lambda \qquad (\text{all } n \in \omega).$$

From (8) and (6) we see that

$$g^\wedge = \int g dF,$$

where F is the function that was defined in 8.1. Since $F \in \mathfrak{F}$, it follows from Theorem G (7.14) that the mapping

$$\text{BV} \ni g \to g^\wedge \tag{9}$$

is Helly-type; the same theorem also enables us to assert that (9) is a continuous mapping of the locally convex space V_b into $L^p(\omega)$, and from 7.12 the known result that (9) also maps the Banach space V_0 into $L^p(\omega)$.

8.5. REMARK. In attempting to prove the Helly-type property for integral transforms such as (9), one might be tempted to use definition 4.2 in conjunction with the Lebesgue dominated convergence theorem: however, this theorem is not applicable to nets (c.f., [2], p. 111).

8.6. SECOND APPLICATION. Let M be a Hausdorff barreled space, $\mathfrak{N}$ a complete locally convex Hausdorff space, and let $\mathfrak{A}$ be the result of endowing $\mathfrak{L}[M:\mathfrak{N}]$ with the strong operator topology (as in 2.9). In case $M = \mathfrak{N}$ is a Hilbert space, any resolution of the identity gives rise to a finite interval $[a, b]$ and to an element of $\mathfrak{F}$ (see 1.7).

8.7. THIRD APPLICATION. Let $\Phi(S)$ be the family of all complex-valued functions on an arbitrary set S; let $\mathfrak{A}$ be the result of endowing $\Phi(S)$ with the topology of pointwise convergence on S. Finally, let f be a mapping of S into the interior of some interval $[a, b]$. The mapping

$$\text{BV} \ni g \to g \circ f \tag{10}$$

is easily seen to be a Helly-type mapping into $\mathfrak{A} = \Phi(S)$. Let u be the mapping (13) and note that

$$|ug(s)| = |g \circ f(s)| = |g(f(s))| \leq \|g\|_0 \qquad (\text{all } s \in S)$$

(see 3.1(3)). Accordingly, we may use Theorem C (6.1) to infer that

$$ug = g \circ f = \int g d\Gamma_u = \int g(\lambda) d\Gamma_u(\lambda).$$

In the particular case $g(\lambda) = \lambda$, we get

$$f = \int \lambda d\Gamma_u(\lambda). \tag{11}$$

Both f and $\Gamma_u(\lambda)$ are complex-valued functions on S; the equality (12) indicates that f is the limit (under pointwise convergence on S) of Stieltjes sums: it is a disguised form of a well-known approximation theorem. If $\mathfrak{A}$ is the result of endowing $\Phi(S)$ with the topology of uniform convergence on S, then (11) is an approximation theorem involving uniform convergence; in particular, if f is a measurable function on a measure space (S, μ), then (11) represents the classical property of approximation such a function by step-functions (c.f., [7, p. 56]).

9. APPROXIMATION BY POLYNOMIALS

Let P be the family of all polynomials in one variable restricted to the open interval (a, b). Henceforth, we suppose that the interval (a, b) is finite: consequently, P is a linear subspace of BV. Although P is not dense in the Banach space V_0, we shall prove that it is dense in the locally convex space V_b (defined in 7.7).

9.1. LEMMA. Suppose that $\theta \in [a, b]$: there exists a V_0-bounded sequence in P which converges pointwise to the function $\chi(a, \theta]$.

Proof. Set $h = \chi(a, \theta]$; recall that h is the characteristic function of the interval $(a, \theta] \cap (a, b)$: therefore, $\chi(a, \theta]$ is a constant polynomial when $\theta = a$ and when $\theta = b$; accordingly, in both cases the V_0-bounded sequence can be chosen to be the sequence $\{p_n, n\}$, where $p_n = h$ for all n. Let us consider the remaining case $a < \theta < b$; thus,

$$h(\lambda) = \begin{cases} 1 \text{ if } a < \lambda \leq \theta \\ 0 \text{ if } \theta < \lambda < b. \end{cases}$$

We shall construct a sequence $\{p_n, n\}$ in P which converges pointwise to h, and such that

$$\operatorname{var} p_n \leq 2 \qquad \text{(for all } n). \tag{12}$$

To that effect, take any integer $n > 0$, and define on (a, b) the continuous function f_n which coincides with the function $(1 + n^{-1})h$ outside of the interval $[\theta, \theta + n^{-1}]$ and whose derivative is constant inside the interval $[\theta, \theta + n^{-1}]$; thus, the graph of f_n (sketched below) consists of straight line segments.

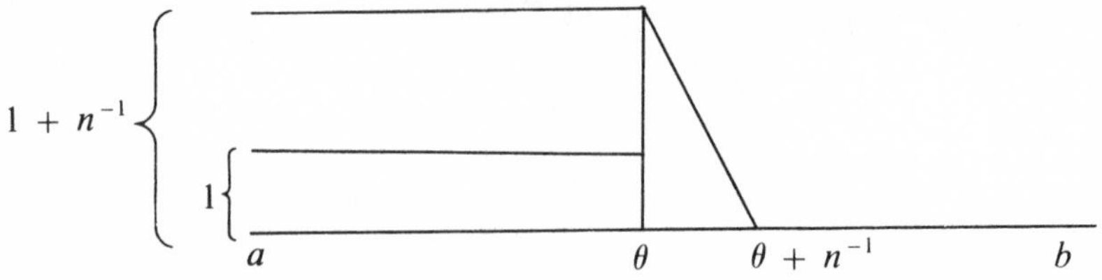

the intermediate horizontal line is the graph of $h = \chi(a, \theta]$. Clearly,

$$h(\tau) = \lim_{n \to \infty} f_n(\tau) \qquad (\text{all } \tau \in (a, b)). \tag{13}$$

Let $[\nu]_n$ be the Bernstein polynomial of order ν of the function f_n (thus, $[\nu]_n \in P$). Since f_n is continuous, it follows from [12, p. 5] that

$$0 = \lim_{n\to\infty} \sup\{\,|f_n(\tau) - [\nu]_n(\tau)| : \tau \in (a,b)\},$$

which implies the existence of an integer ν_n such that, if we set $p_n = [\nu_n]_n$, then

$$\sup_{a<\tau<b} |f_n(\tau) - p_n(\tau)| \leq n^{-1}. \tag{14}$$

But p_n is a Bernstein polynomial of the monotone function f_n; consequently,

$$\operatorname{var} p_n \leq \operatorname{var} f_n \leq 1 + n^{-1}; \tag{15}$$

the first inequality is from [12, p. 23], and the second inequality is obvious from the graph of f_n. The conclusion

$$h(\tau) = \lim_{n\to\infty} p_n(\tau) \qquad (\text{all } \tau \in (a,b)) \tag{16}$$

is immediate from (13) and (14). On the other hand, (15) implies that the sequence $\{p_n, n\}$ satisfies (12); since $p_n \in P$, a look at (16) completes the proof.

9.2. UNIQUENESS THEOREM. Suppose that u_1 and u_2 belong to the family $\mathcal{H}$ of all Helly-type mappings of BV into the QC-space $\mathfrak{A}$. If

$$u_1 p = u_2 p \qquad (\text{all } p \in P), \tag{17}$$

then $u_1 = u_2$.

Proof. It follows from 7.2 that

$$u_k g = \langle g, F_k \rangle \qquad (\text{for } k = 1, 2 \text{ and } g \in \mathrm{BV}), \tag{18}$$

where $F_1 F_2$ are functions in $\mathfrak{F}$ that are defined on $[a,b]$ by the formula

$$F_k(\theta) = u_k \chi(a,\theta] \qquad (\text{for } a \leq \theta \leq b); \tag{19}$$

consequently, it will suffice to prove that

$$u_1 \chi(a,\theta] = u_2 \chi(a,\theta] \qquad (\text{for } a \leq \theta \leq b). \tag{20}$$

From 9.1 we see that the V_0-bounded sequence $\{p_n, n\}$ converges to $\chi(a,\theta]$, whence the Helly-type property (see 4.3) now implies

$$u_k \chi(a,\theta] = \lim_{n\to\infty} u_k p_n \qquad (\text{both } k = 1, 2). \tag{21}$$

Hypothesis (17) implies $u_1 p_n = u_2 p_n$, whence (20) is a consequence of (21). Thus, (20) and (19) imply that $F_1 = F_2$, so that the conclusion $u_1 = u_2$ now comes from (18).

9.3. EXTENSION THEOREM. Let V_b be the locally convex space that was defined in 7.7, and let P_b be the result of endowing P with the topology of V_b. Any continuous linear mapping of P_b into $\mathfrak{A}$ has a unique continuous extension to all of BV; moreover, the space P is dense in V_b.

Proof. See 9.6.

9.4. Let Q be the family of all step-functions on (a, b); thus, $q \in Q$ if there exists a set $z = \{z_k : 0 \leq k \leq N + 1\}$ belonging to Z (see 3.2) such that

$$q = \sum_{k=0}^{N} c_k \chi(z_k, z_{k+1}] \tag{22}$$

for some family $\{c_k : 0 \leq k \leq N\}$ of complex numbers.

9.5. LEMMA. If $q \in Q$ there exists a sequence $\{q_n, n\}$ in P such that

$$q = \lim_{n \to \infty} q_n \qquad (V_b\text{-convergence}). \tag{23}$$

Proof. If $\theta \in [a, b]$ it follows from 9.1 the existence of a V_0-bounded sequence $\{\langle\theta\rangle_n, n\}$ such that

$$\chi(a, \theta](\tau) = \lim_{n \to \infty} \langle\theta\rangle_n(\tau) \qquad (\text{all } \tau \in (a, b));$$

from 7.10 it now results that

$$\chi(a, \theta] = \lim_{n \to \infty} \langle\theta\rangle_n \qquad (V_b\text{-convergence}). \tag{24}$$

Since $q \in Q$, it has the form (22); set

$$q_n = \sum_{k=0}^{N} c_k\{\langle z_{k+1}\rangle_n - \langle z_k\rangle_n\}; \tag{25}$$

obviously, $q_n \in P$, and (23) is now easily seen to be a consequence of (25), (24), and (22).

9.6. *Proof of 9.3.* Suppose that $v \in \mathcal{L}[P_b{:}\mathfrak{A}]$; we must establish the existence of an element $\bar{u}$ of $\mathcal{L}[V_b{:}\mathfrak{A}]$ such that

$$\bar{u}p = vp \qquad (\text{all } p \in P). \tag{26}$$

Since $\mathcal{L}[V_b{:}\quad]\ \mathfrak{A}\,\mathcal{H}$ (by Theorem G (7.14)), any two such extensions $\bar{u}_1$, $\bar{u}_2$ belong to $\mathcal{H}$: their equality is a consequence of 9.2 and the hypothesis $\bar{u}_1 p = vp = \bar{u}_2 p$.

Let Q_b be the result of endowing Q with the topology of V_b: it is clearly a locally convex space. In view of 9.5, any $q \in Q_b$ is the limit of a sequence in P; a convergent sequence being necessarily a bounded net (see 2.3), Extension Theorem A (2.8) (with $D = P$, $X = Q_b$, and $\mu = v$) implies that there is an extension $\bar{v}$ of v such that $\bar{v} \in \mathcal{L}[Q_b{:}\mathfrak{A}]$; in particular,

$$\bar{v}p = vp \qquad (\text{all } p \in P). \tag{27}$$

We have just seen that any q in Q is the limit of a sequence in P: therefore,

$$Q \subset \text{clsr}\, P, \tag{28}$$

where clsr = closure in the topology of V_b. On the other hand, it follows from 3.5–3.6 that any g in BV is the pointwise limit of a V_0-bounded net in Q (compare 9.4 with 4.5(10)): from 7.10 we may now conclude that any g in V_b is the limit of a bounded net in Q. Consequently,

$$\text{BV} \subset \text{clsr}\, Q; \tag{29}$$

also, Extension Theorem A (2.8) (with $D = Q$, $X = V_b$, and $\mu = \bar{v}$) implies that there is an extension $\bar{u}$ of $\bar{v}$ such that $\bar{u} \in \mathfrak{L}\,[V_b{:}\mathfrak{A}]$; in particular,

$$\bar{u}p = \bar{v}p \qquad (\text{all}\, p \in P). \tag{30}$$

The proof is concluded by noting that the equality $\bar{u}p = vp$ comes from (27) and (30). The denseness of P is obtained by combining (28) and (29):

$$\text{BV} \subset \text{clsr clsr}\, P = \text{clsr}\, P.$$

REFERENCES

1. Adams, C. R. and A. P. Morse, Continuous additive functionals on the space(BV) and certain subspaces, *Trans. Amer. Math. Soc.*, **48**(1940), 82–100.
2. Bourbaki, N., Intégration, Chapitres I–IV, Actualités Scient. Indust. No. 1175, Hermann, Paris 1952.
3. Bourbaki, N., Espaces vectoriels topologiques, Chapitres III–V, Actualités Sci. Indust. No. 1229, Hermann, Paris 1955.
4. Bourbaki, N., Espaces vectoriels topologiques, Fascicule de résultats, Actualités Sci. Indust. No. 1230, Hermann, Paris 1955.
5. Dunford, N. and J. Schwartz, Linear operators. I, General theory, Interscience, New York 1958.
6. Gokhman, E. Kh., Integral Stil't'esa i ego priloženiya, Gosudarstv. Izdat. Fiz.-Mat.-Lit., Moscow 1958.
7. Halmos, P. R., Introduction to Hilbert space and the theory of spectral multiplicity, Chelsea, New York 1951.
8. Hildebrandt, T. H., Linear continuous functionals on the space (BV) with weak topologies, Proc. Amer. Math. Soc., Vol. 17, No. 3, (1966), 658–664.
9. Hildebrandt, T. H., Introduction to the theory of integration, Academic Press, New York 1963.
10. Kelley, J. L., General topology, D. Van Nostrand, New York 1955.
11. Kelley, J. L. and I. Namioka, Linear topological spaces, Van Nostrand, New York 1963.
12. Lorentz, G. G., Bernstein polynomials, U. of Toronto Press, Toronto 1953.
13. Natanson, I. P., Theorie der Funktionen einer reelen Veränderlichen, Akademie-Verlag, Berlin 1954.
14. Taylor, A. E., Introduction to functional analysis, New York 1958.

Functorial Measure Theory

F. E. J. Linton

1. INTRODUCTION

In the appendix to his thesis [**2**], J. R. Büchi makes an elegant plea for nonatomic mathematics. To quote, in part:

> "At the foundation of today's mathematics lies the notion of a Set of Elements. . . . If, however, we scrutinize the definitions and theorems of various mathematical disciplines . . . , it is singularly remarkable how seldom the Element is explicitly used. On the contrary, it serves only for the definition of subsets and of relations. . . . Thereafter, the Element is used only implicitly."

These considerations led Büchi to the notion of a *Gefüge* as the proper basis for mathematics. Similar ideas regarding the irrelevancy of the elementhood relation are the force behind Lawvere's recent work [**17**] toward a categorical foundation for mathematics. A measure of his probable success is his ability to recover ordinary set theory [**16**]. A much more modest scheme is the attempt to take the points out of measure spaces, so as to put arbitrary boolean σ-rings on an equal footing with σ-fields of sets.

A number of authors [**3, 4, 10, 14, 24, 25, 28, 32**] have worked toward such a nonatomic or pointless measure theory. The first obstacle is to find the proper counterpart of a function, but it turns out, as we will see, that formal spectral resolutions (for equivalent constructions, see [**9**]) play the role of, say, real-valued functions quite adequately, and have the advantage that equivalence classes of "functions" mod "null functions" are again "functions" on a suitable quotient ring. In this way, the irritating and basically irrelevant locution "almost everywhere" can be banished from measure theory. Incidentally, such formal spectral resolutions, apart from their familiar role in operator theory and in quantum mechanics [**26, 33**], also play a decisive role in a number of representation theorems for Banach lattices, among others [**1, 7, 8, 31**], Kakutani's characterizations [**11, 12**] of L- and M-spaces. Compare also Theorem 2 below.

An important reason that these formal spectral resolutions have not yet gained wider acceptance as suitable "functions" and that the resulting nonatomic measure theory (shown by Carathéodory's book [**4**] to be quite as rich in content as the usual) has seemed so pointless, is the extreme intricacy (e.g., two whole chapters in [**4**]) of the maneuvers hitherto deemed necessary simply to endow the formal spectral resolutions with the usual algebraic and lattice theoretic operations of addition, multiplication, sup, inf, absolute value, positive part, etc.

This, however, is the first of many places where universal techniques from the theory of categories and functors virtually eradicate all difficulty. Another, briefly described elsewhere [**20**], is the description of the dual of L_1. Yet another is the Fubini Theorem: functorial notions not only help prove it, but even help formulate it in this context where it is senseless to write $f_x(y) = f(x, y) = f^y(x)$. And finally, the familiar philosophy, at the very heart of measure theory, that measures extend to linear functionals, finds a precise and usable formulation in the language of adjoint functors: most succinctly put, *Measures are adjoint to functions*.

The following section outlines the algebraic structure with which the formal spectral resolutions are canonically endowed. Section 3 elucidates the cryptic assertion that measures are adjoint to functions. The forms assumed in this setting by some standard results not treated in Carathéodory's book ($L_1{}^*, L_p - L_q$ duality, Fubini Theorem) are sketched in Section 4.

Thanks are due to the National Academy of Sciences and to the National Science Foundation, respectively, for support during the writing of this paper and during the research leading to the results therein embodied.

2. SPECTRAL RESOLUTIONS AND THEIR ALGEBRAIC STRUCTURE

A boolean σ-ring is simply an ordinary ring with idempotent multiplication and countable suprema in the partial order defined by $\sigma \leqslant \sigma' \equiv \sigma = \sigma\sigma'$. The addition then behaves like "symmetric difference" while the multiplication resembles "intersection." A function between two boolean σ-rings is a σ-homomorphism if it is a ring homomorphism and, in addition, preserves countable suprema. We point out that our rings need not have unit elements, and so we impose no restriction relative to unit elements on our σ-homomorphisms.

To see why formal spectral resolutions so adequately play the role of functions, let us recall briefly the usual definition of a measurable, say real-valued, function on a measurable space (X, S). Every real function $\varphi: X \to \mathbb{R}$ gives rise to an inverse image function $\varphi^{-1}: \mathcal{B}(\mathbb{R}) \to \mathcal{B}(X)$

from the power set of $\mathbb{R}$ to the power set of X. φ is called S-measurable if $\varphi^{-1}(b) \in S$ for each Borel subset b of the nonzero real numbers. Since φ^{-1} obviously preserves all boolean operations (in particular, symmetric differences, intersections, countable unions), we see on the one hand that each S-measurable function induces a σ-homomorphism from $B_{\mathbb{R}}$, the σ-ring of Borel subsets of the nonzero real numbers, to the σ-ring S, i.e., a spectral resolution; on the other hand, standard arguments [**26**, §**3**] guarantee that every such homomorphism arises in this way as the φ^{-1} for a unique S-measurable real function φ. It therefore becomes clear immediately that, taking an arbitrary boolean σ-ring S, the way to construct what ought to be all S-measurable real functions is to form the set $\sigma(B_{\mathbb{R}}, S)$ of all σ-homomorphisms from $B_{\mathbb{R}}$ to S. These, for convenience, let us call *real functionoids*; we can safely entrust to the reader the requisite considerations relative to extended real-valued, complex-valued, etc.-valued functions leading to the definition of the corresponding-valued functionoids.

Experience with measurable functions suggests that algebraic and lattice theoretic operations on functionoids should arise from a more general procedure associating, to each n-tuple of real functionoids $f_i (0 \leqslant i < n)$ and each Borel measurable real-valued function f of n real variables, a new functionoid $f(f_0, f_1, \ldots, f_i, \ldots)$. We shall see not only that this can be done, if f sends the origin of $\mathbb{R}^n$ to zero—a provision arising since our σ-rings need have no units, and natural even in the classical setting when the whole space, and hence, each nonzero constant function, fails to be measurable—but also that this is the best that can be done.

It is convenient to work in reverse, that is, to define the concept of a natural operation on all the possible sets of functionoids, and then to make the observations necessary to identify the natural operations with those optimistically described above. In the process, the reader will be briefly (but painlessly) exposed to some functor theory; nevertheless, it will ultimately be much clearer how all the operations on functionoids operate.

It is useful (and, moreover, common) to think of each of the cardinal numbers $n = 0, 1, \ldots, \aleph_0$ as the set

$$n = \{i / 0 \leqslant i < n\}$$

of all smaller cardinals, and to identify the set X^n of all n-tuples in the set X with the set of functions from n to X. In particular, the obvious identification $X \cong X^1$ enables us to treat the points of X as functions from 1 to X.

Now, let us write simply $F(S)$ for the set $\sigma(B_{\mathbb{R}}, S)$ of real functionoids on the σ-ring S, and $F(s)$, where s is a σ-homomorphism from S to another σ-ring S', for the function

$$F(s)\colon F(S) \to F(S')$$
$$\varphi \to s \circ \varphi = \{F(s)\}(\varphi),$$

induced by composition with s. It is easy to check that $F(s \circ s') = F(s) \circ F(s')$, whenever the source of the σ-homomorphism s is the same as the target of s', and that $F(id_S) = id_{F(S)}$. Thus F is an example of a covariant set valued functor on the category of σ-rings.

A natural n-ary operation on functionoids can be defined simply as a natural transformation from the functor F^n to the functor F. In greater detail, this means that a *natural n-ary operation* on functionoids is a system f of functions

$$f_S\colon (F(S))^n \to (F(S))^1, \tag{1}$$

one such function for each boolean σ-ring S, such that, whatever the σ-homomorphism $s\colon S \to S'$, the diagram of functions

$$\begin{array}{ccc} (F(S))^n & \xrightarrow{f_S} & (F(S))^1 \\ {\scriptstyle (F(s))^n}\downarrow & & \downarrow{\scriptstyle (F(s))^1} \\ (F(S'))^n & \xrightarrow{f_{S'}} & (F(S'))^1 \end{array} \tag{2}$$

commutes. Here the left-hand vertical arrows denote the functions sending each of the components $F(S)$ to the corresponding component $F(S')$ by means of the function $F(s)$. Thus a natural n-ary operation is the selection of an ordinary n-place operation on each set $F(S)$, but in such a way as to render each function $F(s)$ a homomorphism.

For technical reasons, it is necessary to replace each of the right-hand exponents ^{1} in (1) and (2) by ^{k}, producing the definition of a *natural* k-*tuple of* n-*ary operations* on functionoids. If we denote by $\Omega(n, k)$ the totality of natural k-tuples of n-ary operations on functionoids, we can define composition functions

$$\Omega(n, k) \times \Omega(k, r) \to \Omega(n, r)$$

by assigning to the pair (f, g) the natural r-tuple of n-ary operations $g \circ f$ specified by

$$(g \circ f)_S = g_S \circ f_S;$$

it is trivial to check that $h \circ (g \circ f) = (h \circ g) \circ f$. Moreover, among the natural k-tuples of n-ary operations are the following: pick any function

$\alpha: k \to n$, and, for each boolean σ-ring S, define

$$F_S^\alpha: (F(S))^n \to (F(S))^k$$
$$x \to x \circ \alpha = F_S^\alpha(x).$$

One verifies without difficulty that $F^\alpha \in \Omega(n, k)$, and that, when $\gamma: r \to k$, $F^\gamma \circ F^\alpha = F^{\alpha\gamma} \cdot F^\alpha$ is called the projection operation corresponding to α; using the projection operations F^i corresponding to the elements of k, it is straightforward to see that, given any k-tuple of natural n-ary operations, i.e., any element of $(\Omega(n, 1))^k$, there is precisely one natural k-tuple of n-ary operations, i.e., element of $\Omega(n, k)$, the k-tuple of whose compositions with the F^i's is the given k-tuple. In other words, via the F^i's, k-tuples of natural n-ary operations are identifiable with natural k-tuples of n-ary operations, or, to put it more graphically,

$$\Omega(n, k) \cong (\Omega(n, 1))^k.$$

Configurations of this sort, special kinds of categories, called *clones* or *theories*, are playing an important and exciting role in the rejuvenation of universal algebra: see [**5, 6, 15, 22**]. For our purposes, we must restrict n, k, r, etc. to be cardinals $\leqslant \aleph_0$.

THEOREM 1. The clone Ω is completely isomorphic to the following clone Λ: for each pair of cardinal numbers n, $k \leqslant \aleph_0$, let $\Lambda(n, k)$ denote the set of all Borel measurable functions from $\mathbb{R}^n$ to $\mathbb{R}^k$ sending origin to origin. The composition rules $\Lambda(n, k) \times \Lambda(k, r) \to \Lambda(n, r)$ are given by the usual composition of functions. The projection operation $\mathbb{R}^\alpha$ corresponding to a function $\alpha: k \to n$ is defined by

$$\mathbb{R}^\alpha(x) = x \circ \alpha \qquad (x \in \mathbb{R}^n).$$

The isomorphism puts each set $\Lambda(n, k)$ in one-to-one correspondence with all of $\Omega(n, k)$ in such a way as to associate F^α to $\mathbb{R}^\alpha$ and to ensure that the composition of two measurable functions in Λ is carried to the composition of the corresponding tuples of operations in Ω.

Proof. Let $B_{\mathbb{R}^n}$ denote the boolean σ-ring of Borel subsets of $\mathbb{R}^n - \{0\}$, the result of removing the origin from the n-fold iterated cartesian product of the real line with itself. The formula $B_f(b) = f^{-1}(b) - \{0\}$ $(b \in B_{\mathbb{R}^k})$ assigns to each $f \in \Lambda(n, k)$ a σ-homomorphism $B_f: B_{\mathbb{R}^k} \to B_{\mathbb{R}^n}$. A standard result [**30, Th. 32.5**] on the representation of boolean homomorphisms, moreover, shows that every σ-homomorphism $B_{\mathbb{R}^k} \to B_{\mathbb{R}^n}$ arises in this way as the B_f for a unique $f \in \Lambda(n, k)$, provided n, $k \leqslant \aleph_0$. [Incidentally, it is only because of the hypotheses of this result that we are forced to restrict the arities of our operations away from uncountable cardinals.]

Take, on the other hand, a natural k-tuple of n-ary operations on functionoids, i.e., a family of functions

$$f_S: (\sigma(B_{\mathbb{R}}, S))^n \to (\sigma(B_{\mathbb{R}}, S))^k.$$

The same result permits us to assert that for each n-tuple of σ-homomorphisms $\varphi_i: B_{\mathbb{R}} \to S$ $(0 \leqslant i < n \leqslant \aleph_0)$, there is a unique σ-homomorphism φ: $B_{\mathbb{R}n} \to S$ satisfying $\varphi \circ B_{\mathbb{R}i} = \varphi_i$ for each $i \in n$. Thus a natural k-tuple of n-ary operations on functionoids can be viewed equally well as a family of functions

$$\bar{f}_S: \sigma(B_{\mathbb{R}n}, S) \to \sigma(B_{\mathbb{R},k}, S)$$

making each diagram

$$\begin{array}{ccc} \sigma(B_{\mathbb{R}n}, S) & \xrightarrow{\bar{f}_S} & \sigma(B_{\mathbb{R}k}, S) \\ \downarrow & & \downarrow \\ \sigma(B_{\mathbb{R}n}, S') & \xrightarrow{\bar{f}_{S'}} & \sigma(B_{\mathbb{R}k}, S') \end{array}$$

commute, whatever the σ-homomorphism s: $S \to S'$ (here the vertical arrows are again the functions "compose with s").

Each such family $\bar{f}$ can now be used to obtain a single σ-homomorphism $\bar{\bar{f}}$: $B_{\mathbb{R}k} \to B_{\mathbb{R}n}$ as follows: set $S = B_{\mathbb{R}n}$ and let

$$\bar{\bar{f}} = \bar{f}_S(id_S).$$

An extremely useful result in functor theory, the so-called Yoneda Lemma [**23, p. 54**], can be invoked here to justify the assertion that the passage from $\bar{f}$ to $\bar{\bar{f}}$ just described, sets up a one-to-one correspondence between the natural transformations $\bar{f}$ and the set of σ-homomorphisms $B_{\mathbb{R}k} \to B_{\mathbb{R}n}$. The following procedure for proving the assertion itself is essentially that for proving the Yoneda Lemma, too. Namely, one verifies that an inverse (two-sided) to the passage $\bar{f} \to \bar{\bar{f}}$ is provided by the following construction: given the σ-homomorphism s: $B_{\mathbb{R}k} \to B_{\mathbb{R}n}$, define $\bar{s}$ by so specifying each $\bar{s}_S$:

$$\bar{s}_S: \sigma(B_{\mathbb{R}n}, S) \to \sigma(B_{\mathbb{R}k}, S)$$
$$x \to x \circ s = \bar{s}_S(x).$$

Thus, via $\sigma(B_{\mathbb{R}k}, B_{\mathbb{R}n})$, we produce the one-to-one correspondences between $\Omega(n, k)$ and $\Lambda(n, k)$ called for by the theorem. We omit the computation verifying the side conditions.

Now it is quite straightforward to follow a given real function along this explicit chain of correspondences to see how it acts on functionoids, and we have, in particular, operations corresponding to the functions of addition, absolute value, multiplication, roots of absolute values, truncation above (below) with any fixed positive (negative) real number; an operation of conditional supremum (acting like $\bigvee_{i\geq 1}(f_0 \wedge f_i)$) determined by the function

$$f(x_0, x_1, \cdots, x_i, \cdots) = \sup_{i\geq 1}(\min(x_0, x_i));$$

an operation acting like "take the characteristic function of the support of . . ." determined by the characteristic function of $\mathbb{R} - \{0\}$; and many more.

We close this section with an interesting specimen of a spectral representation theorem.

THEOREM 2. Any Λ-algebra (i.e., any set X equipped with one function $t_f: X^n \to X^k$ for each $f \in \Lambda(n, k)$ in such a way as to have both $t_{gf} = t_g t_f$ and $t_{\mathbb{R}\alpha}(x) = x \circ \alpha$) is canonically isomorphic to the Λ-algebra $\sigma(B_{\mathbb{R}}, B)$, where B is the boolean σ-ring of elements idempotent under the multiplication provided by $t_{\text{multiplication}}$.

3. MEASURES ARE ADJOINT TO FUNCTIONOIDS

By use of the truncation operations, we can say when a functionoid is bounded: $f \in \sigma(B_{\mathbb{R}}, S)$ is *bounded* if there is a positive real number r such that

$$(-r) \vee (f \wedge r) = f. \tag{3}$$

The infimum of all such r will be called the bound of f, denoted $\|f\|$. Under this norm and the relevant operations on $F(S) = \sigma(B_{\mathbb{R}}, S)$, the subset of bounded functionoids becomes both a Banach algebra and a conditionally countably complete Banach lattice, which will be designated $\mathfrak{F}_S(\mathbb{R})$. Moreover, each function $F(s)$ (s a σ-homomorphism $S \to S'$) sends the bounded elements of $F(S)$ to elements with no higher bound in $F(S')$ (since equation (3) must be preserved), and hence induces a norm decreasing, multiplicative, countable lattice operation preserving, linear transformation

$$\mathfrak{F}_S(\mathbb{R}): \mathfrak{F}_S(\mathbb{R}) \to \mathfrak{F}_{S'}(\mathbb{R}).$$

One observes easily that

$$\mathfrak{F}_s(\mathbb{R}) \circ \mathfrak{F}_{s'}(\mathbb{R}) = \mathfrak{F}_{s \circ s'}(\mathbb{R}), \tag{4}$$

$$\mathfrak{F}_{id_S}(\mathbb{R}) = id\, \mathfrak{F}_S(\mathbb{R}), \tag{5}$$

and that, when N is a σ-ideal in the σ-ring S with quotient $S/N = S'$, the inclusion and projection maps induce transformations

$$F(N) \to F(S),\ F(S) \to F(S')$$

yielding an isomorphism

$$F(S)/F(N) \cong F(S/N), \tag{6}$$

which in turn almost automatically induces an isomorphism

$$\mathfrak{F}_S(\mathbb{R})/\mathfrak{F}_N(\mathbb{R}) \cong \mathfrak{F}_{S/N}(\mathbb{R}). \tag{7}$$

Virtually all that is needed for the proof is the fact that $B_{\mathbb{R}}$ is a projective object in the category of boolean σ-rings, a consequence of the fact [**26**, §**3**] that it is free, which says considerably more. [Remark: relations (4), (5), and (7) indicates the fact that $\mathfrak{F}(\mathbb{R})$ is an *exact functor* from the category of σ-rings to that of Banach spaces, and it is the isomorphism (6) that enables one to divide out by the "null functions" first and not carry a.e.'s around later.]

To continue, define $\chi: S \to F(S) = \sigma(B_{\mathbb{R}}, S)$ by

$$\chi_\sigma(b) = \left\{\begin{matrix} \sigma & (1 \in b) \\ 0 & (1 \in b) \end{matrix}\right\} \quad (\sigma \in S, \quad b \in B_{\mathbb{R}}).$$

χ turns out to be an isomorphism of S onto the boolean ring of multiplicatively idempotent functionoids in $F(S)$. Letting $\mathbb{R} \# S$ denote the real linear span of the set of characteristic functionoids $\{\chi_\sigma / \sigma \in S\}$, we have

LEMMA. Every functionoid in $\mathbb{R} \# S$ (stepfunctionoid) is bounded, the stepfunctionoids are bound-norm dense in the bounded functionoids, and the passage from a linear transformation $T: \mathfrak{F}_S(\mathbb{R}) \to E$ (E a Banach space) to its restriction $T \circ \chi: S \to E$ sets up a linear isometric isomorphism

$$\mathcal{B}(\mathfrak{F}_S(\mathbb{R}), E) \xrightarrow{\cong} M_S(E)$$

between the Banach space of continuous linear transformations from $\mathfrak{F}_S(\mathbb{R})$ to E and the Banach space of all E-valued measure of bounded quasivariation on S, taken with the quasivariation norm.

Making use of the Grothendieck-Schatten (projective) tensor product of Banach spaces (in the largest crossnorm), we define G-valued functionoids on S (G a Banach space) as the tensor product $\mathfrak{F}_S(G) = \mathfrak{F}_S(\mathbb{R}) \otimes G$. (When S is a σ-field of sets, this construction is closely related to the measurable functions Rieffel uses [**27**] for the Bochner integral.) With very little work, we now prove

THEOREM 3. For each boolean σ-ring S and pair of Banach spaces E, G, there is an isometric isomorphism

$$A_{S,E,G}: \mathcal{B}(G, M_S(E)) \xrightarrow{\cong} \mathcal{B}(\mathfrak{F}_S(G), E);$$

moreover, these can be chosen in such a way that whatever the σ-homomorphism $s: S' \to S$ and the continuous linear transformations $g: G' \to G$, $e: E \to E'$, the diagram

$$\begin{array}{ccc} \mathcal{B}(G, M_S(E)) & \xrightarrow{A_{S,E,G}} & \mathcal{B}(\mathfrak{F}_S(G), E) \\ \downarrow & & \downarrow \\ \mathcal{B}(G', M_{S'}(E')) & \xrightarrow{A_{S',E',G'}} & \mathcal{B}(\mathfrak{F}_S(G'), E') \end{array}$$

(in which the vertical arrows send $T \in \mathcal{B}(G, M_S(E))$ resp. $R \in \mathcal{B}(\mathfrak{F}_S(G), E)$ to the composite transformations

$$G' \xrightarrow[g]{} G \xrightarrow[T]{} M_S(E) \xrightarrow[\circ s]{} M_{S'}(E) \xrightarrow[e\circ]{} M_{S'}(E'), \text{ resp.}$$

$$\mathfrak{F}_{S'}(G') \xrightarrow[id \otimes g]{} \mathfrak{F}_{S'}(G) \xrightarrow[\mathfrak{F}_s(\mathbb{R}) \otimes id]{} \mathfrak{F}_S(G) \xrightarrow[R]{} E \xrightarrow[e]{} E')$$

commutes.

[Technically, this says that the functor M_S is *adjoint* to the functor $\mathfrak{F}_S$ by an adjunction natural in S, in short, measures are adjoint to functionoids.]

Proof. We merely define the maps $A_{S,E,G}$ and leave the verification of naturality to the reader. First observe that the necessary and sufficient conditions on a function $G \times S \to E$ for it to give rise to a bounded linear transformation $G \to M_S(E)$ are the same as those for it to give rise to an element of $M_S(\mathcal{B}(G, E))$. There ensues an isometric isomorphism

$$\mathcal{B}(G, M_S(E)) \xrightarrow{\cong} M_S(\mathcal{B}(G, E)).$$

On the other hand, the lemma gives us an isomorphism

$$M_S(\mathcal{B}(G, E) \xrightarrow{\cong} \mathcal{B}(\mathfrak{F}_S(\mathbb{R}), \mathcal{B}(G, E)),$$

and it is the defining property of the tensor product that there be an isometric isomorphism

$$\mathcal{B}(\mathfrak{F}_S(\mathbb{R}), \mathcal{B}(G, E)) \xrightarrow{\cong} \mathcal{B}(\mathfrak{F}_S(\mathbb{R}) \otimes G, E) = \mathcal{B}(\mathfrak{F}_S(G), E).$$

$A_{S,E,G}$ is simply the composite of these three maps.

If we call the linear transformation $A_{S,E,G}(\mu)$ the E-valued integral corresponding to the measure-valued transformation μ, it becomes easy to integrate G-valued functionoids f against E-valued measures μ in the presence of a pairing π: $E \otimes G \to W$, obtaining a value $\int_\pi f\,d\mu \in W$; indeed, there is a bounded linear transformation

$$\begin{array}{l}
\mathfrak{F}_S(G) \otimes M_S(E) \otimes \mathcal{B}(E \otimes G, W) \\
\quad\downarrow \cong \\
\mathfrak{F}_S(G) \otimes M_S(E) \otimes \mathcal{B}(E, \mathcal{B}(G, W)) \\
\quad\downarrow \text{composition on the last two factors} \\
\mathfrak{F}_S(G) \otimes M_S(\mathcal{B}(G, W)) \\
\quad\downarrow \cong \\
\mathfrak{F}_S(G) \otimes \mathcal{B}(G, M_S(W)) \\
\quad\downarrow \text{composition} \\
\mathfrak{F}_S(M_S(W)) \\
\quad\downarrow A_{S,W,M_S(W)}(\mathrm{id}_{M_S(W)}) \\
W
\end{array}$$

and its value at the elementary tensor product $f \otimes \mu \otimes \pi$ is the integral $\int_\pi f\,d\mu$. From its very definition, the linearity of the integral in f and μ (and π, too!) is self evident, and change of variable rules with respect to maps to or from S,E,G or W are immediate consequences of the naturality of each of the transformations used in the composite.

4. POINTLESS MEASURE THEORY: SAMPLE RESULTS

Let there be given a boolean σ-ring S and a non negative, extended real valued, countably additive measure μ on S. E_μ, F_μ, and N_μ will denote the sets of μ-σ-finite, μ-finite, and μ-null somas of S, respectively; E_μ is a σ-ring, F_μ is a boolean ring every principal ideal of which is a σ-ring, and N_μ is a σ-ideal as well in S as in E_μ and F_μ. The quotients of S, E_μ, and F_m by N_μ will be $\bar{S}$, $\bar{E}_\mu$, $\bar{F}_\mu$, and μ clearly drops to a measure $\bar{\mu}$ on $\bar{S}$ whose $\bar{\mu}$-σ-finite, $\bar{\mu}$-finite, and $\bar{\mu}$-null somas are just $\bar{E}_\mu$, $\bar{F}_\mu$, and $\{0\}$, respectively.

The spaces $L_p(\mu)$ are defined as follows. In $\sigma(B_{\mathbb{R}}, S)$, pick out those functionoids which are bounded and live on some principal ideal of F_μ. This set of functionoids is a linear normed lattice $L(\mu)$, and μ extends to a (usually discontinuous) positive linear functional I_μ on $L(\mu)$, in terms of which a new seminorm $\| \ \|_p$ can be introduced on $L(\mu)$ by the formula

$$\|f\|_p = [I_\mu(|f|^p)]^{1/p} \qquad (1 \leq p < \infty).$$

Then $L_p(\mu)$ is the completion of $L(\mu)$ under $\| \ \|_p$. The first observation is that L_p is the same before or after dividing out by null somas and consists of functionoids on $\bar{E}_\mu$.

THEOREM 4. The canonical projection $L(\mu) \longrightarrow L(\bar{\mu})$ induces isometric isomorphisms $L_p(\bar{\mu}) \overset{\cong}{\rightarrow} L_p(\bar{\mu})$, and the inclusion $L(\bar{\mu}) \hookrightarrow \sigma(B_{\mathbb{R}}, \bar{S})$ extends to an embedding of $L_p(\bar{\mu})$ identifying $L_p(\bar{\mu})$ with those functionoids f on $\bar{S}$ living on $\bar{E}_\mu$ for which the ordinary integral

$$\int_0^\infty \lambda \, d(\bar{\mu} \circ |f|^p)$$

is finite (here $\bar{\mu} \circ |f|^p$ is the Borel measure on $\mathbb{R}$ assigning measure $\bar{\mu}(|f|^p(b - \{0\}))$ to the Borel set b in $\mathbb{R}$).

The definition of $L_\infty(\mu)$ follows a different pattern, because we want $L_\infty(\mu)$ to be, without exception, the dual of $L_1(\mu)$. Questions of localizability arising in the calculation of $(L_1(\mu))^*$ necessitate the introduction of the inverse limit $\beta(\bar{E}_\mu)$ of the inverse system of all principal ideals in the σ-ring $\bar{E}_\mu$, and all but force the definition: $L_\infty(\mu) = \mathfrak{F}_B(\mathbb{R})$, where $B = \beta\bar{E}_\mu$. An indication of the proof of the following theorem and further comments concerning the β construction and its relation to the usual localizability of measure spaces are to be found in [**20**].

THEOREM 5. $L_\infty(\bar{\mu}) = L_\infty(\mu) = (L_1(\mu))^*$. If $\bar{E}_\mu$ has a unit—for example, if (totally σ-finite case) E_μ has a unit—then $\beta\bar{E}_\mu = \bar{E}_\mu$, and so $L_\infty(\mu) \cong \mathfrak{F}_{E_\mu}(\mathbb{R})/\mathfrak{F}_{N_\mu}(\mathbb{R}) \cong (L_1(\mu))^*$. More generally, $L_\infty(\mu)$ has a representation as locally measurable functionoids on E_μ, i.e., functionoids on βE_μ, modulo locally null functionoids, in some appropriate sense, if and only if E_μ is localizable [**20**] over N_μ.

An important ingredient in the proof, of course, is the Radon-Nikodym Theorem, which, in the present setting, is conveniently combined with the Mean Value Theorem to characterize the indefinite integrals of positive functionoids on E_μ with respect to μ as μ-absolutely continuous countably additive extended real valued positive measures on principal ideals of E_μ. For further details, see [**19, §2.4**] or [**4, §159, Satz 2** and **§171, Satz 2**].

As is to be expected, the usual $L_p - L_q$ duality can also be established. We give no details here, since the only arguments we know are the exact analogues of the classical ones.

The Fubini Theorem, on the other hand, is far from an exact replica of its classical counterpart (indeed, the error pointed out by Sikorski [**29**] in the only previous attempt to develop a Fubini Theorem in this context some twenty years ago [**13**] arose largely because of too close imitation of the classical version: see [**30, §38C**]). The first (and, as it happens, only) obstacle is the matter of deciding what functionoids "of two variables" should be, now that there are no variables. The decision is rendered by choosing the functionoids on the tensor product (in the sense of universal algebra, see [**21**] or also [**18**]) of the various given σ-rings. The theorem that comes out says:

THEOREM 6 (Fubini). Let μ_1 and μ_2 be positive extended-real valued countably additive measures on σ-rings S_1, S_2. There is then a unique measure of the same sort, denoted $\mu = \mu_1 \otimes \mu_2$, on the tensor product $E_{\mu_1} \otimes_\sigma E_{\mu_2}$ subject to the requirement

$$\mu(a \otimes b) = \mu_1(a)\mu_2(b) \qquad (a \in E_{\mu_1}, b \in E_{\mu_2})$$

(the convention is $0 \cdot \infty = 0$). In addition, there is a canonical isometric isomorphism

$$L_1(\mu_1) \otimes L_1(\mu_2) \cong L_1(\mu_1 \otimes \mu_2),$$

where the left hand $\otimes$ denotes the usual Grothendieck-Schatten tensor product of Banach spaces.

Proof sketch. The uniqueness of μ is the consequence of a standard result [**4, §206, Satz 1**] on the generation of measures. Existence is shown as follows. Map $F_{\mu_1} \times F_{\mu_2}$ into $L_1(\mu_1) \otimes L_1(\mu_2)$ by sending (a, b) to $\chi_a \otimes \chi_b$, and map $L_1(\mu_1) \otimes L_1(\mu_2)$ to $\mathbb{R}$ by $I_{\mu_1} \otimes I_{\mu_2}$. The composite extends to the desired measure μ on $E_{\mu_1} \otimes_\sigma E_{\mu_2}$. Moreover, the first of these maps extends to an isometry of the algebraic tensor product $L(\mu_1) \otimes_{\mathbb{R}} L(\mu_2)$ onto a dense subspace of $L_1(\mu)$, from which the second assertion of the theorem can be established.

Remark: the usual double integration formula is now trivial, for, modulo the isometry of the theorem, $I_\mu = I_{\mu_1} \otimes I_{\mu_2}$, and the double integration formula is just the commutative diagram

$$\begin{array}{ccc} L_1(\mu) \cong L_1(\mu_1) \otimes L_1(\mu_2) & \xrightarrow[\mathrm{id} \otimes I_{\mu_2}]{} & L_1(\mu_1) \otimes \mathbb{R} \\ {\scriptstyle I_{\mu_1} \otimes \mathrm{id}} \downarrow & & \downarrow {\scriptstyle I_{\mu_1} \otimes \mathrm{id}} \\ \mathbb{R} \otimes L_1(\mu_2) & \xrightarrow[\mathrm{id} \otimes I_{\mu_2}]{} & \mathbb{R} \otimes \mathbb{R} = \mathbb{R} \end{array}$$

In effect, though the sections of functionoids on a tensor product of boolean σ-rings do not exist, they can nevertheless be integrated with respect to one of the measures to obtain a functionoid on the other σ-ring, and the familiar painful hedging about the integrability of "almost every section" is entirely avoided.

BIBLIOGRAPHY

1. Bohnenblust, F., An axiomatic characterization of L_p spaces, *Duke J. Math.* **6**(1940), 627–640.
2. Büchi, J. R., Die Boole'sche Partialordnung und die Paarung von Gefügen, *Portugaliae Math.* **7**(1948), 119–180.
3. Carathéodory, C., Entwurf für eine Algebraisierung des Integralbegriffs, Sitzungsber. d. Bayer. Akad. d. Wiss. (1938), 27–69.
4. Carathéodory, C., *Mass und Integral und ihre Algebraisierung*, Birkäuser, Basel, 1956.
5. Cohn, P. M., *Universal Algebra*, Harper and Row, New York, 1965.
6. Eilenberg, S., Automata theory (forthcoming).
7. Freudenthal, H., Uber teilweise geordnete Moduln, *Proc. Kon.* Akad. van Wettenschappen Amsterdam **39**(1936), 641–651.
8. Goffman, C., Remarks on lattice-ordered groups and vector lattices, I. Carathéodory functions, *Trans. Amer. Math. Soc.* **88**(1958), 107–120.
9. Götz, A., O odpowiednikach pojecia funkcji punktu w cialach Boole'a (on the equivalents of the notion of point function in Boolean fields), *Prace Mat.* **1**(1955), 145–161 (Polish; English summary).
10. Horn, A., and Tarski, A., Measures in Boolean algebras, *Trans. Amer. Math. Soc.* **64**(1948), 467–497.
11. Kakutani, S., Concrete representation of abstract (L)-spaces and the mean ergodic theorem, *Ann. of Math.* **42**(1941), 523–537.
12. Kakutani, S., Concrete representation of abstract (M)-spaces, *Ann. of Math.* **42**(1941), 994–1024.
13. Kappos, D. A., Die Cartesischen Produkte und die Multiplication von Massfunktionen in Booleschen Algebren, I and II, *Math. Ann.* **120**(1947), 43–74 and 121 (1949), 223–233.
14. Kappos, D. A., Strukturtheorie der Wahrscheinlichkeitsfelder und -räume, Ergebnisse der Math **24**(1960), Springer, Berlin.
15. Lawvere, F. W., *Functorial Semantics of Algebraic Theories*, Columbia University (dissertation), 1963; summarized in *Proc. Nat. Acad. Sci.* **50**(1963), 869–872.
16. Lawvere, F. W., An elementary theory of the category of sets, Univ. of Chicago and ETH Zürich (mimeographed); summarized in *Proc. Nat. Acad. Sci.* **52**(1964), 1506–1511.
17. Lawvere, F. W., The category of categories as a foundation for mathematics, Univ. of Chicago and ETH Zürich, 1965 (mimeographed).
18. Linton, F. E. J., Tensor products of Boolean σ-rings, Notices *Amer. Math. Soc.* **10**(1963), 271.
19. Linton, F. E. J., *The functorial foundations of measure theory*, Columbia University (dissertation), 1963.
20. Linton, F. E. J., The obstruction to the localizability of a measure space, *Bull. Amer. Math. Soc.* **71**(1965), 353–356.
21. Linton, F. E. J., Autonomous equational categories, *J. Math. Mech.* (to appear)
22. Linton, F. E. J., Some aspects of equational categories, Proc. of the Conference on Categorical Algebra (La Jolla, 1965), Springer, Berlin, 1966.
23. Mac Lane, S., Categorical algebra, *Bull. Amer. Math. Soc.* **71**(1965), 40–106.
24. MacNeille, H., Partially ordered sets, *Trans. Amer. Math. Soc.* **42**(1937), 416–460.
25. Olmsted, J. M. H., Lebesgue theory on a Boolean algebra, *Trans. Amer. Math. Soc.* **51**(1942), 164–193.
26. Ramsay, A., A theorem on two commuting observables (to appear).

27. Rieffel, M. A., The Radon-Nikodym theorem for the Bochner integral (to appear).
28. Sikorski, R., The integral in a Boolean algebra, *Coll. Math.* **2**(1949), 20–26.
29. Sikorski, R., On measures in Cartesian products of Boolean algebras, *Coll. Math* **2**(1951), 124–129.
30. Sikorski, R., Boolean algebras, *Ergebnisse der Math* **25**(1960), Springer, Berlin.
31. Vulih, B. Z., *Vvedenie v teoriyu poluuporyadočennih prostranstv* (Introduction to the theory of partially ordered spaces), FizMatGiz, Moscow, 1961.
32. Wecken, F., Abstrakte Integrale und fastperiodische Funktionen, *Math. Z.* **45**(1939), 377–404.
33. Zierler, N., Order properties of bounded observables, *Proc. Amer. Math. Soc.* **14**(1963), 346–351.

On Spaces of Holomorphic Functions of a Given Type[1]

by
LEOPOLDO NACHBIN[2]
University of Chicago
and
University of Rochester

INTRODUCTION

The purpose of this article is to describe a natural method of endowing certain vector spaces of holomorphic mappings with locally convex topologies, and to derive a few results, for the sake of illustration, of the simple ideas involved in such a method.

The need of the following considerations [5] was prompted by the remark that the largest natural locally convex topology to be used on $\mathcal{H}(U; F)$ (see §1 for notation and terminology) is not the one induced on it by the compact-open topology on the vector space $\mathcal{C}(U; F)$ of all continuous F-valued functions on U (unlike what happens when E is finite dimensional and thus locally compact). A seminorm p on $\mathcal{H}(U; F)$ is said to be ported by a compact subset K of U if, given any open subset V of U containing K, we can find a real number $c(V) > 0$ for which

$$p(f) \leq c(V) \cdot \sup_{x \in V} \|f(x)\|$$

holds for every $f \in \mathcal{H}(U; F)$. It is to be noted that f is not necessarily bounded on V; however, once $f \in \mathcal{H}(U; F)$ and the compact subset K of U are given, there is clearly an open subset V of U containing K on which f is bounded. In other words, the above estimate imposes a restric-

---

[1]The research reported in the present article was sponsored in part by the National Science Foundation through grant GP 5793 at the University of Rochester.

[2]On leave from the Centro Brasileiro de Pesquisas Fisicas and the Instituto de Matematica Pura e Aplicada, Universidade do Brasil, Rio de Janeiro, GB, Brasil.

tion on p for every f, although its right-hand side may occasionally be infinite. The natural topology $\mathfrak{T}_\omega$ on $\mathcal{H}(U; F)$ is defined by the seminorms on $\mathcal{H}(U; F)$ that are ported by compact subsets of U. It is much larger than the topology on $\mathcal{H}(U; F)$ induced by the compact open topology on $\mathcal{C}(U; F)$ whenever $\dim E = \infty$ and $F \neq 0$; otherwise the two topologies on $\mathcal{H}(U; F)$ coincide. The same natural method used here, namely that of estimating functions on arbitrarily small neighborhoods of fixed compact subsets (as expressed by the above estimate), can be of course applied to $\mathcal{C}(U; F)$ itself; but then it gives back the compact-open topology on $\mathcal{C}(U; F)$ and not a larger one. It is only in the case of certain vector subspaces of $\mathcal{C}(U; F)$ which are not too large, or too small, that such a method leads to a topology actually bigger than the one induced by the compact-open topology on $\mathcal{C}(U; F)$.

On the other hand, certain questions about convolution and partial differential operators, Fourier and Borel transforms, distributions, etc., in infinite dimensions (see [**2**] and [**6**]) lead to important types of holomorphy, and of differentiability or real-analyticity as well, and so to corresponding spaces of mappings and their natural topologies. Important examples of such types are found in the nuclear, the integral, the Hilbert-Schmidt cases, etc., all stemming from the corresponding kinds of continuous m-homogeneous polynomials (or equivalently, except perhaps for the norms, of continuous m-linear mappings; see [**1**]).

Section 2 introduces the concept of holomorphy type θ from E to F; and §4 deals with the natural topology $\mathfrak{T}_{\omega,\theta}$ on the vector subspace $\mathcal{H}_\theta(U; F)$ of $\mathcal{H}(U; F)$. Simplifications arising in the case $\mathcal{H}(U; F)$ are described in §7. The rest of the article is devoted to sampling a few results. We refrain here from being as complete in the case $\dim E = \infty$ as one would hope for in view of the existing knowledge in the case $\dim E < \infty$ (see [**3**], and the literature quoted there as well). Thus we do not deal at all with the standard properties of locally convex spaces to be investigated in this connection, with spaces of functions holomorphic about a fixed set not necessarily open or compact, with spaces of real-analytic or differentiable functions, or with the dislinearization of the theory through the use of Banachizable manifolds, etc. A thorough exposition of such aspects deserves a monograph to itself.

1. NOTATION AND TERMINOLOGY

Throughout this article, E and F will represent two complex Banach spaces.

N and **C** will denote respectively the systems of all natural integers $0, 1, \ldots,$ and of all complex numbers.

For each $m \in \mathbf{N}$, we shall represent by $\mathcal{P}(^mE; F)$ the Banach space of all continuous m-homogeneous polynomials from E to F. Notice that $\mathcal{P}(^0E; F) = F$.

The open ball with center ξ and radius $\rho > 0$ in a normed space will be denoted by $B_\rho(\xi)$. Correspondingly, we set

$$B_\rho(X) = \bigcup_{x \in X} B_r(x)$$

for a subset X of a normed space.

U will denote a nonvoid open subset of E; and $\mathcal{H}(U; F)$ will represent the vector space of all holomorphic mappings from U to F. We say that U is equilibrated with respect to one of its points ξ in case $(1 - \lambda)\xi + \lambda x \in U$ for every $x \in U$ and $\lambda \in \mathbf{C}$, $|\lambda| \leq 1$.

If $f \in \mathcal{H}(U; F)$, we denote by $\hat{d}^m f(x) \in \mathcal{P}(^mE; F)$ its m-differential at $x \in U$ looked at as a continuous m-homogeneous polynomial (and not as a continuous symmetric m-linear mapping), for every $m \in \mathbf{N}$. We have correspondingly the mapping

$$\hat{d}^m f \in \mathcal{H}(U; \mathcal{P}(^mE; F)).$$

The Taylor polynomial $\tau_{m,f,\xi}$ of order $m \in \mathbf{N}$ of $f \in \mathcal{H}(U; F)$ at $\xi \in U$ is given by

$$\tau_{m,f,\xi}(x) = \sum_{l=0}^{m} \frac{1}{l!} \hat{d}^l f(\xi) \cdot (x - \xi)$$

for every $x \in E$.

θ will always denote a holomorphy type from E to F, as defined in §2.

We refer to [**4**] in the References as a general source for notation and terminology, as well as for certain results used in this article without further explanation.

2. HOLOMORPHY TYPES

DEFINITION 1. A *holomorphy type* θ from E to F is a sequence of Banach spaces $\mathcal{P}_\theta(^mE; F)$, for $m \in \mathbf{N}$, the norm on each of them being denoted by $P \to \|P\|_\theta$, such that the following conditions hold true:

(1) Each $\mathcal{P}_\theta(^mE; F)$ is a vector subspace of $\mathcal{P}(^mE; F)$.

(2) $\mathcal{P}_\theta(^0E; F)$ coincides with $\mathcal{P}(^0E; F) = F$, as a normed vector space.

(3) There is a real number $\sigma \geq 1$ for which the following is true. Given any $l \in \mathbf{N}$, $m \in \mathbf{N}$, $|l \leq m|$, $x \in E$ and $P \in \mathcal{P}_\theta(^mE; F)$, we

have

$$\hat{d}^l P(x) \in \mathcal{P}_\theta({}^l E; F), \qquad \text{and}$$

$$\left\| \frac{1}{l!} \hat{d}^l P(x) \right\|_\theta \leq \sigma^m \cdot \| P \|_\theta \cdot \| x \|^{m-l}$$

PROPOSITION 1. Each inclusion mapping

$$\mathcal{P}_\theta({}^m E; F) \subset \mathcal{P}({}^m E; F)$$

is continuous and of norm inferior to σ^m, $m \in \mathbf{N}$.

Proof. Set $l = 0$ in Condition (3) and use Conditions (1) and (2) of Definition 1 to get

$$\| P(x) \| \leq \sigma^m \cdot \| P \|_\theta \cdot \| x \|^m$$

that is

$$\| P \| \leq \sigma^m \| P \|_\theta. \qquad \text{Q.E.D.}$$

DEFINITION 2. A given $f \in \mathcal{H}(U; F)$ is said to be of *θ-holomorphy type at $\xi \in U$* if:

(1) $\hat{d}^m f(\xi) \in \mathcal{P}_\theta({}^m E; F)$ for $m \in \mathbf{N}$

(2) There are real numbers $C \geq 0$ and $c \geq 0$ such that

$$\left\| \frac{1}{m!} \hat{d}^m f(\xi) \right\|_\theta \leq C \cdot c^m \text{ for } m \in \mathbf{N}.$$

Moreover, f is said to be of *θ-holomorphy type on U* if f is of θ-holomorphy type at every point of U. We shall denote by $\mathcal{H}_\theta(U; F)$ the vector subspace of $\mathcal{H}(U; F)$ of all such f of θ-holomorphy type on U.

PROPOSITION 2. If $f \in \mathcal{H}_\theta(U; F)$, then corresponding to every compact subset K of U there are real numbers $C \geq 0$ and $c \geq 0$, and an open subset V of U containing K, such that

$$\left\| \frac{1}{m!} \hat{d}^m f(x) \right\|_\theta \leq C \cdot c^m$$

for every $x \in V$ and $m \in \mathbf{N}$.

The proof will be based on the following lemma.

LEMMA 1. Let $f \in \mathcal{H}(U; F)$ be of θ-holomorphy type at $\xi \in U$. Then there exists a real number $\rho > 0$ such that $B_\rho(\xi) \subset U$, and such that:

(1) $\hat{d}^m f(x) \in \mathcal{P}_\theta({}^m E; F)$ for every $x \in B_\rho(\xi)$ and $m \in \mathbf{N}$.

(2) There are real numbers $C \geq 0$ and $c \geq 0$ such that

$$\left\| \frac{1}{m!} \hat{d}^m f(x) \right\|_\theta \leq C \cdot c^m$$

for every $x \in B_\rho(\xi)$ and $m \in \mathbf{N}$.

(3) For every $x \in B_\rho(\xi)$ and $l \in \mathbf{N}$, we have

$$\hat{d}^l f(x) = \sum_{m=l}^{\infty} \hat{d}^l P_m(x - \xi),$$

where

$$P_m = \frac{1}{m!}\hat{d}^m f(\xi) \qquad (m \in \mathbf{N}),$$

convergence of the series being in the sense of $\mathcal{P}_\theta({}^lE; F)$.

Proof. Consider the Taylor series

$$f(x) \cong \sum_{m=0}^{\infty} P_m(x - \xi)$$

of f at ξ. Then there exists some real number $\rho > 0$ such that $B_\rho(\xi) \subset U$, and such that, letting $x \in B_\rho(\xi)$ and $l \in \mathbf{N}$, we have

$$\hat{d}^l f(x) = \sum_{m=l}^{\infty} \hat{d}^l P_m(x - \xi), \tag{*}$$

convergence of this series being in the sense of $\mathcal{P}({}^lE; F)$. By Condition (1) of Definition 2, we have $P_m \in \mathcal{P}_\theta({}^mE; F)$. Hence $\hat{d}^l P_m(x - \xi) \in \mathcal{P}_\theta({}^lE; F)$, by Condition (3) of Definition 1. Using Condition (3) of Definition 1, we have

$$\sum_{m=l}^{\infty} \| \hat{d}^l P_m(x - \xi) \|_\theta \leq l! \sum_{m=l}^{\infty} \sigma^m \cdot \| P_m \|_\theta \cdot \| x - \xi \|^{m-l}.$$

There are real numbers $C \geq 0$ and $c \geq 0$ such that $\| P_m \|_\theta \leq C \cdot c^m$ for every $m \in \mathbf{N}$, by Condition (2) of Definition 2. If, in addition, we assume that ρ was chosen sufficiently small so that $\sigma c \rho < 1$, we shall have have

$$\sum_{m=l}^{\infty} \| \hat{d}^l P_m(x - \xi) \|_\theta \leq \frac{l!C}{1 - \sigma c \rho} \cdot (\sigma c)^l$$

for every $x \in B_\rho(\xi)$ and $l \in \mathbf{N}$, so that the series in (*) will converge in the sense of $\mathcal{P}_\theta({}^lE; F)$, by completeness of this normed space. Since that series converges to $\hat{d}^l f(x)$ in the sense of $\mathcal{P}({}^lE; F)$, by assumption, it follows, by virtue of Proposition 1, that actually $\hat{d}^l f(x) \in \mathcal{P}_\theta({}^lE; F)$, that (*) is true in the sense of $\mathcal{P}_\theta({}^l E; F)$, and also that

$$\left\| \frac{1}{l!} \hat{d}^l f(x) \right\|_\theta \leq \frac{C}{1 - \sigma c \rho} \cdot (\sigma c)^l$$

for every $x \in B_\rho(\xi)$ and $l \in \mathbf{N}$. Q.E.D.

Proof of Proposition 2. Apply Condition (2) of Lemma 1. Q.E.D.

3. DIFFERENTIATION OF HOLOMORPHY TYPES

DEFINITION 1. Once a holomorphy type θ from E to F and $l \in \mathbf{N}$ are given, the vector space isomorphism

$$P \in \mathcal{P}({}^{l+m}E; F) \rightarrow \frac{1}{l!} \hat{d}^l P \in \mathcal{P}({}^m E; \mathcal{P}({}^l E; F))$$

(for each $m \in \mathbf{N}$) induces, by Condition (3) of Definition 1, §2, a vector space isomorphism of $\mathcal{P}_\theta({}^{l+m}E; F)$ onto a vector subspace of $\mathcal{P}({}^m E; \mathcal{P}_\theta({}^l E; F))$. Such a vector subspace will be denoted by

$$\frac{1}{l!} \hat{d}^l \mathcal{P}_\theta({}^{l+m}E; F);$$

it becomes a Banach space when normed in an isometric way by

$$\left\| \frac{1}{l!} \hat{d}^l P \right\|_\tau = \| P \|_\theta$$

for $P \in \mathcal{P}_\theta({}^{l+m}E; F)$.

PROPOSITION 1. For each fixed holomorphy type θ from E to F and $l \in \mathbf{N}$, the sequence of Banach spaces

$$\frac{1}{l!} \hat{d}^l \mathcal{P}_\theta({}^{l+m}E; F) \qquad (m \in \mathbf{N})$$

is a holomorphy type τ from E to $\mathcal{P}_\theta({}^l E; F)$ $\left(\text{to be denoted by } \frac{1}{l!} \hat{d}^l \theta\right)$.

Proof. We have to verify conditions (1), (2) and (3) of Definition 1, §2 for the prospective holomorphy type τ from E to $\mathcal{P}_\theta({}^l E; F)$. Condition (1) is clearly satisfied.

As to Condition (2), if

$$P \in \mathcal{P}_\theta({}^{l+0}E; F) \subset \mathcal{P}({}^l E; F),$$

then

$$\frac{1}{l!} \hat{d}^l P = P,$$

showing that

$$\frac{1}{l!}\hat{d}^l \mathcal{P}_\theta(^{l+0}E; F)$$

coincides with $\mathcal{P}_\theta(^lE; F)$ as a normed space.

To verify Condition (3), let $k \in \mathbf{N}$, $m \in \mathbf{N}$, $k \leq m$, $x \in E$ and

$$P \in \frac{1}{l!}\hat{d}^l \mathcal{P}_\theta(^{l+m}E; F)$$

be given. This means that

$$P = \frac{1}{l!}\hat{d}^l Q$$

for a unique $Q \in \mathcal{P}_\theta(^{l+m}E; F)$. We then have

$$\frac{1}{k!}\hat{d}^k P(x) = \frac{1}{k!}\hat{d}^k\left(\frac{1}{l!}\hat{d}^l Q\right)(x) = \frac{1}{l!}\hat{d}^l\left[\frac{1}{(l+k)!}\hat{d}^{l+k}Q(x)\right].$$

Since

$$\hat{d}^{l+k}Q(x) \in \mathcal{P}_\theta(^{l+k}E; F)$$

by Condition (3) of Definition 1, §2, we see that

$$\hat{d}^k P(x) \in \frac{1}{l!}\hat{d}^l \mathcal{P}_\theta(^{l+k}E; F).$$

Moreover, we claim that

$$\left\|\frac{1}{k!}\hat{d}^k P(x)\right\|_\tau \leq (\sigma^{l+1})^m \cdot \|P\|_\tau \cdot \|x\|^{m-k},$$

where σ is associated with the holomorphy type θ from E to F by Condition (3) of Definition 1, §2. In fact, this inequality amounts to

$$\left\|\frac{1}{(l+k)!}\hat{d}^{l+k}Q(x)\right\|_\theta \leq (\sigma^{l+1})^m \cdot \|Q\|_\theta \cdot \|x\|^{m-k}.$$

This is true in case $m = 0$, for then $k = 0$, $Q \in \mathcal{P}_\theta(^lE; F)$ and

$$\frac{1}{l!}\hat{d}^l Q = Q.$$

This is also true in case $m \geq 1$. In fact, using Condition (3) of Definition 1, §2 for θ, we have

$$\left\|\frac{1}{(l+k)!}d^{l+k}Q(x)\right\|_\theta \leq \sigma^{l+m} \cdot \|Q\|_\theta \cdot \|x\|^{m-k}.$$

It remains to notice that $\sigma^{l+m} \leq \sigma^{lm+m} = (\sigma^{l+1})^m$. Q.E.D.

PROPOSITION 2. Let θ be a holomorphy type from E to F, and

$$\tau = \frac{1}{l!}\hat{d}^l\theta$$

be the corresponding holomorphy type from E to $\mathcal{P}_\theta({}^lE; F)$, where $l \in \mathbf{N}$ (see Proposition 1). If $f \in \mathcal{H}_\theta(U; F)$, then

$$\hat{d}^l f \in \mathcal{H}_\tau(U; \mathcal{P}_\theta({}^lE; F)).$$

Proof. Letting $\xi \in U$ and

$$P_m = \frac{1}{m!}\hat{d}^m f(\xi) \qquad (m \in \mathbf{N}),$$

choose some real number $\rho > 0$ such that $B_\rho(\xi) \subset U$, and such that

$$\frac{1}{l!}\hat{d}^l f(x) = \sum_{m=l}^{\infty} \frac{1}{l!}\hat{d}^l P_m(x - \xi) = \tag{1}$$

$$= \sum_{m=0}^{\infty} \frac{1}{l!}\hat{d}^l P_{l+m}(x - \xi)$$

for every $x \in B_\rho(\xi)$ and $l \in \mathbf{N}$, where the series is assumed to be convergent in the sense of $\mathcal{P}_\theta({}^lE; F)$, by (3) of Lemma 1, §2. Since we can use Conditions (1) and (2) of Definition 2, §2, we see that

$$\left\| \frac{1}{l!}\hat{d}^l P_{l+m}(x - \xi) \right\|_\theta \leq \sigma^{l+m} \cdot \| P_{l+m} \|_\theta \cdot \| x - \xi \|^m$$

$$\leq C \cdot (\sigma c)^l \cdot (\sigma c)^m \cdot \| x - \xi \|^m, \tag{2}$$

by virtue also of Condition (3) of Definition 1, §2. It follows from (1) and (2) that

$$\hat{d}^l f \in \mathcal{H}(U; \mathcal{P}_\theta({}^lE; F)). \tag{3}$$

Moreover we see that

$$\frac{1}{l!}\hat{d}^l P_{l+m} \in \frac{1}{l!}\hat{d}^l \mathcal{P}_\theta({}^{l+m}E; F), \tag{4}$$

and that

$$\left\| \frac{1}{l!}\hat{d}^l P_{l+m} \right\|_\tau = \| P_{l+m} \|_\theta \leq C \cdot c^l \cdot c^m. \tag{5}$$

Equations (3), (4) and (5) complete the proof. Q.E.D.

COROLLARY 1. Let $f \in \mathcal{H}_\theta(U; F)$ and $B_\rho(\xi) \subset U$. Then

$$\left\| \frac{1}{l!} \hat{d}^l f(x) \right\|_\theta \leq \sum_{m=l}^{\infty} \sigma^m \rho^{m-l} \cdot \left\| \frac{1}{m!} \hat{d}^m f(\xi) \right\|_\theta$$

for every $x \in B_\rho(\xi)$ and $l \in \mathbf{N}$.

Proof. By Proposition 2, we have

$$\frac{1}{l!} \hat{d}^l f \in \mathcal{H}(U; \mathcal{P}_\theta({}^l E; F)).$$

Hence the Taylor series of this function at ξ, namely

$$\frac{1}{l!} \hat{d}^l f(x) = \sum_{m=l}^{\infty} \frac{1}{l!} \hat{d}^l P_m(x - \xi),$$

where

$$P_m = \frac{1}{m!} \hat{d}^m f(\xi) \qquad (m \in \mathbf{N}),$$

converges to the indicated sum, in the sense of $\mathcal{P}_\theta({}^l E; F)$, for every $x \in B_\rho(\xi)$. By using Condition (3) of Definition 1, §2, we get

$$\left\| \frac{1}{l!} \hat{d}^l f(x) \right\|_\theta \leq \sum_{m=l}^{\infty} \sigma^m \| P_m \|_\theta \rho^{m-l}$$

if $x \in B_\rho(\xi)$. Q.E.D.

COROLLARY 2. Let $f \in \mathcal{H}_\theta(U; F)$ and $B_\rho(X) \subset U$. Then

$$\sum_{l=0}^{\infty} \epsilon^l \cdot \sup_{x \in B_\rho(X)} \left\| \frac{1}{l!} \hat{d}^l f(x) \right\|_\theta \leq \sum_{m=0}^{\infty} [\sigma(\rho + \epsilon)]^m \cdot \sup_{x \in X} \left\| \frac{1}{m!} \hat{d}^m f(x) \right\|_\theta$$

for every real number $\epsilon > 0$.

Proof. Apply Corollary 1. Q.E.D.

4. TOPOLOGY ON SPACES OF HOLOMORPHIC MAPPINGS

LEMMA 1. Let p be a seminorm on $\mathcal{H}_\theta(U; F)$ and K be a compact subset of U. Then the following conditions are equivalent:

(1) Given any real number $\epsilon > 0$, we can find a real number $c(\epsilon) > 0$ such that

$$p(f) \leq c(\epsilon) \sum_{m=0}^{\infty} \epsilon^m \cdot \sup_{x \in K} \left\| \frac{1}{m!} \hat{d}^m f(x) \right\|_\theta$$

for every $f \in \mathcal{H}_\theta(U; F)$.

(2) Given any real number $\epsilon > 0$ and any open subset V of U containing K, we can find a real number $c(\epsilon, V) > 0$ such that

$$p(f) \leq c(\epsilon, V) \sum_{m=0}^{\infty} \epsilon^m \cdot \sup_{x \in V} \left\| \frac{1}{m!} \hat{d}^m f(x) \right\|_\theta$$

for every $f \in \mathcal{H}_\theta(U; F)$.

Proof. It is clear that (1) implies (2). To prove that (2) implies (1), we apply Corollary 2 of §3 by taking $X = K$ and by assuming further that $\rho \leq \epsilon$. Q.E.D.

DEFINITION 1. A seminorm p on $\mathcal{H}_\theta(U; F)$ is said to be *ported* by a compact subset K of U if the equivalent conditions (1) and (2) of Lemma 1 hold. The natural topology $\mathfrak{J}_{\omega,\theta}$ on $\mathcal{H}_\theta(U; F)$, also denoted simply by $\mathfrak{J}_\omega$, is defined by the seminorms on $\mathcal{H}_\theta(U; F)$ that are ported by compact subsets of U. It is plainly separated.

REMARK 1. It is to be observed that, by Proposition 1, §2, once $f \in \mathcal{H}_\theta(U; F)$ and a compact subset K of U are given, we can find a real number $\epsilon > 0$ and an open subset V of U containing K such that

$$\sum_{m=0}^{\infty} \epsilon^m \cdot \sup_{x \in V} \left\| \frac{1}{m!} \hat{d}^m f(x) \right\|_\theta < \infty,$$

and, in particular,

$$\sum_{m=0}^{\infty} \epsilon^m \cdot \sup_{x \in K} \left\| \frac{1}{m!} \hat{d}^m f(x) \right\|_\theta < \infty.$$

These facts are to be compared, respectively, with conditions (2) and (1) in Lemma 1.

PROPOSITION 1. Let Λ be a set, $\mathfrak{F}$ a filter on Λ, $(f_\lambda)_{\lambda \in \Lambda}$ a family of elements of $\mathcal{H}_\theta(U; F)$ indexed by Λ and $f \in \mathcal{H}_\theta(U; F)$. Assume that, corresponding to every compact subset K of U, we can find a real number $\epsilon > 0$ such that

$$\lim_{l \to \mathfrak{F}} \sum_{m=0}^{\infty} \epsilon^m \cdot \sup_{x \in K} \left\| \frac{1}{m!} \hat{d}^m (f_\lambda - f) \right\|_\theta = 0.$$

Then

$$\lim_{\lambda \to \mathfrak{F}} f_\lambda = f$$

in the sense of the topology $\mathfrak{J}_\omega$ on $\mathcal{H}_\theta(U; F)$.

The proof is trivial.

REMARK 2. From Corollary 2, §3, it follows that the assumption in Proposition 1 is equivalent to requiring that, corresponding to every compact subset K of U, we can find a real number $\epsilon > 0$ and an open subset V of U containing K such that

$$\lim_{\lambda \to \mathfrak{F}} \sum_{m=0}^{\infty} \epsilon^m \cdot \sup_{x \in V} \left\| \frac{1}{m!} d^m(f_\lambda - f) \right\|_\theta = 0.$$

PROPOSITION 2. Let $f \in \mathcal{H}_\theta(U; F)$, $\xi \in U$ and U be ξ-equilibrated. Then the Taylor series of f at ξ converges to f in the sense of the topology $\mathfrak{I}_\omega$ on $\mathcal{H}_\theta(U; F)$.

The proof will be based on the following lemmas.

LEMMA 2. Let $f \in \mathcal{H}(U; F)$, $\xi \in U$, $x \in U$, and the real number $\rho > 1$ be such that we have $(1 - \lambda)\xi + \lambda x \in U$ for every $\lambda \in \mathbf{C}$, $|\lambda| \leq \rho$. Then

$$\|f(x) - \tau_{l,f,\xi}(x)\| \leq \frac{1}{\rho^l(\rho - 1)} \cdot \sup_{|\lambda| = \rho} \|f[(1 - \lambda)\xi + \lambda x]\|,$$

for every $l \in \mathbf{N}$.

Proof. By Cauchy's integral, we have

$$f(x) = \frac{1}{2\pi i} \int_{|\lambda| = \rho} \frac{f[(1 - \lambda)\xi + \lambda x]}{\lambda - 1} d\lambda \quad \text{and}$$

$$\frac{1}{k!} \hat{d}^k f(\xi) \cdot (x - \xi) = \frac{1}{2\pi i} \int_{|\lambda| = \rho} \frac{f[(1 - \lambda)\xi + \lambda x]}{\lambda^{k+1}} d\lambda$$

for $k \in \mathbf{N}$. If we use the identity

$$\frac{1}{\lambda - 1} = \sum_{k=0}^{l} \frac{1}{\lambda^{k+1}} + \frac{1}{\lambda^{l+1}(\lambda - 1)} \qquad (\lambda \neq 0, 1),$$

we then get

$$f(x) - \tau_{l,f,\xi}(x) = \frac{1}{2\pi i} \int_{|\lambda| = \rho} \frac{f[(1 - \lambda)\xi + \lambda x]}{\lambda^{l+1}(\lambda - 1)} d\lambda,$$

from which the lemma follows. Q.E.D.

LEMMA 3. Let $f \in \mathcal{H}_\theta(U; F)$, $\xi \in U$ and U be ξ-equilibrated. Then, given any compact subset K of U, there exist real numbers $\gamma (0 < \gamma < 1)$, $C \geq 0$ and $c \geq 0$, and an open subset V of U containing K, such that

$$\sup_{x \in V} \left\| \frac{1}{m!} \hat{d}^m(f - \tau_{l,f,\xi})(x) \right\|_\theta \leq C \cdot c^m \cdot \gamma^l$$

for every $l \in \mathbf{N}$, $m \in \mathbf{N}$.

Proof. By Proposition 2, §2, choose an open subset W of U containing the given compact subset K of U, and real numbers $C \geq 0$ and $c \geq 0$, such that W is ξ-equilibrated and

$$\left\| \frac{1}{m!} \hat{d}^m f(x) \right\|_\theta \leq C \cdot c^m$$

for every $x \in W$ and $m \in \mathbf{N}$. Next choose a real number $\rho > 1$ and an open subset V of W containing K such that $\lambda \in \mathbf{C}$, $|\lambda| \leq \rho$, $x \in V$ imply that $(1 - \lambda)\xi + \lambda x \in W$. Use

$$\hat{d}^m f \in \mathcal{H}(U; \mathcal{P}_\theta(^m E; F)),$$

by Proposition 2, §3, and apply Lemma 2 to $\hat{d}^m f$ to get

$$\| \hat{d}^m f(x) - \tau_{l, \hat{d}^m f, \xi}(x) \|_\theta \leq \frac{C \cdot c^m \cdot m!}{\rho^l(\rho - 1)}$$

for $x \in V, l \in \mathbf{N}$ and $m \in \mathbf{N}$. Now

$$\tau_{l, \hat{d}^m f, \xi} = \hat{d}^m \tau_{l+m, f, \xi},$$

so that

$$\left\| \frac{1}{m!} \hat{d}^m (f - \tau_{l+m, f, \xi})(x) \right\|_\theta \leq \frac{C \cdot c^m}{\rho^l(\rho - 1)}$$

for $x \in V, l \in \mathbf{N}$ and $m \in \mathbf{N}$. In other notation,

$$\left\| \frac{1}{m!} \hat{d}^m (f - \tau_{l, f, \xi})(x) \right\|_\theta \leq \frac{C \cdot (\rho c)^m}{\rho^l(\rho - 1)} \tag{1}$$

for $x \in V, l \in \mathbf{N}$, $m \in \mathbf{N}$ and $l \geq m$. However, (1) remains true for $l < m$. In fact, then

$$\hat{d}^m \tau_{l, f, \xi} = 0;$$

and since $V \subset W$, we have

$$\left\| \frac{1}{m!} \hat{d}^m f(x) \right\|_\theta \leq C \cdot c^m \leq \frac{C \cdot (\rho c)^m}{\rho^l(\rho - 1)}$$

for $x \in V$, because $\rho - 1 < \rho \leq \rho^{m-l}$. Thus (1) is true for $x \in V$, $l \in \mathbf{N}$ and $m \in \mathbf{N}$. The lemma is thus proved if we replace

$$\frac{C}{\rho - 1} \text{ and } \rho c$$

by C and c respectively, and also set $\gamma = 1/\rho$. Q.E.D.

Proof of Proposition 2. Apply Lemma 3. Then corresponding to every compact subset K of U, we can find real numbers $\gamma (0 < \gamma < 1)$, $C \geq 0$

and $c \geq 0$, and an open subset V of U containing K, such that if the real number $\epsilon > 0$ satisfies $\epsilon c < 1$, then

$$\sum_{m=0}^{\infty} \epsilon^m \cdot \sup_{x \in V} \left\| \frac{1}{m!} \hat{d}^m (f - \tau_{l,f,\xi})(x) \right\|_\theta \leq \frac{C\gamma^l}{1 - \epsilon c}$$

for $l \in \mathbf{N}$. Then apply Proposition 1 (compare with Remark 2). Q.E.D.

PROPOSITION 3. Each inclusion mapping

$$\mathcal{H}_\theta(U; F) \subset \mathcal{H}(U; F)$$

is continuous for the corresponding topologies $\mathfrak{I}_\omega$.

Proof. Apply Proposition 1, §2. Q.E.D.

PROPOSITION 4. Let θ be a holomorphy type from E to F and

$$\tau = \frac{1}{l!} \hat{d}^l \theta$$

be the corresponding holomorphy type from E to $\mathcal{P}_\theta({}^l E; F)$, where $l \in \mathbf{N}$ (see Proposition 1, §3). Then the linear mapping

$$f \in \mathcal{H}_\theta(U; F) \to \frac{1}{l!} \hat{d}^l f \in \mathcal{H}_\tau(U; \mathcal{P}_\theta({}^l E; F))$$

(see Proposition 2, §3) is continuous for the corresponding $\mathfrak{I}_\omega$ topologies.

Proof. Let p be a seminorm on $\mathcal{H}_\tau(U; \mathcal{P}_\theta({}^l E; F))$ ported by a compact subset K of U. Let the real number $c(\epsilon) > 0$ correspond to every real number $\epsilon > 0$ so that, for every $g \in \mathcal{H}_\tau(U; \mathcal{P}_\theta({}^l E; F))$, we have

$$p(g) \leq c(\epsilon) \sum_{m=0}^{\infty} \epsilon^m \cdot \sup_{x \in K} \left\| \frac{1}{m!} \hat{d}^m g(x) \right\|_\tau .$$

If then $f \in \mathcal{H}_\theta(U; F)$, we have

$$\left\| \frac{1}{m!} \hat{d}^m \left(\frac{1}{l!} \hat{d}^l f(x) \right) \right\|_\tau =$$

$$\left\| \frac{1}{l!} \hat{d}^l \left[\frac{1}{(l+m)!} \hat{d}^{l+m} f(x) \right] \right\|_\tau =$$

$$\left\| \frac{1}{(l+m)!} \hat{d}^{l+m} f(x) \right\|_\theta ,$$

and so

$$p\left(\frac{1}{l!} \hat{d}^l f \right) \leq c(\epsilon) \sum_{m=0}^{\infty} \epsilon^m \cdot \sup_{x \in K} \left\| \frac{1}{(l+m)!} \hat{d}^{l+m} f(x) \right\|_\theta$$

$$\leq \frac{c(\epsilon)}{\epsilon^l} \sum_{m=0}^{\infty} \epsilon^m \cdot \sup_{x \in K} \left\| \frac{1}{m!} \hat{d}^m f(x) \right\|_\theta ,$$

proving the desired continuity. Q.E.D.

5. BOUNDED SUBSETS

PROPOSITION 1. Each of the following equivalent conditions is necessary and sufficient for a subset $\mathfrak{X}$ of $\mathcal{H}_\theta(U; F)$ to be bounded for $\mathfrak{J}_\omega$:

(1) Corresponding to every $\xi \in U$, there are real numbers $C \geq 0$ and $c \geq 0$ such that

$$\left\| \frac{1}{m!} \hat{d}^m f(\xi) \right\|_\theta \leq C \cdot c^m$$

for every $m \in \mathbf{N}$ and $f \in \mathfrak{X}$.

(2) Corresponding to every compact subset K of U, there are real numbers $C \geq 0$ and $c \geq 0$ such that

$$\left\| \frac{1}{m!} \hat{d}^m f(x) \right\|_\theta \leq C \cdot c^m$$

for every $m \in \mathbf{N}, f \in \mathfrak{X}$ and $x \in K$.

(3) Corresponding to every compact subset K of U, there are real numbers $C \geq 0$ and $c \geq 0$, and an open subset V of U containing K, such that

$$\left\| \frac{1}{m!} \hat{d}^m f(x) \right\|_\theta \leq C \cdot c^m$$

for every $m \in \mathbf{N}, f \in \mathfrak{X}$ and $x \in V$.

Proof. Let $\mathfrak{X}$ be bounded for $\mathfrak{J}_\omega$. We shall then prove (2). If $K \subset U$ is compact and $\alpha_m \geq 0$ $(m \in \mathbf{N})$ are real numbers such that $(\alpha_m)^{1/m} \to 0$ as $m \to \infty$, we have correspondingly a seminorm p on $\mathcal{H}_\theta(U; F)$ defined by

$$p(f) = \sum_{m=0}^{\infty} \alpha_m \cdot \sup_{x \in K} \left\| \frac{1}{m!} \hat{d}^m f(x) \right\|_\theta$$

for $f \in \mathcal{H}_\theta(U; F)$, by Proposition 2, §2. It is immediate that p is ported by K, hence continuous for $\mathfrak{J}_\omega$. Therefore p is bounded on $\mathfrak{X}$. Now it is classical that if $s_{m,\lambda} \geq 0$ are real numbers for $m \in \mathbf{N}$ and $\lambda \in \Lambda$, where Λ is a set, then

$$\sup_{\lambda \in \Lambda} \sum_{m=0}^{\infty} \alpha_m s_{m,\lambda} < \infty$$

holds true for every sequence $(\alpha_m)_{m\in\mathbf{N}}$ of positive real numbers such that $(\alpha_m)^{1/m} \to 0$ as $m \to \infty$ if and only if there are real numbers $C \geq 0$ and $c \geq 0$ such that

$$s_{m,\lambda} \leq C \cdot c^m$$

for every $m \in \mathbf{N}$ and $\lambda \in \Lambda$. Therefore, the fact that every seminorm p of the above form is bounded on $\mathfrak{X}$ implies (2).

Conversely, it is clear that (2) implies that $\mathfrak{X}$ is bounded for $\mathfrak{J}_\omega$.

The implications (3)⟹(2)⟹(1) are clear too.

Let us finally prove (1)⟹(3). In fact, if $\xi \in U$ and $C \geq 0$ and $c \geq 0$ correspond by (1), we may apply Corollary 1, §3 to get

$$\left\| \frac{1}{l!} \hat{d}^l f(x) \right\|_\theta \leq \frac{C}{1 - \sigma\rho c} (\sigma c)^l$$

for every $x \in B_\rho(\xi)$, $l \in \mathbf{N}$ and $f \in \mathfrak{X}$, provided we choose $\rho > 0$ so that $B_\rho(\xi) \subset U$ and $\sigma\rho c < 1$. This suffices to show that (3) holds. Q.E.D.

DEFINITION 1. Corresponding to every compact subset K of U and every $m \in \mathbf{N}$, we have the seminorm p on $\mathcal{H}_\theta(U; F)$ defined by

$$p(f) = \sup_{x \in K} \| \hat{d}^m f(x) \|$$

for $f \in \mathcal{H}_\theta(U; F)$. The $\mathfrak{J}_\infty$ topology on $\mathcal{H}_\theta(U; F)$ is defined by all such seminorms. Clearly $\mathfrak{J}_\infty \subset \mathfrak{J}_\omega$ and $\mathfrak{J}_\infty$ is separated.

PROPOSITION 2. On every $\mathfrak{J}_\omega$-bounded subset $\mathfrak{X}$ of $\mathcal{H}_\theta(U; F)$, the uniform structures associated with $\mathfrak{J}_\omega$ and $\mathfrak{J}_\infty$ induce the same uniform structure. In particular, $\mathfrak{J}_\omega$ and $\mathfrak{J}_\infty$ induce on $\mathfrak{X}$ the same topology.

Proof. Let us assume first that $0 \in \mathfrak{X}$ and prove that a subset of $\mathfrak{X}$ is a neighborhood of 0 in the topology on $\mathfrak{X}$ induced by $\mathfrak{J}_\omega$ if and only if it is a neighborhood of 0 in the topology on $\mathfrak{X}$ induced by $\mathfrak{J}_\infty$. One half of this assertion is clear from $\mathfrak{J}_\infty \subset \mathfrak{J}_\omega$. Conversely, let p be a $\mathfrak{J}_\omega$-continuous seminorm on $\mathcal{H}_\theta(U; F)$. Assume that p is ported by a compact subset K of U, and let $c(\epsilon)$ be as described in (1) of Lemma 1, §4. Since $\mathfrak{X}$ is $\mathfrak{J}_\omega$-bounded, there are C and c according to Condition (2) of Proposition 1. Next choose $\epsilon > 0$ so that $\epsilon c < 1$ and $\mu \in \mathbf{N}$ by

$$C \cdot c(\epsilon) \sum_{m > \mu} (\epsilon c)^m \leq \frac{1}{2}.$$

Define the $\mathfrak{J}_\infty$-continuous seminorm q by

$$q(f) = c(\epsilon) \sum_{m=0}^{\mu} \epsilon^m \cdot \sup_{x \in K} \left\| \frac{1}{m!} \hat{d}^m f(x) \right\|_\theta .$$

It is then clear that, if $f \in \mathfrak{X}$ and $q(f) \leq \frac{1}{2}$, then $p(f) \leq 1$. This proves the remaining half of the above assertion.

If we next consider any subset $\mathfrak{X}$ bounded for $\mathfrak{J}_\omega$, the set $\mathfrak{X} - \mathfrak{X}$ of all differences of two elements of $\mathfrak{X}$ is bounded for $\mathfrak{J}_\omega$ and contains 0. Since the neighborhoods of 0 in the topologies on $\mathfrak{X} - \mathfrak{X}$ induced by $\mathfrak{J}_\omega$ and $\mathfrak{J}_\infty$ are identical, it follows that the uniform structures on $\mathfrak{X}$ induced by the uniform structures associated to $\mathfrak{J}_\omega$ and $\mathfrak{J}_\infty$ are identical too. Q.E.D.

COROLLARY 1. If $f_l \in \mathcal{H}_\theta(U; F)$ for $l \in \mathbf{N}$, and $f \in \mathcal{H}_\theta(U; F)$, then $f_l \to f$ for $\mathfrak{J}_\omega$ as $l \to \infty$ if and only if $(f_l)_{l \in \mathbf{N}}$ is bounded for $\mathfrak{J}_\omega$ and $f_l \to f$ for $\mathfrak{J}_\infty$ as $l \to \infty$.

Proof. If $f_l \to f$ for $\mathfrak{J}_\omega$ as $l \to \infty$, then clearly $(f_l)_{l \in \mathbf{N}}$ is $\mathfrak{J}_\omega$-bounded and also $f_l \to f$ for $\mathfrak{J}_\infty$ as $l \to \infty$.

Conversely, let us assume that $(f_l)_{l \in \mathbf{N}}$ is $\mathfrak{J}_\omega$-bounded and that $f_l \to f$ for $\mathfrak{J}_\infty$ as $l \to \infty$. To prove that $f_l \to f$, for $\mathfrak{J}_\omega$ it suffices to notice that the subset of $\mathcal{H}_\theta(U; F)$ formed by all $f_l (l \in \mathbf{N})$, and by f, is $\mathfrak{J}_\omega$-bounded, and then to apply Proposition 2. Q.E.D.

PROPOSITION 3. Each subset $\mathfrak{X}$ of $\mathcal{H}_\theta(U; F)$ bounded for $\mathfrak{J}_\omega$ is equicontinuous at every point of U.

Proof. Let $\xi \in U$ and C and c correspond to it by Condition (1) of Proposition 1. We have

$$f(x) = \sum_{m=0}^{\infty} \frac{1}{m!} \hat{d}^m f(\xi) \cdot (x - \xi)$$

for every $f \in \mathcal{H}(U; F)$ provided $x \in B_\rho(\xi) \subset U$. Using Proposition 1, §2, we get

$$\|f(x) - f(\xi)\| \leq \sum_{m=1}^{\infty} \left\| \frac{1}{m!} \hat{d}^m f(\xi) \right\| \cdot \|x - \xi\|^m$$

$$\leq \sum_{m=1}^{\infty} \sigma^m \cdot \left\| \frac{1}{m!} \hat{d}^m f(\xi) \right\|_\theta \cdot \|x - \xi\|^m$$

$$\leq \sum_{m=1}^{\infty} \sigma^m \cdot C \cdot c^m \cdot \|x - \xi\|^m$$

$$= \frac{C\sigma c \|x - \xi\|}{1 - \sigma c \|x - \xi\|}$$

provided $x \in B_\rho(\xi)$, $\sigma c \rho \leq 1$ and $f \in \mathfrak{X}$, from which equicontinuity follows. Q.E.D.

REMARK 1. Proposition 3 for arbitrary θ follows simply from the particular case in which θ is the current holomorphy type (see §7), in view of Proposition 3, §4.

6. RELATIVELY COMPACT SUBSETS

DEFINITION 1. A subset $\mathfrak{X}$ of $\mathcal{H}_\theta(U; F)$ is said to be *relatively compact at a point* $\xi \in U$ if, for every $m \in \mathbf{N}$, the set

$$\{\hat{d}^m f(\xi) \mid f \in \mathfrak{X}\}$$

is relatively compact in $\mathcal{P}_\theta(^m E; F)$.

PROPOSITION 1. A subset $\mathfrak{X}$ of $\mathcal{H}_\theta(U; F)$ is relatively compact for $\mathfrak{J}_\omega$ if and only if $\mathfrak{X}$ is bounded for $\mathfrak{J}_\omega$, and $\mathfrak{X}$ is relatively compact at every point of U.

Proof. Assume that $\mathfrak{X}$ is relatively compact for $\mathfrak{J}_\omega$. Then $\mathfrak{X}$ is bounded for $\mathfrak{J}_\omega$. Moreover the mapping

$$f \in \mathcal{H}_\theta(U; F) \to \hat{d}^m f(\xi) \in \mathcal{P}_\theta(^m E; F)$$

is continuous, for every $\xi \in U$ and $m \in \mathbf{N}$. Hence the image of $\mathfrak{X}$ is relatively compact in $\mathcal{P}_\theta(^m E; F)$ for every $m \in \mathbf{N}$, that is, $\mathfrak{X}$ is relatively compact at every $\xi \in U$.

Conversely, let us assume that $\mathfrak{X}$ is bounded for $\mathfrak{J}_\omega$ and that $\mathfrak{X}$ is relatively compact at every point of U. By Proposition 2, §5, the closure of $\mathfrak{X}$ in the topology $\mathfrak{J}_\omega$ coincides with the closure of $\mathfrak{X}$ in the topology $\mathfrak{J}_\infty$. Moreover since such a closure is $\mathfrak{J}_\omega$-bounded, the topologies induced on it by $\mathfrak{J}_\omega$ and by $\mathfrak{J}_\infty$ are identical. Hence, in order to prove that $\mathfrak{X}$ is relatively compact for $\mathfrak{J}_\omega$, we shall show that $\mathfrak{X}$ is relatively compact for $\mathfrak{J}_\infty$.

To this end, consider the cartesian product

$$S = \prod_{m=0}^{\infty} \mathcal{P}_\theta(^m E; F) = F_\theta[[E]]$$

(vector space of all formal power series from E to F) endowed with its Cartesian product topology. We define a natural mapping Φ from $\mathcal{H}_\theta(U; F)$ into the vector space $\mathcal{C}(U; S)$ of all continuous S-valued functions on U by associating with every $f \in \mathcal{H}_\theta(U; F)$ the function $\Phi(f)$ defined at every point $x \in U$ by

$$\Phi(f)(x) = \left(\frac{1}{m!}\hat{d}^m f(x)\right)_{m \in \mathbf{N}} \in S.$$

It is immediate that $\Phi(f) \in \mathcal{C}(U; S)$, because each $\hat{d}^m f$ is holomorphic, hence continuous, from U to $\mathcal{P}_\theta(^m E; F)$. The mapping Φ is linear and one-to-one. It is a homeomorphism if we endow $\mathcal{H}_\theta(U; F)$ with the $\mathfrak{J}_\infty$ topology and $\mathcal{C}(U; S)$ with the compact-open topology. By the assumption that $\mathfrak{X}$ is relatively compact at every point of U, we see that the set

$$\{\Phi(f)(x) \mid f \in \mathfrak{X}\}$$

is relatively compact in S. Therefore, in view of Ascoli's theorem, in order to show that the image set $\Phi(\mathfrak{X})$ is relatively compact in $\mathcal{C}(U; S)$, we must show that it is equicontinuous at every point of U. In other words, we must show that, for every $m \in \mathbf{N}$, the subset

$$\{\hat{d}^m f \mid f \in \mathfrak{X}\}$$

of $\mathcal{C}(U; \mathcal{P}_\theta({}^m E; F))$ is equicontinuous. This follows from the fact that $\mathfrak{X}$ is bounded for $\mathfrak{J}_\omega$, from Proposition 4, §4 and from Proposition 3, §5.

Q.E.D.

PROPOSITION 2. If U is connected, a subset $\mathfrak{X}$ of $\mathcal{H}_\theta(U; F)$ is relatively compact for $\mathfrak{J}_\omega$ if and only if $\mathfrak{X}$ is bounded for $\mathfrak{J}_\omega$, and $\mathfrak{X}$ is relatively compact at a single point of U.

The proof will be based on the following lemma.

LEMMA 1. Let $\mathfrak{X}$ be a subset of $\mathcal{H}_\theta(U; F)$ such that

(1) $\mathfrak{X}$ is relatively compact at some $\xi \in U$, and

(2) There exist real numbers $\rho > 0$ and $C \geq 0$ such that $B_\rho(\xi) \subset U$ and

$$\left\| \frac{1}{m!} \hat{d}^m f(\xi) \right\|_\theta \leq \frac{C}{(\sigma\rho)^m}$$

for every $f \in \mathfrak{X}$ and $m \in \mathbf{N}$.

Then $\mathfrak{X}$ is relatively compact at every point of $B_\rho(\xi)$.

Proof. For every $f \in \mathcal{H}_\theta(U; F)$ set

$$P_{m,f} = \frac{1}{m!} \hat{d}^m f(\xi) \qquad (m \in \mathbf{N}).$$

We then have

$$\hat{d}^l f(x) = \sum_{m=l}^{\infty} \hat{d}^l P_{m,f}(x - \xi)$$

for $x \in B_\rho(\xi)$ and $l \in \mathbf{N}$, convergence being in the sense of $\mathcal{P}_\theta({}^m E; F)$, by Proposition 2, §3. Using (2) and Condition (3) of Definition 1, §2, we have

$$\| \hat{d}^l P_{m,f}(x - \xi) \|_\theta \leq \sigma^m \cdot \frac{C}{(\sigma\rho)^m} \cdot \| x - \xi \|^{m-l}$$

for every $f \in \mathfrak{X}$, $l \in \mathbf{N}$, $m \in \mathbf{N}$, $l \leq m$. Using this estimate and the above series, we see that $\mathfrak{X}$ is relatively compact at every point x such that $\| x - \xi \| < \rho$.

Q.E.D.

Proof of Proposition 2. Assume that $\mathfrak{X}$ is bounded for $\mathfrak{J}_\omega$. Let X be the set of points of U where $\mathfrak{X}$ is relatively compact. Lemma 1 shows immediately that X is open. We now show that X is closed. Let $\eta \in U$ be in the closure of X. Since $\mathfrak{X}$ is $\mathfrak{I}_\omega$-bounded, there are $\rho > 0$ and $C \geq 0$ such that $B_\rho(\eta) \subset U$ and

$$\left\| \frac{1}{m!} \hat{d}^m f(x) \right\|_\theta \leq \frac{C}{(\sigma\rho)^m}$$

for every $f \in \mathfrak{X}$, $m \in \mathbf{N}$ and $x \in B_\rho(\eta)$, by Proposition 1, Condition (3), §5. Let $r = \rho/2$, $\xi \in X \cap B_r(\eta)$. Then the fact that $\xi \in X$ and $\xi \in B_\rho(\eta)$, hence that

$$\left\| \frac{1}{m!} \hat{d}^m f(\xi) \right\|_\theta \leq \frac{C}{(\sigma\rho)^m} \leq \frac{C}{(\sigma r)^m}$$

for every $f \in \mathfrak{X}$ and $m \in \mathbf{N}$, implies that $\mathfrak{X}$ is relatively compact at every point of $B_r(\xi)$, by Lemma 1, since $B_r(\xi) \subset B_\rho(\eta) \subset U$. Now $\eta \in B_r(\xi)$. Hence $\eta \in X$, proving that X is closed in U. The lemma then follows by connectedness of U. Q.E.D.

We shall not discuss further results concerning relative compactness, equicontinuity, etc., which follow from the results already proved and known general principles. Let us, however, make the following remark.

REMARK 1. Proposition 2 of §5 can be improved as follows. Let X be a subset of U. Denote by $\mathfrak{I}_{\infty,X}$ the topology on $\mathfrak{H}_\theta(U;F)$ defined by the family formed by each of the following seminorms

$$p(f) = \| \hat{d}^m f(x) \|_\theta$$

for $f \in \mathfrak{H}_\theta(U;F)$, where $x \in X$ and $m \in \mathbf{N}$. Then it follows from Proposition 2 and 3 of §5, and from general principles concerning equicontinuity, that if X is dense in U, then $\mathfrak{I}_\omega$ and $\mathfrak{I}_{\infty,X}$ induce the same topology on every $\mathfrak{I}_\omega$-bounded subset; and analogously for uniform structures. However the above proofs of Propositions 1 and 2 will show that the same conclusion about the identity of $\mathfrak{I}_\omega$ and $\mathfrak{I}_{\infty,X}$ on every $\mathfrak{I}_\omega$-bounded subset, as well as of their uniform structures, remains true if X intersects every connected component of U. This in turn could be used to provide short proofs of the above Propositions 1 and 2. A corresponding remark applies to Corollary 1, §5.

7. THE CURRENT HOLOMORPHY TYPE

DEFINITION 1. The *current* holomorphy type from E to F is the holomorphy type θ for which $\mathcal{P}_\theta(^mE;F) = \mathcal{P}(^mE;F)$, as normed vector spaces, for every $m \in \mathbf{N}$. Then $\mathfrak{H}_\theta(U;F) = \mathfrak{H}(U;F)$.

Certain of the preceding considerations simplify for the current holomorphy type, as we shall try to explain in the present section. It will be tacitly assumed that all considerations on $\mathcal{H}(U; F)$ are taken with respect to the current holomorphy type.

LEMMA 1. A seminorm p on $\mathcal{H}(U; F)$ is ported by a compact subset K of U if and only if, given any open subset V of U containing K, we can find a real number $c(V) > 0$ such that

$$p(f) \leq c(V) \cdot \sup_{x \in V} \|f(x)\|$$

for every $f \in \mathcal{H}(U; F)$.

Proof. Let p be ported by K in the sense of Definition 1 of §4, so that there exists a real number $c(\epsilon) > 0$ corresponding to every real number $\epsilon > 0$, such that

$$p(f) \leq c(\epsilon) \sum_{m=0}^{\infty} \epsilon^m \sup_{x \in K} \left\| \frac{1}{m!} \hat{d}^m f(x) \right\|$$

holds for every $f \in \mathcal{H}(U; F)$. Now, given any open subset V of U containing K, choose a real number $\rho > 0$ in such a way that any closed ball of radius ρ whose center lies in K will be contained in V. By Cauchy's inequality, we shall have

$$\sup_{x \in K} \left\| \frac{1}{m!} \hat{d}^m f(x) \right\| \leq \frac{1}{\rho^m} \sup_{x \in V} \|f(x)\| .$$

Take $\epsilon = \rho/2$ and set $c(V) = 2c(\epsilon)$ to conclude that p is ported by K in the sense of the statement of Lemma 1. The converse is obvious, by Condition (2) of Lemma 1, §4. Q.E.D.

REMARK 1. The topology $\mathfrak{J}_\omega$ on $\mathcal{H}(U; F)$ is therefore defined by the seminorms on it that are ported by compact subsets of U in the sense of the statement of Lemma 1.

In the case of boundedness in the sense of $\mathfrak{J}_\omega$ for subsets of $\mathcal{H}(U; F)$, in addition to the three equivalent conditions provided by Proposition 1, §5, we have also the following.

PROPOSITION 1. Each of the following equivalent conditions is necessary and sufficient for a subset $\mathfrak{X}$ of $\mathcal{H}(U; F)$ to be bounded for $\mathfrak{J}_\omega$:

(1) Corresponding to every compact subset K of U, there is a real number $C \geq 0$ such that

$$\|f(x)\| \leq C$$

for every $f \in \mathfrak{X}$ and $x \in K$.

(2) Corresponding to every compact subset K of U, there are a real number $C \geq 0$ and an open subset V of U containing K such that

$$\|f(x)\| \leq C$$

for every $f \in \mathfrak{X}$ and $x \in V$.

Proof. If (2) holds true, then $\mathfrak{X}$ is bounded for $\mathfrak{J}_\omega$, by Remark 1. If $\mathfrak{X}$ is bounded for $\mathfrak{J}_\omega$, then (1) is true. As a matter of fact, the seminorm p given on $\mathcal{H}(U; F)$ by

$$p(f) = \sup_{x \in K} \|f(x)\|$$

for all $f \in \mathcal{H}(U; F)$ is obviously continuous for $\mathfrak{J}_\omega$; hence p must be bounded on $\mathfrak{X}$. Finally (1) implies (2). In fact, (1) means that $\mathfrak{X}$ is bounded for the topology induced on $\mathcal{H}(U; F)$ by the compact-open topology on the vector space $\mathcal{C}(U; F)$ of all continuous F-valued functions on U. Since U is metrizable, bounded subsets of $\mathcal{C}(U; F)$ have the property expressed by (2). Q.E.D.

REFERENCES

1. Grothendieck, A., Produits tensoriels topologiques et espaces nucléaires, Memoirs of of the American Mathematical Society, nr. 16 (1955).
2. Gupta, C. P., Malgrange theorem for nuclearly entire functions of bounded type on a Banach space, Notas de Matematica, no. 37 (1966), Instituto de Matematica Pura e Aplicada, Rio de Janeiro, GB, Brazil.
3. Martineau, A., Sur la topologie des espaces de fonctions holomorphes, *Mathematische Annalen*, vol. **163** (1966), pp. 62–88.
4. Nachbin, L., Lectures on the theory of distributions, University of Rochester (1963). Reproduced in Textos de Matematica, no. 15 (1964), Universidade do Recife, Brazil.
5. Nachbin, L., On the topology of the space of all holomorphic functions on a given open subset, to appear.
6. Nachbin, L. and C. P. Gupta, On Malgrange's theorem for nuclearly entire functions, to appear.

Dentable Subsets of Banach Spaces, with Application to a Radon-Nikodym Theorem

M. A. RIEFFEL

This work originated as an attempt to give a new proof of Phillips' Radon-Nikodym theorem [**5**, p. 130] using techniques analogous to those developed in [**6**]. Instead, we have obtained a new Radon-Nikodym theorem—one which is not a consequence of Phillips' theorem. However, we have not been able to show that our theorem implies Phillips' theorem in its full generality.

DEFINITION 1. A subset, K, of a Banach space will be called *dentable* if for every $\epsilon > 0$ there is a $b \in K$ such that $b \notin \bar{c}(K - \text{ball}(b, \epsilon))$ (where $\bar{c}$ denotes "closed convex hull").

We shall discuss the question of which subsets of Banach spaces are dentable after we have stated and proved the Radon-Nikodym theorem referred to above.

THEOREM 1. Let (X, S, μ) be a σ-finite positive measure space, and let B be a Banach space. Let m be a B-valued measure on S. Then there is a B-valued Bochner integrable function, f, on X such that

$$m(E) = \int_E f\,d\mu$$

for all $E \in S$, if and only if

1. m is μ-continuous, that is, $m(E) = 0$ whenever $\mu(E) = 0$, $E \in S$.
2. the total variation, $|m|$, of m is a finite measure.
3. locally m almost has dentable average range, that is, given $E \in S$, $\mu(E) < \infty$, and given $\epsilon > 0$, there is an $F \subseteq E$, such that $\mu(E - F) < \epsilon$ and

$$A_F = \{m(F')/\mu(F') \colon F' \subseteq F, \mu(F') > 0\}$$

is dentable.

The slight generalization of Phillips' theorem for which we tried to find a new proof is obtained by replacing the word "dentable" in hypothesis 3 of Theorem 1 by "relatively weakly compact."

The necessity of hypotheses 1 and 2 is well known. In [**6**, Prop. 1.12] it was shown that an additional necessary condition is obtained if in hypothesis 3 the word "dentable" is replaced by "relatively norm compact." But,

PROPOSITION 1. Any relatively norm compact subset of a Banach space is dentable.

Proof. First, suppose that K is a norm compact convex subset of a Banach space. Let b be any extreme point of K. Then, since the norm closure of $K - \text{ball}(b, \epsilon)$ does not contain b for any $\epsilon > 0$, it follows from part of the Krein-Milman theorem that $b \notin \bar{c}(K - \text{ball}(b, \epsilon))$.

The general case follows from

PROPOSITION 2. Let K be any subset of a Banach space. If $\bar{c}(K)$ is dentable, then so is K.

Proof. Given $\epsilon > 0$, choose $b' \in \bar{c}(K)$ such that $b' \notin Q$, where

$$Q = \bar{c}(\bar{c}(K) - \text{ball}\,(b', \epsilon/2)).$$

Since $b' \in \bar{c}(K) - Q$, and Q is closed and convex, Q can not contain K. Choose $b \in K - Q$. Then $b \in \text{ball}(b', \epsilon/2)$, and so $(K - \text{ball}(b, \epsilon)) \subseteq Q$. Thus $b \notin \bar{c}(K - \text{ball}(b, \epsilon))$.

We now turn to the proof of the sufficiency of the hypotheses of Theorem 1. Since finite measures are carried on measurable sets, it suffices to prove sufficiency under the assumption that (X, S, μ) is totally σ-finite. From now on we restrict our attention to this case.

As in [**6**], the key step in the proof of sufficiency is a decomposition theorem analogous to the classical Hahn decomposition theorem. We recall the following definition from [**6**].

DEFINITION 2. Given $b \in B$ and $\epsilon > 0$ we say that a set $E \in S$ is (b, ϵ)-pure (for m with respect to μ) if $m(F)/\mu(F)$ is in $\text{ball}(b, \epsilon)$ for all $F \subseteq E$ such that $0 < \mu(F) < \infty$.

The appropriate decomposition theorem for the present situation is

THEOREM 2. Let (X, S, μ) be a totally σ-finite measure space, and let m be a B-valued measure on S which satisfies hypotheses 1, 2 and 3 of Theorem 1. Then, given $\epsilon > 0$, there are (possibly finite) sequences $\{b_i\}$ and $\{E_i\}$ of elements of B and S respectively such that E_i is (b_i, ϵ)-pure for each i, and $X = \bigcup E_i$.

LEMMA 1. Let the hypotheses of Theorem 2 be satisfied, and let $E \in S$ and $\epsilon > 0$ be given, with $\mu(E) > 0$. Then there is an $F \subseteq E$ and a $b \in B$ such that $\mu(F) > 0$ and F is (b, ϵ)-pure.

Proof. By hypothesis 3 of Theorem 1 choose $E_d \subseteq E$, $\mu(E_d) > 0$ such that A_{E_d} is dentable. Choose $b \in A_{E_d}$ such that $b \notin Q$, where $Q = \bar{c}(A_{E_d} - \text{ball}(b, \epsilon))$. Let $b = m(F_0)/\mu(F_0)$ where $F_0 \subseteq E_d$ and $0 < \mu(F_0) < \infty$. Suppose that F_0 is not (b, ϵ)-pure. Let k_1 be the smallest integer ≥ 2 for which there is an $E_1 \subseteq F_0$ such that $\mu(E_1) \geq 1/k_1$ and $m(E_1)/\mu(E_1)$ is in Q. Let $F_1 = F_0 - E_1$, and suppose that F_1 is not (b, ϵ)-pure. Let k_2 be the smallest integer ≥ 2 for which there is an $E_2 \subseteq F_1$ such that $\mu(E_2) \geq 1/k_2$ and $m(E_2)/\mu(E_2)$ is in Q. Let $F_2 = F_1 - E_2$. Continuing in this way we obtain a sequence $\{E_i\}$ of disjoint subsets of F_0, and a nondecreasing sequence $\{k_i\}$ of integers with the property that $m(E_i)/\mu(E_i)$ is in Q and $\mu(E_i) \geq 1/k_i$ for each i, and if $E' \subseteq F_0 - \bigcup_{i=1}^{n} E_i$ and $m(E')/\mu(E')$ is in Q, then $\mu(E') < 1/(k_n - 1)$. Since F_0 has finite measure and the E_i are disjoint, k_i must converge to ∞.

Let $E_0 = \bigcup E_i$, and let $F = F_0 - E_0$. Then F is (b, ϵ)-pure, for if $F' \subseteq F$, $\mu(F') > 0$ and $m(F')/\mu(F')$ is in Q, then, since $F' \subseteq F_0 - \bigcup_{i=1}^{n} E_i$ for each n, it follows that $\mu(F') < 1/(k_n - 1)$ for each n. But, k_n converges to ∞, and so $\mu(F') = 0$.

Finally, we show that $\mu(F) > 0$. Suppose that $\mu(F) = 0$. Then since m is μ-continuous, $m(F) = 0$, and so $m(F_0)/\mu(F_0) = m(E_0)/\mu(E_0)$. Now

$$m(E_0)/\mu(E_0) = \sum_i (m(E_i)/\mu(E_i))(\mu(E_i)/\mu(E_0)).$$

Then, since $\sum_i \mu(E_i)/\mu(E_0) = 1$, and $m(E_i)/\mu(E_i)$ is in Q for each i, and since Q is closed and convex, it follows that $m(E_0)/\mu(E_0)$ is in Q. Thus $m(F_0)/\mu(F_0)$ is in Q, contradicting the way in which F_0 was chosen.

Proof of Theorem 2. Since X is the union of a countable number of subsets of finite measure, it suffices to prove Theorem 2 under the assumption that X has finite measure.

Let k_1 be the smallest integer ≥ 2 for which there is a $b_1 \in B$ and an $E_1 \subseteq X$ such that E_1 is (b_1, ϵ)-pure and $\mu(E_1) \geq 1/k_1$. Let k_2 be the smallest integer ≥ 2 such that there is a $b_2 \in B$ and an $E_2 \subseteq X - E_1$ such that E_2 is (b_2, ϵ)-pure and $\mu(E_2) \geq 1/k_2$. Continuing in this way we obtain a sequence $\{E_i\}$ of disjoint subsets of X, a sequence $\{b_i\}$ of elements of B, and a nondecreasing sequence $\{k_i\}$ of integers with the property that E_i is (b_i, ϵ)-pure and $\mu(E_i) \geq 1/k_i$ for each i, and if $F \subseteq X - \bigcup_{i=1}^{n} E_i$ and F is (b, ϵ)-pure for some $b \in B$ then $\mu(F) < 1/(k_n - 1)$. Since X is assumed to have finite measure, k_i must converge to ∞.

Let $E = X - \bigcup E_i$. We show that $\mu(E) = 0$. Suppose that $\mu(E) > 0$. Then by Lemma 1 there is an $F \subseteq E$ and a $b \in B$ such that $\mu(F) > 0$ and F is (b, ϵ)-pure. But $F \subseteq X - \bigcup_{i=1}^{n} E_i$ for each n and so $\mu(F) < 1/(k_n - 1)$ for each n. But k_n converges to 0, and so $\mu(F) = 0$.

Since $\mu(E) = 0$, E can be adjoined to E_1 and E_1 will still be (b_1, ϵ)-pure. With this change made, $X = \bigcup E_i$.

Proof of Theorem 1. As in [**6**] let Π denote the set of all collections, π, consisting of a finite number of disjoint elements of S of strictly positive finite measure. Then Π becomes a directed set (up to null sets) if $\pi_1 \geq \pi$ is defined to mean that every element of π is, except for possible null sets, the union of elements of π_1. For each $\pi \in \Pi$ we define a simple integrable function f_π by

$$f_\pi = \sum_{E \in \pi} (m(E)/\mu(E))\chi_E$$

(where χ_E denotes the characteristic function of E). We show that the f_π form a mean Cauchy net.

Let $\epsilon > 0$ be given. We seek a $\pi_0 \in \Pi$ such that if $\pi \geq \pi_0$ then $\|f_\pi - f_{\pi_0}\| < \epsilon$. Since $|m|$ is assumed to be a finite measure, we can find $E \in S$ such that $\mu(E) < \infty$ and $|m|(X - E) < \epsilon/3$. Since m is μ-continuous, so is $|m|$, and so, since $|m|$ is a finite measure, there is a $\delta > 0$ such that if $\mu(F) < \delta$ then $|m|(F) < \epsilon/6$.

By Theorem 2 we can find (possibly finite) sequences $\{E_i\}$ and $\{b_i\}$ of elements of S and B respectively such that E_i is $(b_i, \epsilon/6\mu(E))$-pure for each i, $\mu(E_i) > 0$, and $E = \bigcup E_i$, the union being disjoint. Since E has finite measure, there is an integer n such that if $E_0 = E - \bigcup_{i=1}^{n} E_i$ then $\mu(E_0) < \delta$. Let $\pi_0 = \{E_i\colon 0 \leq i \leq n\}$ unless $\mu(E_0) = 0$, in which case let $\pi_0 = \{E_i\colon 1 \leq i \leq n\}$. Then a routine calculation, as given in [**6**], shows that $\|f_\pi - f_{\pi_0}\| < \epsilon$ whenever $\pi \geq \pi_0$.

Since the f_π form a mean Cauchy net, there is an integrable function, f, to which f_π converges in mean. In particular,

$$\int_E f\,d\mu = \lim_\pi \int_E f_\pi\,d\mu$$

for all $E \in S$. We show that

$$m(E) = \int_E f\,d\mu$$

for all $E \in S$. If $\mu(E) = 0$, the result follows from the μ-continuity of m.

If $0 < \mu(E) < \infty$, let $\pi_0 = \{E\}$. It is easily checked that $\int_E f_\pi \, d\mu = m(E)$ whenever $\pi \geq \pi_0$, and so

$$m(E) = \lim_\pi \int_E f_\pi \, d\mu = \int_E f \, d\mu.$$

The case $\mu(E) = \infty$ then follows easily using the σ-finiteness of μ.

We remark that the proof of Theorem 1 is essentially measure theoretic. All the geometric difficulties involved in obtaining Radon-Nikodym theorems for the Bochner integral with values in some particular Banach space are contained in the problem of determining which subsets of the Banach space are dentable.

In particular, in view of the fact that we should like to obtain Phillips' Radon-Nikodym theorem as a consequence of Theorem 1, we are led to ask

QUESTION 1. Is every relatively weakly compact subset of a Banach space dentable?

The proof of Proposition 1 does not work in this case, since an extreme point b of a closed convex set K may well be in the *weak* closure of K – ball(b, ϵ). This is illustrated by the following well known example.

EXAMPLE 1. Let H be an infinite dimensional Hilbert space, and let $\{e_i\}$ be an infinite orthonormal sequence in H. Let $K = \overline{c}(\{e_i\})$. Then $0 \in K$, since the e_i converge weakly to 0, and norm closed convex sets are weakly closed. It is also easily checked that 0 is an extreme point of K. But it is clear that $K = \overline{c}(K - \text{ball}(0, \epsilon))$ for any $\epsilon < 1$.

We have not been able to answer Question 1 completely, but the answer is affirmative in many cases. To begin with, it can be shown by a routine argument that any bounded subset of a uniformly convex Banach space is dentable. Since uniformly convex spaces are reflexive, the bounded subsets coincide with relatively weakly compact subsets, and so Question 1 is answered affirmatively in this case.

To describe a much deeper result, we first recall from [**3**]

DEFINITION 3. A point b of a set K is called *strongly exposed* if there is a continuous linear functional f such that $f(b) > f(b')$ for all $b' \in K$, $b' \neq b$, and such that if $f(b_n) \rightarrow f(b)$ for $\{b_n\} \subseteq K$ then $b_n \rightarrow b$.

Also, in view of Definition 1, it is natural to make

DEFINITION 4. A point b of a set K is called a *denting point* if $b \notin \overline{c}(K\text{-ball}(b, \epsilon))$ for all $\epsilon > 0$.

It is easily checked that any strongly exposed point is a denting point. Namioka has pointed out to us that the converse is not true, as there are norm compact sets which have extreme points which are not exposed. In Example 1 the point 0 is an extreme point which is not a denting point. It is clear that any set whose closed convex hull has a denting point is dentable.

Now Lindenstrauss has shown in [**3**] that if B is a Banach space that can be given an equivalent norm which is locally uniformly convex, then any weakly compact convex subset of B is the closed convex hull of its strongly exposed points. In particular, Question 1 has an affirmative answer in all such Banach spaces. Furthermore, Kadec has shown in [**1, 2**] that any separable Banach space can be given an equivalent norm which is locally uniformly convex. Thus Question 1 has an affirmative answer for all separable Banach spaces.[1]

To describe a result in the opposite direction, let us call a subset K of a Banach space *subset-dentable* if every subset of K is dentable. Then it is natural to ask whether every subset-dentable subset of a Banach space is relatively weakly compact. That this need not be the case is shown by the following result (it is a pleasure to thank B. Kripke for several stimulating conversations which led us to this result).

THEOREM 3. Let X be any (possibly uncountable) set. Then any bounded subset of $l^1(X)$ is dentable.

Proof. In view of Proposition 2 it suffices to show that any bounded closed convex subset of $l^1(X)$ is dentable. Let K be such a subset, and let $\epsilon > 0$ be given. Let

$$s = \sup\{\|a\| : a \in K\}.$$

There need not be an element of K whose norm attains the value s, but we can choose an element $a \in K$ such that $\|a\| > s - \epsilon/6$. Then there is a finite subset, F, of X such that $\sum_{x \in F} |a(x)| > s - \epsilon/6$.

For any element, b, of $l^1(X)$ let b_F denote its natural projection into the subspace $l^1(F)$. Then K_F, the projection of K into $l^1(F)$, is bounded and convex, though it need not be closed. Let $\bar{K}_F$ denote its closure. Since $l^1(F)$ is finite dimensional, $\bar{K}_F$ is norm compact. Since $a_F \in K_F$ and $\|a_F\| > s - \epsilon/6$, $\bar{K}_F$ must have an extreme point, e, such that $\|e\| > s - \epsilon/6$. By the Krein-Milman theorem, as in Proposition 1, $e \notin \bar{c}(K_F - \text{ball}(e, \epsilon/6))$ and so there is an f in $l^\infty(F)$ which separates e from $\bar{c}(K_F - \text{ball}(e, \epsilon/6))$, that is, such that there is a constant, r, for which $f(e) > r$ but $f(b_F) < r$ for any b_F in $K_F - \text{ball}(e, \epsilon/6)$.

Choose $b \in K$ such that $f(b_F) > r$ (so that necessarily $\|b_F - e\| \leq e/6$). We show that $b \notin \bar{c}(K - \text{ball}(b, \epsilon))$. Suppose that $c \in K$ and $f(c_F) \geq r$. Then $\|c_F - e\| \leq \epsilon/6$ and so $\|c_F - b_F\| \leq \epsilon/3$. Also, since

[1]Added in proof: A short, elegant proof of this fact, independent of the work of Lindenstrauss and Kadec, has recently been given by I. Namioka and E. Asplund in "A geometric proof of Ryll-Nardzewski's fixed point theorem" Bull. A.M.S. 73 (1967) 443–445.

$\|e\| > s - \epsilon/6$, we have $\|c_F\| > s - \epsilon/3$, as well as $\|b_F\| > s - \epsilon/3$. But $\|b\| \leq s$ and $\|c\| \leq s$, and so $\|b - b_F\| < \epsilon/3$ and $\|c - c_F\| < \epsilon/3$. Thus $\|b - c\| < \epsilon$. It follows that if $c \in K - \text{ball}(b, \epsilon)$, then $f(c_F) \leq r$, and so the same inequality holds for all elements of $\bar{c}(K - \text{ball}(b, \epsilon))$. But $f(b_F) > r$, and so $b \notin \bar{c}(K - \text{ball}(b, \epsilon))$.

With this result in mind it is not at all clear how one might hope to characterize the dentable subsets of Banach spaces. Since every Banach space can be isometrically embedded in $C(X)$ (the Banach space of all continuous functions on some compact Hausdorff space X), this problem is equivalent to

QUESTION 2. Which are the dentable subsets of $C(X)$?

In view of Theorem 3 one is also led to ask

QUESTION 3. Which Banach spaces have the property that all bounded subsets are dentable?[2]

We remark that it is easily checked that the unit balls of the Banach spaces c_0, $C([0, 1])$, and $L^1(m)$, where m is Lebesgue measure, are not dentable.

Another question which we have not been able to resolve is whether dentability always comes about essentially because of the presence of strongly exposed points. Put another way

QUESTION 4. Does there exist a closed, bounded, convex set which is dentable but which has no strongly exposed points?

In view of Theorem 3 the Banach space l^1 would seem to be an excellent place in which to look for such an example. But we have not been able to answer Question 4 even for l^1. We remark that in connection with this problem we asked whether there is a closed, bounded, convex subset of l^1 which has no extreme points at all. This question has now been answered by Lindenstrauss [**4**], who shows that every closed, bounded, convex subset of l^1 is the closed convex hull of its extreme points.

UNIVERSITY OF CALIFORNIA, BERKELEY

REFERENCES

1. Kadec, M. I., On spaces which are isomorphic to locally uniformly convex spaces. *Izvestia Vys. Uch. Zav.* (1959) **6**, 51–57.
2. Kadec, M. I., Letter to the editor. *Izvestia Vys. Uch. Zav.* (1961) **6**, 186–187.
3. Lindenstrauss, J., On operators which attain their norm. *Israel J. Math.* **1**(1963), 139–148.
4. Lindenstrauss, J., On extreme points in l_1. *Israel J. Math.* **4** (1966), 59–61.
5. Phillips, R. S., On weakly compact subsets of a Banach space. *Amer. J. Math.* **65**(1943), 108–136.
6. Rieffel, M. A., The Radon-Nikodym theorem for the Bochner integral. To appear.

[2]Added in proof: I. Namioka has recently shown, in "Neighborhoods of Extreme Points" (to appear), that every dual Banach space which is separable has this property.

II

OPERATORS

On Wiener-Hopf Operators

by
ALLEN DEVINATZ[1]

During the past decade considerable progress has been made in the study of Wiener-Hopf equations on the group of integers ([7], [**16**], [**22**]), on the straight line ([**16**]) and in other rather general situations [**8**]. In particular a great deal of attention has been centered on the 'finite-section' equation ([**5**], [**9**], [**11**], [**17**], [**18**]) which is of great importance for applications. Most of these investigations have been carried out by Banach algebra techniques. However, it has been shown in [**9**] and [**10**] that for some applications the study of these equations in a Hilbert space topology would lead to better results.

The object of this paper is to study Wiener-Hopf equations in the Hardy space H^2 of the real line. In particular we shall apply our ideas to obtain a sharpened version of an asymptotic formula originally obtained by G. Szegö [**21**] for the circle group, and subsequently by M. Kac [**14**], N. I. Achiezer [**2**], and very recently a sharp version due to I. I. Hirschman, Jr. [**13**] for the real line.

1. PRELIMINARIES

We shall designate the real line by R and shall use the letters x, y to stand for the elements of R. The Haar measure on R will be taken as $dx/2\pi$. It will be convenient to denote the dual group of R by $\hat{R}$ and we shall usually use the letters s, t, etc., to stand for the elements of $\hat{R}$. The Haar measure in $\hat{R}$ will be taken as dt. Complex valued functions on R will usually be designated by f, g, u, v, etc. The circle group will be designated by T and its dual by $\hat{T}$. The Haar measure on T will be taken as $d\theta/2\pi$ and the Haar measure on $\hat{T}$ is the measure which counts the number of points in any given set.

[1]Research supported by NSF Grant No. GP-3583.

If $g \in L^2(R)$ its Fourier transform is given by

$$\hat{g}(t) = \frac{1}{2\pi}\int_{-\infty}^{\infty} e^{-itx}g(x)dx, \tag{1.1}$$

and hence the inverse transform is

$$g(x) = \int_{-\infty}^{\infty} e^{itx}\hat{g}(t)dt. \tag{1.2}$$

The Hardy space $H^2(R)$ is that subspace of $L^2(R)$ consisting of those (equivalence classes of) functions $g(x)$ that are the nontangential limits of analytic functions $g(z)$, $z = x + iy$, defined on the half-plane $\{z: \operatorname{Im} z > 0\}$ and so that

$$\frac{1}{2\pi}\int_{-\infty}^{\infty} |g(x)|^2dx = \|g\|^2 = \sup_{y>0}\frac{1}{2\pi}\int_{-\infty}^{\infty} |g(x+iy)|^2dx. \tag{1.3}$$

Any function, analytic in the upper half-plane, for which the right-hand side of this equation is finite has a nontangential limit, a.e., which defines a function in $H^2(R)$ and the equality in (1.3) is satisfied. $H^2(R)$ may also be characterized as that subspace of all $g \in L^2(R)$ such that $\hat{g}(t) = 0$ for $t < 0$.

The Hardy space $H^2(T)$ is that subspace of $L^2(T)$ consisting of those functions $g(e^{i\theta})$ which are the nontangential limits of analytic functions $g(w)$, $w = re^{i\theta}$, defined on the open unit disk $\{w: |w| < 1\}$ and so that

$$\frac{1}{2\pi}\int_{0}^{2\pi} |g(e^{i\theta})|^2d\theta = \|g\|^2 = \sup_{r<1}\frac{1}{2\pi}\int_{0}^{2\pi} |g(re^{i\theta})|^2d\theta. \tag{1.4}$$

Any function, analytic on the open unit disk, for which the right side is bounded has a nontangential limit, a.e., which defines a function in $H^2(T)$ and the equality (1.4) holds. The space $H^2(T)$ may also be characterized as the collection of functions $g \in L^2(T)$ such that $\hat{g}(n) = 0$ for $n < 0$.

The Hardy classes $H^p(R)$ and $H^p(T)$, $1 \le p < \infty$ are defined in an analogous way. The only difference is that in (1.3) and (1.4) the exponent 2 is replaced by the exponent p. They may also be characterized as those elements of $L^p(R)$ whose (distribution) Fourier transforms have support in $[0, \infty)$.

There is a useful unitary map from $L^2(R)$ onto which takes $H^2(T)$ onto $H^2(R)$ and allows us to obtain a number of results about $H^2(R)$ from results known about $H^2(T)$. This unitary map is defined with the help of the Cayley transform which takes the upper half-plane conformally onto the open unit disk. The Cayley transform is given by

$$\kappa z = \frac{z - i}{z + i}. \tag{1.5}$$

We first define an operator V as follows. For any g, defined on T, we set

$$Vg(x) = g(\kappa x) \tag{1.6}$$

It is an easy matter to compute that for any real number p,

$$\frac{1}{2\pi}\int_0^{2\pi} |g(e^{i\theta})|^p d\theta = \frac{1}{\pi}\int_{-\infty}^{\infty} \frac{|Vg(x)|^p}{1 + x^2} dx. \tag{1.7}$$

For any function g, defined on T, we now set

$$Ug(x) = \sqrt{2}\frac{Vg(x)}{x + i}. \tag{1.8}$$

If we set $p = 2$ in (1.7), then this equation shows that when U is restricted to $L^2(T)$ it is an isometric map from $L^2(T)$ into $L^2(R)$. To show that this map is onto, let $h \in L^2(R)$ and set

$$g(w) = -\sqrt{2}i\frac{h(\kappa^{-1}w)}{w - 1}, \qquad |w| = 1, w \neq 1.$$

It follows that $Ug(x) = h(x)$ and therefore from (1.7), with $p = 2$, it follows that $g \in L^2(T)$ and U restricted to $L^2(T)$ is onto. From now on we shall suppose that the U acts only on $L^2(T)$.

In order to prove that U takes $H^2(T)$ onto $H^2(R)$ it is convenient to consider the classes $H^\infty(R)$ and $H^\infty(T)$. The space $H^\infty(R)$ is defined as the set of functions $g(x) \in L^\infty(R)$ which are nontangential limits of analytic functions $g(z)$, $z = x + iy$, $y > 0$, so that

$$\text{ess. sup}\,\{|g(x)| : x \in R\} = \|g\|_\infty = \sup\,\{|g(z)| : \text{Im}\, z > 0\}. \tag{1.9}$$

Any function analytic in the upper half plane for which the right-hand side of (1.9) is finite has nontangential limits and the equalities in (1.9) are satisfied. The Hardy class $H^\infty(T)$ can be defined in an analogous way.

If g is defined on T it is clear that

$$\|g\|_\infty = \|Vg\|_\infty \tag{1.10}$$

where the left-hand side is the supremum norm on T and the right-hand side is the supremum norm on R. This makes the restriction of V to $L^\infty(T)$ an isometric map from $L^\infty(T)$ into $L^\infty(R)$. A moment's reflection will convince the reader that this map is onto.

Let us return to the proof that U takes $H^2(T)$ onto $H^2(R)$. We begin with a function $g \in H^\infty(T)$. The functions $Ug(x)$ and $Vg(x)$ may be extended analytically into the upper half-plane to get functions $Ug(z)$ and $Vg(z)$ and from (1.8) these analytic extensions satisfy the equation

$$Ug(z) = \sqrt{2}\, Vg(z)/(z + i),$$

since the boundary values uniquely determine the analytic extensions. Hence we get

$$\int_{-\infty}^{\infty} |Ug(x + iy)|^2 dx = 2 \int_{-\infty}^{\infty} \left|\frac{Vg(z)}{z + i}\right|^2 dx$$

$$\leq 2 \| Vg \|_\infty \int_{-\infty}^{\infty} \frac{dx}{x^2 + (y + 1)^2} \leq 2 \| g \|_\infty \int_{-\infty}^{\infty} \frac{dx}{x^2 + 1}.$$

It follows that $Ug(x) \in H^2(R)$. Since $H^\infty(T)$ is dense in $H^2(T)$ it follows that U maps $H^2(T)$ into $H^2(R)$.

To show that the map is onto suppose that $\hat{f}$ is a continuously differentiable function which vanishes outside a compact set in $(0, \infty)$. The class of such functions is dense in $L^2(0, \infty)$ and hence the class of functions

$$f(x) = \int_0^\infty e^{ixt} \hat{f}(t) dt$$

is dense in $H^2(R)$. Since $\hat{f}$ is continuously differentiable and vanishes outside a compact set it is clear that $g(x) = (x + i) f(x)$ belongs to $H^\infty(R)$. Let us set $\sqrt{2}\, h = V^{-1} g$; then $h \in H^\infty(T)$ and $Uh(x) = f(x)$. This shows that U takes $H^2(T)$ onto $H^2(R)$.

2. CONJUGATE FUNCTIONS AND OUTER FACTORS

There are several possibilities for defining conjugate functions for certain classes of functions defined on R. We shall use that definition which is most congenial to our purpose. The class W_p shall be taken as those equivalence classes of functions u for which

$$\frac{|u(x)|^p}{1 + x^2} \in L^1(R). \tag{2.1}$$

It follows from formulas (1.6) and (1.7) that if $u \in W_p$, then $V^{-1}u \in L^p(T)$. If we designate the usual conjugation operator on $L^1(T)$ by K, then we define

$$Cu = VKV^{-1}u, \qquad u \in W_1, \tag{2.2}$$

and call C the conjugation operator. Since it is always true that $KV^{-1} \in L^p(T)$, $0 \leq p < 1$, (see [**23**], p. 254) it follows that

$$\frac{|Cu(x)|^p}{1 + x^2} \in L^1(R), 0 \leq p < 1.$$

Actually, it is possible to exhibit an integral transform which will give the operator C. The function $V^{-1}u(e^{i\theta}) + iKV^{-1}u(e^{i\theta})$ may be extended analytically into the open disk by means of the formula

$$V^{-1}u(w) + iKV^{-1}u(w) = \frac{1}{2\pi}\int_0^{2\pi} V^{-1}u(e^{i\theta})\frac{e^{i\theta} + w}{e^{i\theta} - w}d\theta. \tag{2.3}$$

Suppose z is in the upper half-plane and $w = \kappa z$. Transform the integral in (2.3) by means of $e^{i\theta} = \kappa x = (x - i)/(x + i)$. After a little computation it turns out that

$$V^{-1}u\left(\frac{z - i}{z + i}\right) + iKV^{-1}u\left(\frac{z - i}{z + i}\right) = -\frac{i}{\pi}\int_{-\infty}^{\infty} u(x)\frac{zx + 1}{x - z}\frac{dx}{1 + x^2}.$$

Supposing u is real and $\xi = Re\, z$, if we equate the imaginary part of both sides of this equation and then allow Im $z \to 0$, it follows that for almost all ξ

$$Cu(\xi) = KV^{-1}u\left(\frac{\xi - i}{\xi + i}\right) = -\frac{1}{\pi}\int_{-\infty}^{\infty} u(x)\frac{x\xi + 1}{x - \xi}\frac{dx}{1 + x^2}, \tag{2.4}$$

where the integral is to be taken as an improper integral. By breaking up a function into its real and imaginary part we get (2.4) for complex functions as well.

If $u(x)/(1 + |x|)$ is summable then the Hilbert transform exists and indeed from (2.4) we have

$$Cu(\xi) = -\frac{1}{\pi}\int_{-\infty}^{\infty}\frac{u(x)}{x - \xi}dx + \frac{1}{\pi}\int_{-\infty}^{\infty} u(x)\frac{x}{1 + x^2}dx.$$

Thus the Hilbert transform of u differs from Cu by an additive constant. In case $u(x)/(1 + x^2)$ is in $L^2(R)$ the conjugate function can be defined by means of the Fourier transform of $u(x)/(x + i)$ (see Achiezer [**1**]) or can be taken as the operator UKU^{-1}. The conjugate function obtained in these ways will differ from the conjugate function we have defined by, at most, an additive constant.

If $g \in L^p(T)$, $1 \leq p \leq \infty$, then g is an *outer factor* in $H^p(T)$ if and only if g can be written

$$g = \exp(u + iKu + i\alpha),$$

where u is a real function in $L^1(T)$ and α is a real constant (see [**6**]). An equivalent condition for $g \in H^p(T)$, $1 \leq p < \infty$, to be an outer factor is that the closure in the norm topology of $H^p(T)$ of the linear manifold determined by $\{e^{ik\theta}g(e^{i\theta})$: $k = 0, 1, 2, \ldots\}$ is all of $H^p(T)$. For $p = \infty$, the closure of this manifold in the weak* topology of $H^\infty(T)$ is all of $H^\infty(T)$.

If we go over to $H^p(R)$, $1 \leq p < \infty$, then in analogy with the last statement we could define $g \in H^p(R)$ to be an outer factor if and only if the linear space generated by the set $\{e^{itx}g(x)$: $t \geq 0\}$ is dense in $H^p(R)$. We can show that if this is taken as the definition then $g \in H^p(R)$ is an outer factor if and only if $g \in L^p(R)$ and

$$g = \exp(u + iCu + i\alpha), \tag{2.5}$$

where u is a real function in W_1 and α is a real constant. In general, functions which can be written in the form (2.5) do not belong to any of the Lebesgue spaces $L^p(R)$. The functions g which appear in our later applications will usually belong to a class W_p, $1 \leq p \leq \infty$. However, we find it convenient to define an outer factor without attaching it to any class.

DEFINITION 2.1. A function g, defined on R, is said to be an outer factor if and only if it can be written in the form (2.5) where u is a real function in W_1 and α is a real constant.

From this definition it is clear that the product and quotient of two outer factors is an outer factor. Further, g is an outer factor in W_p if and only if $V^{-1}g$ is an outer factor in $H^p(T)$, $1 \leq p \leq \infty$. Indeed, if g is in W_p it follows from the formula (1.7) (or (1.10) if $p = \infty$),

$$\frac{1}{2\pi}\int_0^{2\pi} |V^{-1}g(e^{i\theta})|^p d\theta = \frac{1}{\pi}\int_{-\infty}^{\infty} \frac{|g(x)|^p}{1 + x^2}dx,$$

that $V^{-1}g \in L^p(T)$. If g is an outer factor then from (2.5) we get

$$V^{-1}g = \exp(V^{-1}u + iV^{-1}Cu + i\alpha). \tag{2.6}$$

Since $u \in W_1$, it follows from (1.7), with $p = 1$, that $V^{-1}u \in L^1(T)$. Since $V^{-1}Cu = KV^{-1}u$, it follows from (2.6) that $V^{-1}g$ is outer in $H^P(T)$. Conversely, suppose $g \in W_p$ and $V^{-1}g$ is outer in $H^p(T)$. Then there is a $v \in L^1(T)$ so that

$$V^{-1}g = \exp(v + iKv + i\alpha).$$

If we set $u = Vv$, then $VKv = VKV^{-1}u = Cu$. From (1.7) it follows that $u \in W_1$ and hence g is outer in W_p.

Using this method one can establish, for example, that the function $1/(x + i)$ is outer in $H^2(R)$. The fact that it is in $H^2(R)$ is clear. Now,

$$V^{-1}\left(\frac{1}{x+i}\right) = \frac{i}{2}(e^{i\theta} - 1); \quad e^{i\theta} = \frac{x-i}{x+i}.$$

We claim that $e^{i\theta} - 1$ is outer in $H^2(T)$. Indeed, suppose $h \in H^2(T)$ and

$$\int_0^{2\pi} e^{in\theta}(e^{i\theta} - 1)\bar{h}(\theta)\, d\theta = 0,\ n = 0, 1, \cdots$$

It follows that $(e^{-i\theta} - 1)h(\theta) \in (H^2)^{\perp}$; i.e.,

$$(e^{-i\theta} - 1)h(\theta) \sim \sum_{k=-\infty}^{-1} \hat{g}(k)e^{ik\theta}.$$

But we also have

$$h(\theta) \sim \sum_{k=0}^{\infty} \hat{h}(k)e^{ik\theta},$$

and these two statements together imply that

$$\hat{h}(k+1) - \hat{h}(k) = 0,\ k = 0, 1, 2, \cdots.$$

This means $\hat{h}(0) = \hat{h}(1) = \hat{h}(2) = \ldots$, which is impossible unless $h = 0$ since $h \in H^2(T)$. This shows that the set $\{e^{in\theta}(e^{i\theta} - 1): n = 0, 1, \ldots\}$ is dense in $H^2(T)$ which proves our assertion that $e^{i\theta} - 1$ is outer.

Consequently, we may write

$$V^{-1}\left(\frac{1}{x+i}\right) = \exp(u + iKu + i\alpha),$$

where u is real and in $L^1(T)$. Apply V to both sides and we see that $1/(x+i)$ is outer in $H^2(R)$.

PROPOSITION 2.2. The function g is an outer factor in $H^2(R)$ if and only if the closure of the linear manifold generated by the set $\{e^{itx}g(x): t \geq 0\}$ is all of $H^2(R)$.

Proof. Suppose that g is an outer factor in $H^2(R)$. Let us set

$$h(e^{i\theta}) = -\sqrt{2}i\frac{V^{-1}g(e^{i\theta})}{e^{i\theta} - 1} = U^{-1}g(e^{i\theta}). \tag{2.7}$$

We have just shown that $e^{i\theta} - 1$ is an outer factor and hence its inverse is an outer factor. Since $V^{-1}g$ is also an outer factor it follows that $h(e^{i\theta})$ and $(e^{i\theta} - 1)h(e^{i\theta})$ are outer factors in $H^2(T)$.

The closure in $H^2(T)$ of the linear manifold generated by the continuous functions in $H^{\infty}(T)$ times $(e^{i\theta} - 1)h(e^{i\theta})$ is all of $H^2(T)$. From this it is immediate that the closure in $H^2(T)$ of the linear manifold generated by the products of h with continuous functions in $H^\infty(T)$ that vanish at $e^{i\theta} = 1$ is all of $H^2(T)$. If we map this latter linear manifold by U the range is dense in $H^2(R)$. Let $K_0^\infty(R)$ be the collection of continuous functions in $H^\infty(R)$ which vanish at $\pm\infty$. Then the closure in $H^2(R)$ of the linear manifold generated by products of g with elements of $K_0^\infty(R)$ is all of $H^2(R)$.

Let $\hat{\varphi}(t)$ be continuous on $[0, r]$ and set

$$\varphi_r(x) = \int_0^r e^{itx}\hat{\varphi}(t)\,dt.$$

The function φ_r is in $K_0^\infty(R)$ and the collection of such functions (as r and $\hat{\varphi}$ vary) is dense in $K_0^\infty(R)$. There is a sequence of Riemann sums which converge pointwise and boundedly to $\varphi_r(x)$. Hence, by use of Lebesgue's dominated convergence theorem it follows that $\varphi_r(x)g(x)$ is in the closure of the linear manifold generated by $\{e^{itx}g(x): t \geq 0\}$. This proves the necessity part of the proposition.

Conversely, suppose $\{e^{itx}g(x);\ t \geq 0\}$ generates $H^2(R)$. For fixed $t_0 > 0$ and $1/n \leq t_0$ let us set

$$g_n(x) = \frac{n}{2}\int_{t_0-1/n}^{t_0+1/n} e^{itx}\,dt = e^{it_0x}\cdot\left[\frac{\sin x/n}{x/n}\right].$$

We see from this that $g_n(x) \to 0$ as $x \to \pm\infty$. Let us now set

$$g_n(z) = \frac{n}{2}\int_{t_0-1/n}^{t_0+1/n} e^{it(x+iy)}dt, \quad z = x + iy, \quad y \geq 0.$$

It is clear that $g_n(z)$ is an analytic extension of $g_n(x)$ into the upper half-plane. Further,

$$|g_n(z)| \leq \frac{n}{2}\int_{t_0-1/n}^{t_0+1/n} e^{-ty}dt \leq 1.$$

Hence, $g_n(x) \in K_0^\infty(R)$.

Now,

$$\int_{-\infty}^{\infty} |g_n(x)g(x) - e^{it_0x}g(x)|^2dx = \int_{-\infty}^{\infty} |g(x)|^2\left|\frac{\sin x/n}{x/n} - 1\right|^2 dx.$$

As $n \to \infty$, the integrand on the right goes pointwise to zero and is bounded by $4|g(x)|^2$. By Lebesgue's dominated convergence theorem the integral goes to zero. This shows that the linear manifold generated by products of elements of $K_0^\infty(R)$ and g is dense in $H^2(R)$.

If we transform g by U^{-1} we get (2.7). Set $e_n(e^{i\theta}) = e^{in\theta}(e^{i\theta} - 1)$, $n = 0, 1, 2, \ldots$; then

$$e_n(e^{i\theta})U^{-1}g(e^{i\theta}) = -\sqrt{2}i\, e^{in\theta}V^{-1}g(e^{i\theta}) .$$

The linear manifold generated by the set $\{e_n\}$ is dense in the subset of continuous functions in $H^\infty(T)$ which vanish at 1. Hence, the linear manifold generated by the set $\{Ve_n\}$ is dense in $K_0^\infty(R)$. Consequently the linear manifold generated by

$$Ue_nU^{-1}g = (Ve_n)g$$

is dense in $H^2(R)$. This shows that $e^{in\theta}V^{-1}g(e^{i\theta})$ is dense in $H^2(T)$. Thus g is outer in $H^2(R)$.

We can put a metric on W_p by means of the norm

$$\left\{\frac{1}{2\pi}\int_{-\infty}^{\infty}\frac{|g(x)|^p}{1+x^2}dx\right\}^{1/p}, \quad 1 \le p < \infty ,$$

The metric induced by this norm will make W_p a complete metric space which is indeed nothing more than the Lebesgue space with respect to the measure $dx/(1 + x^2)$.

DEFINITION 2.3. The space B_p, $1 \le p < \infty$ shall be the closure in W_p of the linear manifold generated by $\{e^{itx}: t \ge 0\}$. We shall take $B_\infty = B_2 \cap L^\infty(R)$.

PROPOSITION 2.4. The map $W{:}h \to h/(x + i)$ is an isometry from B_2 onto $H^2(R)$.

Proof. If $h \in B_2$, then there exists a sequence of polynomials $\{p_n\}$ of the generic form

$$p(x) = \sum_{k=1}^{m} \alpha_k e^{it_k x}; \quad t_k \ge 0,$$

such that $p_n \to h$ in W_2. Now, $p_n(x)/(x + i)$ is clearly in $H^2(R)$ and $p_n(x)/(x + i) \to h/(x + i)$ in $H^2(R)$. This shows the map W is an isometry into $H^2(R)$. On the other hand we have shown that $1/(x + i)$ is an outer factor and hence by Proposition 2.2 the set $\{e^{itx}/(x + i): t \ge 0\}$ generates $H^2(R)$. This shows the map is onto.

COROLLARY 2.4. The function $g \in W_2$ is outer if and only if the set $\{e^{itx}g(x): t \ge 0\}$ generates B_2.

Proof. If g is outer in W_2, the function $g(x)/(x + i)$ is an outer factor in H^2. Hence by Proposition 2.2 the set $\{e^{itx}g(x)/(x + i): t \ge 0\}$ generates H^2. Apply Proposition 2.4 and we have necessity. The sufficiency follows immediately from Propositions 2.2 and 2.4 and the fact that $1/(x + i)$ is outer.

Another convenient characterization of an outer factor in W_2 is given by the following:

PROPOSITION 2.5. A function $g \in W_2$ is an outer factor if and only if the closure in W_2 of the linear manifold generated by the set

$$\left\{\left(\frac{x-i}{x+i}\right)^n g(x): n = 0, 1, 2, \cdots\right\}$$

is all of B_2.

Proof. Suppose g is an outer factor in W_2. By definition it has the form (2.5) where u is a real element in W_1. Now,

$$V^{-1}g = \exp(V^{-1}u + iV^{-1}Cu + i\alpha),$$

where $V^{-1}g \in L^2(T)$ and $V^{-1}u \in L^1(T)$. Since $V^{-1}Cu = KV^{-1}u$ it follows that $V^{-1}g$ is an outer factor in $H^2(T)$. Consequently the set $\{e^{in\theta}V^{-1}g(e^{i\theta}): n = 0, 1, \ldots\}$ generates a dense linear space in $H^2(T)$. Now

$$Ue^{in\theta}\, V^{-1}g(x) = \frac{\sqrt{2}}{x+i}\left(\frac{x-i}{x+i}\right)^n g(x), \tag{2.8}$$

which shows that the linear space generated by the set of elements on the right is $H^2(R)$. Now apply the map W^{-1} of the previous proposition and we have proved the necessity of the present proposition.

To prove the sufficiency apply the map W of the previous proposition and we see that the set of elements on the right-side of (2.8) generates $H^2(R)$. Apply U^{-1} and we see that the set $\{e^{in\theta}\, V^{-1}g(e^{i\theta}): n = 0, 1, 2, \ldots\}$ generates $H^2(T)$. Hence $V^{-1}g$ is outer which makes g outer.

COROLLARY 2.5. The function $g \in H^2(R)$ is outer if and only if the set

$$\left\{\left(\frac{x-i}{x+i}\right)^n g(x): n = 0, 1, 2, \cdots\right\} \tag{2.9}$$

generates $H^2(R)$.

Proof. We have already seen that $1/(x + i)$ is an outer factor and hence $(x + i)$ is an outer factor. Hence $(x + i)g(x)$ is an outer factor in W_2. Consequently, the space generated by the set

$$\left\{\left(\frac{x-i}{x+i}\right)^n (x+i)g(x): n = 0, 1, 2, \cdots\right\} \tag{2.10}$$

is dense in B_2 by the last corollary. Apply the operator W which proves the necessity.

Conversely if (2.9) generates $H^2(R)$ it follows that (2.10) generates B_2 and thus $(x + i)g(x)$ is outer. This in turn implies g is outer.

By almost identical reasoning we can obtain results corresponding to the previous results when W_2, B_2 and $H^2(R)$ are replaced by W_p, B_p and $H^p(R)$ respectively, $1 \leq p < \infty$.

3. THE INVERTIBILITY OF WIENER-HOPF OPERATORS

Let E be the projection of $L^2(T)$ onto $H^2(T)$ and P the projection of $L^2(R)$ onto $H^2(R)$. Then it is clear that

$$P = UEU^{-1}$$

If $f \in L^\infty(R)$, then the operator defined on $L^2(R)$ by

$$L(f)g = fg$$

is a bounded normal operator. The operator

$$W(f) = PL(f)\mid_{H^2(R)}$$

is a bounded operator from $H^2(R)$ into $H^2(R)$ which we call a Wiener-Hopf operator. If one goes over to the Fourier transform then the Wiener-Hopf operator becomes a convolution operator and if $g \in H^2(R)$ we can write

$$\hat{W}(\hat{f}) = \hat{f} * \hat{g},$$

where $\hat{f}$ is to be considered as the Fourier transform in the distribution sense. Of course the convolution is to be interpreted in the usual way; i.e., $\hat{f}*\hat{g}$ is defined as the usual distribution convolution when $\hat{g}$ vanishes off a compact set in $(0, \infty)$ and since $\hat{W}(f)$ is a bounded operator the convolution operation is uniquely extendable to all functions in $L^2(0, \infty)$.

The first question we are interested in is to give conditions on f so that $W(f)$ is an invertible operator; i.e., $W(f)$ is a one to one transformation of $H^2(R)$ onto $H^2(R)$. Of course $W(f)$ will be an invertible operator if and only if the Toeplitz operator defined by

$$T(\tilde{f}) = U^{-1}W(f)U$$

is an invertible operator on $H^2(T)$. The operator $T(\tilde{f})$ is given by

$$T(\tilde{f})g = E(V^{-1}f)g = E\tilde{f}g,$$

where we have set $\tilde{f} = V^{-1}f$. Necessary and sufficient conditions are known [**8**] that $T(\tilde{f})$ be an invertible operator of $H^2(T)$ onto itself. These conditions are:

(i) $|\tilde{f}| \geq m > 0$, (*$\tilde{f}$ is bounded also*)

(ii) *there exists a* $\tilde{\gamma} \in H^\infty(T)$ *so that* $1/\tilde{\gamma} \in H^\infty(T)$ *and* $\|\operatorname{Arg} \tilde{\gamma}\tilde{f}\|_\infty < \pi/2$, where for any complex number z, Arg z is the principal argument of z, $-\pi < \operatorname{Arg} z \leq \pi$.

We should make a few comments about the meaning of condition (ii). Suppose $\tilde{f}$ is a continuous function on T. By use of the monodromy theorem it is possible to find a function $\arg \tilde{f}$ which is defined and continuous for $0 \leq \theta \leq 2\pi$. The number

$$\Delta \arg \tilde{f} = \frac{1}{2\pi}\{\arg \tilde{f}(2\pi) - \arg \tilde{f}(0)\}$$

is called the index of $\tilde{f}$ and a necessary and sufficient condition that (ii) holds is that $\Delta \arg \tilde{f} = 0$. Indeed, since $\Delta \arg \tilde{f} = 0$, the function $\arg \tilde{f}(\theta)$ may be considered to be a continuous function on T. Hence, there is a real trigonometric polynomial

$$p(e^{i\theta}) = \sum_{k=-n}^{n} \hat{p}(k)e^{ik\theta}$$

so that

$$\| \arg \tilde{f} - p \|_\infty < \pi/2.$$

If we set

$$\tilde{\gamma}(e^{i\theta}) = \exp - 2i\left\{\hat{p}(0)/2 + \sum_{k=1}^{n} \hat{p}(k)e^{ik\theta}\right\},$$

then (ii) is satisfied. The proof of the necessity requires somewhat more refined arguments and can be found in [**8**].

By setting $\gamma = V\tilde{\gamma}$ the conditions (i) and (ii) can be translated over to R and we have the following:

Necessary and sufficient conditions that the Wiener-Hopf operator $W(f)$ *is invertible are:*

(i′) $|f| \geq m > 0$, (f *is bounded also*).

(ii′) *there exists a* $\gamma \in H^\infty(R)$ *so that* $1/\gamma \in H^\infty(R)$ *and so that* $\| \operatorname{Arg} \gamma f \|_\infty < \pi/2$.

There is, however, a more delicate question that must be answered in order to be able to apply the theory of Wiener-Hopf operators to various problems in asymptotic approximation which has found wide application during the past few years. Let us designate by H_r^2 that subspace of $H^2(R)$ consisting of all functions of the form

$$u(x) = \int_0^r e^{itx}\hat{u}(t)\, dt,$$

where $\hat{u} \in L^2(0, r)$. Let P_r be the projection of $L^2(R)$ onto H_r^2 and set

$$W_r(f) = P_r W(f) \mid_{H_r^2}.$$

The problem is to give conditions on f so that $W_r(f)$ is invertible for *all* sufficiently large r and moreover the inverse operators shall be uniformly bounded in norm as r varies. Of course, if we demand this latter condition, $W(f)$ itself must be an invertible operator and hence the conditions (i′) and (ii′) are necessary conditions on f in order that the 'finite section' problem be solvable. It is not known whether or not these conditions are sufficient.

We shall give conditions here for the solvability of the 'finite-section' problem. The theorem we shall give is a generalization of a theorem obtain by E. Reich [**17**] for the circle group.

Before we state and prove our theorem we shall say a few words about the factorizations of functions that satisfy (ii′). We shall suppose that f and $\log |f|$ are in W_1; i.e., $f(x)/(1 + x^2)$ and $\log |f(x)|/(1 + x^2)$ are in $L^1(R)$. This means that the functions $\tilde{f}$ and $\log |\tilde{f}|$ are in $L^1(T)$ and (ii) is satisfied for $\tilde{f}$. Under these conditions it is known (see [**8**]) that $\tilde{f}$ may be factored as

$$f = (\tilde{\phi}\tilde{\psi})(\tilde{\phi}/\tilde{\psi})^*, \qquad (z^* = \text{complex conjugate of } z) \tag{3.1}$$

where $\tilde{\phi}$ is an outer factor in $H^2(T)$ and $\tilde{\psi}$ and $1/\tilde{\psi}$ are outer factors in $H^q(T)$ for some $q > 2$. If we apply V to both sides of (3.1) it follows that

$$f = (\phi\psi)(\phi/\psi)^* = gh^*, \tag{3.2}$$

where ϕ is an outer factor in B_2 and ψ and $1/\psi$ are outer factors in B_q for some $q > 2$.

Let us note that if f and $1/f$ are in $L^\infty(R)$, then it follows that ϕ and $1/\phi$ are outer factors in $H^\infty(R)$. However, it is in general not possible to give a sharper estimate on the function ψ.

Let us designate by $C^-(R)$ the closure in L^∞ of the set of $s \in L^\infty(R)$ so that the support of $\hat{s}$ (as a distribution) lies in some half line $[r, \infty)$, $-\infty < r < \infty$. The elements of $C^-(R)$ form an algebra and from the Fejer approximation theorem for R([**1**], p. 113) this algebra contains the bounded uniformly continuous functions defined on R. We have not, however been able to characterize $C^-(R)$.[1]

THEOREM 3.1. Suppose conditions (i′) and (ii′) are satisfied for f. Then f may be factored as in (3.2) and if either g/g^* or h/h^* belong to $C^-(R)$, then there exists an $r_0 \geq 0$ so that $r \geq r_0$ implies $W_f(f)$ is invertible and the norms of $W_r(f)^{-1}$ remain uniformly bounded.

[1]However, very recently D. Sarason has characterized the corresponding algebra on T as being $C + H^\infty(T)$, where C is the class of continuous functions on T.

Proof. Let $u \in H^2_r$ and set $v = P_r fu$. Then we may write

$$fu = p + v + q, \tag{3.3}$$

where $p \in H^2(R)^\perp$ and $q \in H^2(R) \cap (H^2_r)^\perp$. Multiply (3.3) by $p^*/f\gamma$ and then integrate over R. We get

$$0 = \int_R \frac{up^*}{\gamma} = \int_R \frac{1}{f\gamma}|p|^2 + \int_R v\frac{p^*}{f\gamma} + \int_R \frac{p^*}{f\gamma}. \tag{3.4}$$

We have used the fact that $u/\gamma \in H^2(R)$ and $p \in H^2(R)^\perp$ so that the left side of (3.4) is zero.

Suppose now that $s \in L^\infty(R)$ so that the support of $\hat{s}$ (as a distribution) is in $[-r, \infty)$, $r \geq 0$. Since $q \in H^2(R) \cap (H^2_r)^\perp$ it can be written as

$$q(x) = \int_r^\infty e^{itx}\hat{q}(t)\,dt, \ \hat{q} \in L^2(\hat{R}).$$

Since $1/\gamma$ and $1/\phi$ are in $H^\infty(R)$ and $p^* \in H^2(R)$ it follows that $p^*q/\gamma\phi^2 \in H^1(R)$ and has a Fourier transform which is a function whose support is in $[r, \infty)$. Hence $sp^*q/\gamma\phi^2$ has a Fourier transform which is a continuous function whose support is in $[0, \infty)$. This means in particular that

$$\int_R \frac{s}{\gamma}\frac{p^*q}{\phi^2} = 0. \tag{3.5}$$

If we combine (3.4) and (3.5) we get

$$-\int_R \frac{1}{f\gamma}|p|^2 = \int_R v\frac{p^*}{f\gamma} + \int_R\left(\frac{\varphi}{\phi^*\gamma} - \frac{s}{\phi\gamma}\right)\frac{p^*q}{\phi}, \tag{3.6}$$

where we have set $\varphi = \psi^*/\psi$. Since $\|\operatorname{Arg}\gamma f\|_\infty < \pi/2$ and $\gamma f \in L^\infty(R)$ it follows that there is a $\delta > 0$ so that $Re\ 1/\gamma f \geq \delta > 0$. If we take the absolute value of both sides of (3.6), apply the previous fact, Schwarz's inequality and the facts that $1/\gamma$, $1/f\gamma$ and $1/\phi$ are bounded, we arrive at the fact that there exists a constant M, independent of r and u, so that

$$\|p\| \leq M\|v\| + M\left\|\frac{h}{h^*} - s\right\|_\infty \|q\|. \tag{3.7}$$

Since by hypothesis $h/h^* \in C^-(R)$, for every $\epsilon > 0$ there exists an r_ϵ so that $r \geq r_\epsilon$ implies

$$\|p\| \leq M\|v\| + M\epsilon\|q\|. \tag{3.7'}$$

Next, multiply (3.3) by $(\gamma q)^*/f$ and integrate over R to get

$$0 = \int_R u(\gamma q)^* = \int_R \frac{(\gamma q)^*}{f} p + \int_R v \frac{(\gamma q)^*}{f} + \int_R \frac{\gamma^*}{f} |q|^2. \tag{3.8}$$

The left side is zero since the support of $\hat{u}$ is in $[0, r]$ and the support of $\gamma\hat{q}$ is in $[r, \infty)$. By the hypothesis on the principal argument of γf and the fact that γ^*/f is bounded away from zero it follows that there is an $\eta > 0$ so that $Re\ \gamma^*/f \geq 2\eta > 0$. Using this fact in (3.8) we find that there is an M, independent of r and u, so that

$$2\eta \|q\| \leq M\|p\| + M\|v\|. \tag{3.9}$$

If we use the estimate (3.7′) in (3.9) we get

$$2\eta\|q\| \leq M\|v\| + M\epsilon\|q\|, \tag{3.10}$$

where the values of M in (3.7′), (3.9) and (3.10) are different, but are independent of r and u. If in (3.10) we choose ϵ so that $M\epsilon < \eta$, then for all r sufficiently large we get

$$\|q\| \leq M\|v\|, \tag{3.11}$$

where again M has a different value than before, but is independent of u and r.

Using the estimates (3.7′) and (3.11), and noting that f is bounded below we have arrived at the fact that there exists an M and an r_0 so that $r \geq r_0$ implies that for every $u \in H^2_r$ we have

$$\|u\| \leq M\|v\| = M\|W_r(f)u\|.$$

This proves the theorem except for one minor point. In the proof we supposed that $h/h^* \in C^-(R)$. If we had supposed instead that $g/g^* \in C^-(R)$ a slight adjustment in the proof would give this situation. However, we can reduce the latter situation immediately to the previous situation. Namely we can consider $f^* = hg^*$. Since $\|\text{Arg}\ \gamma f\|_\infty < \pi/2$ implies $\|\text{Arg} f^*/\gamma\|_\infty < \pi/2$ we get under the assumption that g/g^* is in $C^-(R)$ that $W_r(f^*)$ is invertible for all sufficiently large r and the inverses have uniformly bounded norms. Now, an easy calculation shows that $W_r(f)^* = W_r(f^*)$ and hence the theorem follows for $W_r(f)$.

COROLLARY 3.2[1]. If f satisfies the conditions (i′) and (ii′) and in addition f is uniformly continuous, then the conclusions of theorem 3.1 are valid.

Proof. Since $1/f$ is bounded and uniformly continuous it belongs to

[1]This corollary resulted from a conversation with Henry Helson during the course of this conference.

$C^-(R)$. We may write

$$\frac{gh}{f} = \frac{h}{h^*}.$$

Since $gh \in H^\infty(R)$ it belongs to $C^-(R)$, and since $C^-(R)$ is an algebra it follows that $h/h^* \in C^-(R)$.

4. ANALOGUES OF BIORTHOGONAL POLYNOMIALS

In order to obtain results on the asymptotic formula which was mentioned in the introduction it will be necessary for us to restrict the class of Wiener-Hopf operators which we discussed in the last section. We shall consider the class of functions f which satisfy the hypotheses of theorem 3.1 and moreover can be written in the form

$$f(x) = 1 - k(x), \qquad k \in L^2(R). \tag{4.1}$$

If we take δ to be the Dirac distribution which is the Fourier transform of the constant function 1 we get $\hat{f} = \delta - \hat{k}$.

It follows from the results of Theorem 3.1 that there exists an r_0 so that $r \geq r_0$ implies there is a unique $u_r \in H_r^2$ so that the distribution equation

$$(\delta - \hat{k}) * (\delta + \hat{u}_r) = 0 \tag{4.2}$$

is satisfied when applied to C^∞ functions with support in $(0, r)$. This is equivalent with saying that

$$\hat{f} * \hat{u}_r(t) = \hat{k}(t), \qquad t \in [0, r], \text{ a.e.} \tag{4.3}$$

Indeed, if we let $\hat{k}_r$ be the restriction of $\hat{k}$ to $[0, r]$, then equation (4.3) is nothing more than

$$W_r(f)u_r = k_r, \tag{4.4}$$

where, of course, k_r belongs to H_r^2 and is the inverse Fourier transform of $\hat{k}_r$. Theorem 3.1 tells us that equation (4.4) has a unique solution for all sufficiently large r.

From this point on we shall assume that $\hat{k}$ has right and left mean values at the origin; that is to say we shall suppose that the limits

$$\hat{k}(0\pm) = \lim_{h \searrow 0} \pm \frac{1}{h} \int_0^{\pm h} \hat{k}(t)\, dt \tag{4.5}$$

exist. Using equation (4.3) this will imply that

$$\hat{u}_r(0+) = \lim_{h \searrow 0} \frac{1}{h} \int_0^h \hat{u}_r(t)\, dt \tag{4.6}$$

exists. Indeed, for $t \in [0, r]$ we may write equation (4.3) as

$$\hat{u}_r(t) = \hat{k}(t) + \hat{k} * \hat{u}_r(t). \tag{4.7}$$

Consequently,

$$\hat{u}_r(0+) = \hat{k}(0+) + \int_0^r \hat{k}(-t)\hat{u}_r(t)\,dt. \tag{4.6'}$$

Since we have assumed that f satisfies the hypotheses of Theorem 3.1, it follows that there is a unique $u \in H^2(R)$ so that the convolution equation

$$(\delta - \hat{k}) * (\delta + \hat{u}) = 0 \tag{4.8}$$

is satisfied when applied to C^∞ functions with compact support in $(0, \infty)$. As before, this is equivalent with saying that

$$f * \hat{u}(t) = \hat{k}(t), \qquad t \in [0, \infty), \text{ a.e.} \tag{4.9}$$

If we take $\hat{k}_+$ to be the restriction of $\hat{k}$ to $[0, \infty)$, then equation (4.9) is

$$W(f)u = k_+, \tag{4.10}$$

where $k_+ \in H^2(R)$ and is the inverse Fourier transform of $\hat{k}_+$. By the same method that we have used before we find that

$$\hat{u}(0+) = \lim_{h \searrow 0} \frac{1}{h} \int_0^h \hat{u}(t)\,dt$$

$$= \hat{k}(0+) + \int_0^\infty \hat{k}(-t)\hat{u}(t)\,dt. \tag{4.11}$$

THEOREM 4.1. There exists an M so that for all sufficiently large r and for all $p_r \in H^2_r$,

$$\|u_r - p_r\| \leq M \|p_r - u\|. \tag{4.12}$$

Proof. Since $k_+ = Pk$ and $k_r = P_r k$, it follows that $P_r(k_r - k_+) = P_r(P_r - P)k = 0$. Hence, from (4.4) and (4.10) we get

$$P_r W(f)(u_r - u) = P_r(k_r - k_+) = 0.$$

Let $p_r \in H^2_r$; then

$$\|P_r W(f)(u_r - p_r)\| - \|P_r W(f)(p_r - u)\| \leq \|P_r W(f)(u_r - u)\| = 0.$$

Now, $\|P_r W(f)\| \leq \|W(f)\|$ and $P_r W(f)(u_r - p_r) = W_r(f)(u_r - p_r)$. It follows from Theorem 3.1 that there is an $m > 0$ so that for all sufficiently large r,

$$m \| u_r - p_r \| \leq \| W_r(f)(u_r - p_r) \| \leq \| W(f) \| \, \| p_r - u \| .$$

This is the content of Theorem 4.1.

COROLLARY 4.2. There exists an M so that for all sufficiently large r and for all $p_r \in H_r^2$,

$$\| u_r - u \| \leq M \| p_r - u \| . \tag{4.13}$$

In particular,

$$\| u_r - u \|^2 \leq M^2 \int_r^\infty | \hat{u}(t) |^2 \, dt. \tag{4.14}$$

Proof. From Theorem 4.1 we have

$$\| u_r - u \| \leq \| u_r - p_r \| + \| p_r - u \| \leq M \| p_r - u \| ,$$

which gives (4.13). If we take

$$p_r(x) = \int_0^r e^{itx} \hat{u}(t) \, dt$$

we get (4.14).

COROLLARY 4.3. For all sufficiently large r,

$$| \hat{u}_r(0+) - \hat{u}(0+) | \leq \| (\mathrm{I} - P)k \| \, \| u_r - u \| . \tag{4.15}$$

This implies, in particular, that $\hat{u}_r(0+) \to \hat{u}(0+)$ as $r \to \infty$.

Proof. From equations (4.6′) and (4.11) we get

$$\hat{u}_r(0+) - \hat{u}(0+) = \int_0^\infty \hat{k}(-t)[\hat{u}_r(t) - \hat{u}(t)] \, dt.$$

Now apply Schwarz's inequality and we have the first statement of the corollary. The second statement is then a consequence of Corollary 4.2.

In the same way, as we have been considering Wiener-Hopf operators on $H^2(R)$, we may also consider them on $H^2(R)^\perp$. We shall define

$$H(f) = (I - P)L(f) \mid_{H^2(R)^\perp} .$$

A theorem corresponding to Theorem 3.1 holds for the operator $H(f)$ and the proof can be made in a corresponding way.

We shall define H^2_{-r} as that subspace consisting of all functions of the form

$$u(x) = \int_{-r}^0 e^{itx} \hat{u}(t) \, dt,$$

where $\hat{u} \in L^2(-r, 0)$, and denote the projection onto H^2_{-r} by P_{-r}. As before we may prove that there exists a unique $v_r \in H^2_{-r}$ so that the equation

$$(\delta - \hat{k}) * (\delta + \hat{v}_r) = 0 \tag{4.2'}$$

is satisfied when applied to C^∞ functions with support in $(-r, 0)$. This is equivalent with saying that

$$\hat{f} * \hat{v}_r(t) = \hat{k}(t), \qquad t \in [-r, 0], \text{ a.e.} \tag{4.3'}$$

Indeed, if we let $\hat{k}_{-r}$ be the restriction of $\hat{k}$ to $[-r, 0]$, then equation (4.3′) is equivalent with the equation

$$H_r(f)v_r = k_{-r}, \tag{4.4'}$$

where $H_r(f) = P_{-r}H(f) \mid_{H^2_{-r}}$, and k_{-r} is the inverse Fourier transform of $\hat{k}_{-r}$. In the same way as before we may show that

$$\hat{v}_r(0-) = \lim_{h \searrow 0} \frac{1}{h} \int_{-h}^{0} \hat{v}_r(t)\, dt = \hat{k}(0-) + \int_{-r}^{0} \hat{k}(-t)\hat{v}_r(t)\, dt. \tag{4.6'}$$

We may also prove the existence of a unique function $v \in H^2(R)^\perp$ so that the convolution equation

$$(\delta - \hat{k}) * (\delta + \hat{v}) = 0 \tag{4.8'}$$

is satisfied when applied to C^∞ functions with compact support in $(-\infty, 0)$. As before this is equivalent with saying that

$$\hat{f} * \hat{v}(t) = \hat{k}(t), \qquad t \in (-\infty, 0] \text{ a.e.} \tag{4.9'}$$

If we take $\hat{k}$ to be the restriction of $\hat{k}$ to $(-\infty, 0]$, then the equation (4.9′) is equivalent with

$$H(f)v = k_-, \tag{4.10'}$$

where $k_- \in H^2(R)^\perp$ and is the inverse Fourier transform of $\hat{k}_-$. We also get the formula

$$\hat{v}(0-) = \lim_{h \searrow 0} \frac{1}{h} \int_{-h}^{0} \hat{v}(t)\, dt \tag{4.11'}$$

$$= \hat{k}(0-) + \int_{-\infty}^{0} \hat{k}(-t)\hat{v}(t)\, dt.$$

We also can prove the analogues of Theorem 4.1, and Corollaries 4.2 and 4.3.

Let us now consider the distribution convolution equation

$$(\delta - \hat{k}) * (\delta + \hat{u}) = \delta + \hat{w}, \tag{4.16}$$

where, by definition, $\hat{w} = \hat{u} - \hat{k} - \hat{k} * \hat{u}$. Since (4.8) is satisfied for all C^∞ functions with compact support in $(0, \infty)$ it follows that the support of $\hat{w}$ is in $(-\infty, 0]$. If we take the inverse Fourier transform of both sides of (4.16) we get

$$f(1 + u) = 1 + w.$$

The functions $(1 + u)$ and $(1 + w)^*$ are in B_2 and if we set $\tilde{u} = V^{-1}u$, $\tilde{w}^* = V^{-1}w^*$, then these functions are in $H^2(T)$ and

$$\tilde{f}(1 + \tilde{u}) = (1 + \tilde{w}),$$

where $\tilde{f} = V^{-1}f$. Since $1 + \tilde{u} \in H^2(T)$ it can vanish only a.e. and consequently we may write

$$\tilde{f} = \frac{1 + \tilde{w}}{1 + \tilde{u}}. \tag{4.17}$$

On the other hand since $\tilde{f}$ satisfies (i) and (ii) of section 3 we know that there are outer factors $\tilde{g}$, $\tilde{h}$ in $H^q(T)$, for some $q > 2$, so that

$$\tilde{f} = \tilde{g}\,\tilde{h}^* \qquad \text{(see equation (3.1))} \tag{4.18}$$

Further since $1/\tilde{f}$ is bounded, it follows from equation (3.1) that $1/\tilde{g}$ and $1/\tilde{h}$ also belong to $H^q(T)$. Hence, from (4.17) and (4.18) we get

$$\frac{1 + \tilde{w}}{\tilde{h}^*} = \tilde{g}\,(1 + \tilde{u}). \tag{4.19}$$

Since both $\tilde{g}(1 + \tilde{u})$ and $(1 + \tilde{w})^*/\tilde{h}$ belong to $H^1(T)$ it follows that both sides of (4.19) are the same constant. This shows that $(1 + \tilde{w})^*$, $(1 + \tilde{u})$ and their reciprocals are outer factors in $H^q(T)$. This in turn implies that $(1 + w)^*$, $(1 + u)$ and their reciprocals are outer factors in B_q.

We may also consider the equation

$$(\delta - \hat{k}) * (\delta + \hat{v}) = \delta + \hat{w}_1,$$

where $\hat{w}_1 = \hat{v} - \hat{k} - \hat{k} * \hat{v}$. Since (4.8′) is satisfied for all C^∞ functions with compact support in $(-\infty, 0)$, it follows that $\hat{w}_1$ has support in $[0, \infty)$. Running through the same computations as before we find that $(1 + v)^*$ and $(1 + w_1)$ are outer factors in B_q and hence

$$\tilde{f} = \frac{1 + \tilde{w}}{1 + \tilde{u}} = \frac{1 + \tilde{w}_1}{1 + \tilde{v}}.$$

From this equation we get

$$(1 + \tilde{w})(1 + \tilde{v}) = (1 + \tilde{w}_1)(1 + \tilde{u}) \equiv 1, \text{ a.e.}$$

The fact that the right-hand side is 1 can be seen as follows. That the products are constant is clear since $(1 + \tilde{w})^*(1 + \tilde{u})^*$ and $(1 + \tilde{w}_1)\cdot$

$(1 + \tilde{u})$ are both in $H^1(T)$. By applying the operator V we find that $(1 + w)(1 + u)$ is equal to the same constant. Since w and u are in $L^2(R)$, for every $\epsilon > 0$ there is a set of positive measure on which $|w| + |u| < \epsilon$. This shows the constant is 1. Hence we have $1 + w = 1/(1 + v)$, and applying V to both sides of (4.17) we get

$$f = \frac{1}{(1 + u)(1 + v)}. \tag{4.20}$$

We have consequently proved the following proposition.

PROPOSITION 4.4. Suppose f satisfies the conditions (i′) and (ii′) of section 3 and (4.1) of section 4. Then f may be factored in the form (4.20) where u and v are solutions of (4.10) and (4.10′) respectively. The functions $(1 + u)$, $(1 + v)^*$ and their reciprocals are outer factors in B_q for some $q > 2$.

We now turn to the problem of computing the numbers $\hat{u}(0+)$ and $\hat{v}(0-)$. First of all we note that for $p \geq 1$,

$$|\log|1 + u||^p \leq 2^{p-1}\left\{|1 + u|^p + \frac{1}{|1 + u|^p}\right\}.$$

It follows from the fact that since $1 + u$ and $1/(1 + u)$ are in B_q for some $q > 2$, that $\log|1 + u| \in W_q$. From this it follows that $C\log|1 + u| \in W_q$. Since $1 + u$ is an outer factor it follows that the function defined by

$$\log(1 + u(x)) = \log|1 + u(x)| + iC\log|1 + u(x)| + i\alpha \tag{4.21}$$

is a determination of $\log(1 + u(x))$ for each α in a set of constants which differ from each other by an integer multiple of 2π. Since each such function is in B_q, it follows that each such function can be extended analytically into the upper half-plane, and the extended function is $\log(1 + u(z))$, where $u(z)$ is the analytic extension of $u(x)$ into the upper half-plane. These facts have been proved for the circle group and the disk in [**9**] and they are easily carried over to this situation by means of the operator V of (1.6).

Since $u \in H^2(R)$ we have

$$u(z) = \int_0^\infty e^{itz}\hat{u}(t)\,dt, \qquad z = x + iy, y \geq 0, \tag{4.22}$$

where $\hat{u} \in L^2(0, \infty)$. Hence,

$$|u(z)| \leq \int_0^\infty e^{-yt}|\hat{u}(t)|\,dt \leq M/y^{1/2}, y > 0. \tag{4.23}$$

Hence $u(z) \to 0$ as $\operatorname{Im} z \to \infty$. Now the analytic function $\log(1 + u(z))$ is completely determined as soon as its values are known in any neighborhood. Take a neighborhood U so that $|u(z)| \leq 1/2$. We see it is possible to choose the constant α so that

$$\log(1 + u(z)) = u(z) + 0(u^2(z)), \qquad z \in U. \tag{4.24}$$

Hence we see it is possible to choose α so that $\log(1 + u(z)) \to 0$ as $\operatorname{Im} z \to \infty$.

In the same way we can define

$$\log(1 + v) = \log|1 + v| - iC\log|1 + v| - i\beta$$

so that the analytic extension of $\log(1 + v(x))^*$ into the upper half-plane goes to zero as $\operatorname{Im} z \to \infty$. Choosing these values of α and β we define

$$\log f = -\log(1 + u) - \log(1 + v). \tag{4.25}$$

THEOREM 4.5. Under the conditions of Proposition 4.4 we have[1]

$$\hat{u}(0+) = \lim_{r\to\infty} \frac{1}{\pi} \int_{-r}^{r} \left(1 - \frac{|x|}{r}\right) \log(1 + u(x))\, dx$$

(4.26)

$$\hat{v}(0-) = \lim_{r\to\infty} \frac{1}{\pi} \int_{-r}^{r} \left(1 - \frac{|x|}{r}\right) \log(1 + v(x))\, dx,$$

and hence

$$\hat{u}(0+) + v(0-) = -\lim_{r\to\infty} \frac{1}{\pi} \int_{-r}^{r} \left(1 - \frac{|x|}{r}\right) \log f(x)\, dx. \tag{4.27}$$

Proof. As we have already noted, $\log(1 + u(x))$ belongs to B_q for some $q > 2$. This means in particular that $|\log(1 + u(x))|^q/(1 + x^2)$ is in L^1. Let us write

$$\log(1 + u(z)) = \iota(z)\,\omega(z), \qquad \operatorname{Im} z \geq 0,$$

where $\omega(z)$ is an outer factor and $\iota(z)$ is an inner factor; i.e., its boundary function is in $H^\infty(R)$ and has absolute value 1, a.e. Now, $\omega(z)^{q/2}$ is analytic in the upper half-plane for a suitable branch of the $q/2$ root and if we set

$$g(z) = \frac{\omega(z)^{q/2}}{z + i},$$

[1] In this connection see Hirschman [**13**].

then g has a boundary function which is in $H^2(R)$. Hence we may write

$$g(z) = \int_0^\infty e^{itz} \hat{g}(t)\, dt, \qquad \hat{g} \in L^2(0, \infty),$$

and by Schwarz's inequality we get

$$|g(z)| \leq M/y^{1/2},$$

for a suitable constant M. Hence, we get

$$|\log(1 + u(z))| \leq M|x + i(y + 1)|^{2/q}/y^{1/q}. \tag{4.28}$$

Let $y_0 > 0$ and Γ_1 the contour in the clockwise direction which consists of the three sides of the rectangle in the upper half-plane having corners at $(0, 0)$, $(y_0, 0)$, (y_0, r) and $(r, 0)$, $r > 0$. Let Γ_2 be the contour in the clockwise direction which consists of the three sides of the rectangle in the upper half-plane having corners at $(-r, 0)$, $(-r, y_0)$, $(0, y_0)$ and $(0, 0)$. Finally, let us set

$$h(z) = \log(1 + u(z)) - u(z).$$

By Cauchy's theorem we get

$$\int_0^r \left(1 - \frac{x}{r}\right) h(x)\, dx = \int_{\Gamma_1} \left(1 - \frac{z}{r}\right) h(z)\, dz,$$

$$\int_{-r}^0 \left(1 + \frac{x}{r}\right) h(x)\, dx = \int_{\Gamma_2} \left(1 + \frac{z}{r}\right) h(z)\, dz.$$

Hence, if we compute these line integrals we get

$$\int_{-r}^r \left(1 - \frac{|x|}{r}\right) h(x)\, dx = I_1 + I_2 + I_3 + I_4, \tag{4.29}$$

where

$$I_1 = \frac{2}{r} \int_0^{y_0} y h(iy)\, dy,$$

$$I_2 = \frac{1}{r} \int_0^{y_0} -y[h(r + iy) + h(-r + iy)]\, dy,$$

$$I_3 = \frac{iy_0}{r} \int_0^r [h(-x + iy_0] - h(x + iy_0)]\, dx,$$

$$I_4 = \int_{-r}^r \left(1 - \frac{|x|}{r}\right) h(x + iy_0)\, dx.$$

If we take $x = 0$ in (4.28) and use (4.23) and the definition of h we get

$$h(iy) = 0(1/y^{1/2}), \qquad 0 < y \le y_0.$$

Putting this into the integral for I_1 we get

$$I_1 = 0\left(\frac{1}{r}\right).$$

Next from (4.28) we have for $0 < y \le y_0$,

$$|\log(1 + u(\pm r + iy))| \le Mr^{2/q}\left[1 + \frac{y_0 + 1}{r}\right]^{2/q} / y^{1/q}.$$

If we use this estimate in conjunction with (4.23) we get for $r \ge 1$,

$$|I_2| \le \frac{2M}{r^{1-2/q}} \int_0^{y_0} y\left\{\frac{[1 + (y_0 + 1)/r]^{2/q}}{y^{1/q}} + \frac{1}{y^{1/2}}\right\} dy = 0(r^{(2-q)/q}).$$

If we choose y_0 large enough, from (4.24) we have

$$h(x + iy_0) = 0(u^2(x + iy_0)).$$

Since $u^2(x + iy_0) \in L^1(R)$ we have

$$|I_3| = 0\left(\frac{1}{r}\right).$$

Finally for y_0 large enough, from (4.24),

$$|I_4| \le M \int_{-\infty}^{\infty} |u(x + iy_0)|^2 dx,$$

where M is a suitable constant.

From (4.29) and the above estimates we get for all sufficiently large y_0,

$$\limsup_{r\to\infty} \left| \int_{-r}^{r} \left(1 - \frac{|x|}{r}\right) h(x)dx \right| \le M \int_{-\infty}^{\infty} |u(x + iy_0)|^2 dx.$$

Now using (4.22) and Plancherel's theorem we get

$$\int_{-\infty}^{\infty} |u(x + iy_0)|^2 dx = \int_0^{\infty} e^{-2y_0 t} |\hat{u}(t)|^2 dt.$$

The right side clearly goes to zero as $y_0 \to \infty$. Hence we have proved

$$\lim_{r\to\infty} \int_{-r}^{r} \left(1 - \frac{|x|}{r}\right) h(x)\, dx = 0. \tag{4.30}$$

Let us now set

$$K_r(t) = \frac{2}{\pi r}\frac{\sin^2 rt/2}{t^2}.$$

Since $\hat{u}(t)/(1 + t^2)$ is summable and (4.11) is satisfied, it follows (by the methods used in [**1**] pp. 113–116) that

$$\int_0^\infty K_r(t)\,\hat{u}(t)\,dt \longrightarrow \frac{1}{2}\hat{u}(0+) \text{ as } r \longrightarrow \infty .$$

It follows by Plancherel's theorem that

$$\frac{1}{2\pi}\int_{-r}^{r}\left(1 - \frac{|x|}{r}\right)u(x)dx = \int_0^\infty K_r(t)\hat{u}(t)dt \longrightarrow \frac{1}{2}\hat{u}(0+) \text{ as } r \longrightarrow \infty .$$

Consequently by equation (4.30) we get the first formula of (4.26). In an analogous way, but by integrating over contours in the lower half-plane, we get the second formula of (4.26). Finally, considering (4.25) we get (4.27).

5. A REFINED LIMIT THEOREM

Equation (4.27) of Theorem 4.5 when combined with corollary 4.3 may be viewed as an analogue of a theorem of G. Szegö (see [**9**], [**20**]). The purpose of this section is to refine this limit theorem (see [**2**], [**10**], [**13**], [**14**]).

In order to discuss this refined limit theorem it will be necessary to make some remarks about certain Hilbert spaces of functions. The first one, which we call $H_{1/2}$, is the space of all (equivalence classes of) functions in $L^2(R)$ for which

$$\|c\|_{1/2}^2 = \int_{-\infty}^{\infty} |t|\,|\hat{c}(t)|^2 dt < \infty . \tag{5.1}$$

There is an alternate expression for $\|c\|_{1/2}^2$ which is often very useful and is given directly in terms of the function c. This is given by

$$\|c\|_{1/2}^2 = \frac{1}{\pi^2}\int_{-\infty}^{\infty}\int_{-\infty}^{\infty}\left|\frac{c(x) - c(y)}{x - y}\right|^2 dxdy. \tag{5.2}$$

The proof of this equality is a simple application of Plancherel's theorem and Fubini's theorem and we leave its verification to the reader.

Now, it may happen that the right hand side of (5.2) is finite even though the right hand side of (5.1) does not have a meaning since $\hat{c}$ may not be a function. For example if $g \in H_{1/2}$ and $c = 1 + g$, then $\hat{c}$ is not a function but the right side of (5.2) is finite. The set of all (equivalence classes of) functions for which the right side of (5.2) is finite is a Hilbert space which contains $H_{1/2}$ as a subspace. We label it $\mathfrak{H}_{1/2}$.

In case $c \in H^2(R) \cap H_{1/2}$, then c may be extended analytically into the upper half plane P and we get the formula

$$\| c \|_{1/2}^2 = \frac{1}{\pi} \int_P \int | c'(z) |^2 \, dxdy, \qquad z = x + iy, \tag{5.3}$$

where $c'(z)$ is the derivative of the analytic extension of c into P. This formula is also a simple application of Plancherel's theorem and Fubini's theorem.

In case c is an *outer factor* in $H^2(R) \cap H_{1/2}$, it has a nonvanishing analytic extension into P and $\log c$ can be defined as in Section 4. In case $\log c$ belongs to $H^2(R) \cap H_{1/2}$, then formula (5.3) takes the form

$$\| \log c \|_{1/2}^2 = \frac{1}{\pi} \int_P \int | \{\log c(z)\}' |^2 \, dxdy = \frac{1}{\pi} \int_P \int \left| \frac{c'(z)}{c(z)} \right|^2 dxdy. \tag{5.3'}$$

For $\hat{c} \in L^2(R)$ let us set

$$s_r(c)(x) = \int_{-r}^{r} \hat{c}(t) e^{itx} \, dt,$$

$$\sigma_r(c)(x) = \int_{-r}^{r} \left(1 - \frac{|t|}{r}\right) \hat{c}(t) e^{itx} \, dt.$$

We have the following.

PROPOSITION 5.1. If $c \in H_{1/2}$, then

$$\| s_r(c) - \sigma_r(c) \|_\infty \to 0 \text{ as } r \to \infty .$$

Proof. We have

$$| s_r(c)(x) - \sigma_r(c)(x) |^2 = \left| \int_{-r}^{r} \frac{|t|}{r} \hat{c}(t) e^{itx} dt \right|^2$$

$$\leq 2 \int_{-r}^{r} \left| \frac{t}{\sqrt{r}} \right|^2 | \hat{c}(t) |^2 dt.$$

$$\leq 2 \Big[\int_{|t| \leq r^{1/4}}$$

$$+ \int_{r^{1/4} \le |t| \le r} \left| \frac{t}{\sqrt{r}} \right|^2 |\hat{c}(t)|^2 dt$$

$$\le \frac{1}{\sqrt{r}} \int_{-\infty}^{\infty} |\hat{c}(t)|^2 dt$$

$$+ \int_{|t| \ge r^{1/4}} |t| \, |\hat{c}(t)|^2 dt.$$

Since the last two terms go to zero as $r \to \infty$, independent of x, we have completed the proof.

PROPOSITION 5.2. Suppose f satisfies the hypotheses of Theorem 3.1 as well as (4.1), and u_r and u are the functions given in (4.4) and (4.10). Then for sufficiently large r

$$\left.\begin{array}{l} \| u_r - s_r(u) \|_\infty \\ \| u_r - s_r(u) \|_{1/2} \end{array}\right\} \begin{array}{l} = 0(r^{1/2} \| s_r(u) - u \|) \\ = 0(\| s_r(u) - u \|_{1/2}). \end{array}$$

In particular if $u \in H_{1/2}$, both quantities on the left go to zero as $r \to \infty$.

Proof. We may write

$$\begin{aligned} |u_r(x) - s_r(u)(x)|^2 &= \left| \int_0^r \{\hat{u}_r(t) - \hat{u}(t)\} e^{itx} dt \right|^2 \\ &\le r \int_0^r |\hat{u}_r(t) - \hat{u}(t)|^2 dt. \end{aligned} \tag{5.4}$$

In (4.12) take $P_r = s_r(u)$ and putting the result in (5.4) gives

$$|u_r(x) - s_r(u)(x)|^2 \le Mr \| s_r(u) - u \|^2 \le M \| s_r(u) - u \|_{1/2}^2. \tag{5.5}$$

The inequalities (5.5) constitute the first set of inequalities of this proposition.

Similarly

$$\begin{aligned} \| u_r - s_r(u) \|_{1/2}^2 &= \int_0^r |t| \, |\hat{u}_r(t) - \hat{u}(t)|^2 dt \\ &\le r \| u_r - u \|^2 \le Mr \| s_r(u) - u \|^2 \\ &\le M \| s_r(u) - u \|_{1/2}^2. \end{aligned} \tag{5.6}$$

The inequalities (5.6) constitute the second set of inequalities of this proposition.

PROPOSITION 5.3. Suppose f satisfies the hypotheses of proposition 5.2 and moreover $1/(1+u)$, $1/(1+v)$, u and v are in $L^\infty(R)$, and there is a $\gamma \in H^\infty(R)$ so that $1/\gamma \in H^\infty(R)$, $\|\text{Arg } \gamma f\|_\infty < \pi/2$ and γ and $\log \gamma$ belong to $\mathfrak{H}_{1/2}$. Then the following are equivalent:

(α) $k \in H_{1/2}$.

(β) $\log f$ (defined by (4.25)) is in $H_{1/2}$,

(γ) $\log(1+u), \log(1+v) \in H_{1/2}$,

(δ) $u, v \in H_{1/2}$.

Proof. Let us first show that $\log(1+u)$ and $\log(1+v)$ are in $L^2(R)$. It will follow that $\log f \in L^2(R)$. Hence, in order to prove the proposition it will be enough to show that any of the functions in (α) – (γ) are in $\mathfrak{H}_{1/2}$.

We shall only show that $\log(1+u) \in L^2(R)$ since the proof for $\log(1+v)$ will be the same. Since $u \in L^2(R)$ it follows that the set

$$E = \{x: |u(x)| > 1/2\}$$

is of finite Lebesgue measure. Because of the way the branch of $\log(1+u)$ was chosen in section 4 we have that for $x \in E'$ (complement of E),

$$\log(1+u(x)) = 0(u(x)).$$

Hence for u restricted to E', $\log|1+u(x)| \in L^2(E')$. On the other hand since $1/(1+u)$ and $1+u$ are, by hypothesis, bounded, it follows that $\log|1+u|$ is bounded and hence for u restricted to E, $\log|1+u(x)| \in L^2(E)$. Therefore, $\log|1+u|$ is in $L^2(R)$. Let us set

$$g = \log|1+u| + iH\log|1+u|,$$

where H is the Hilbert transform. The function g is in $H^2(R)$ and, as we pointed out in section 2, differs from $\log(1+u)$ by at most an additive constant. However, this additive constant must be zero, otherwise g and $\log(1+u)$ could not both be square summable on E'. This shows $g = \log(1+u)$ and hence $\log(1+u) \in H^2(R)$.

Now, let us set

$$f_1 = \gamma f.$$

The hypotheses on γ imply that it is an outer factor in $H^\infty(R)$. Hence, as in section 4, we can find a determination of $\log \gamma$ which extends analytically into the upper half plane. Any two such determinations will differ by an additive constant which is an integer multiple of 2π. We choose a branch of $\log \gamma$ so that

$$\operatorname{Log} f_1 = \log \gamma + \log f,$$

where $\operatorname{Log} z$ is the principal branch of the logarithm function.

If $k \in H_{1/2}$, then it follows from (5.2) that $f \in \mathfrak{H}_{1/2}$. Hence since both γ and f are bounded it follows that $f_1 \in \mathfrak{H}_{1/2}$. As we shall show in a moment, this will imply that $\log f_1 \in \mathfrak{H}_{1/2}$ and since $\log \gamma \in \mathfrak{H}_{1/2}$ it follows that $\log f \in H_{1/2}$. Clearly, the branch of $\log \gamma$ that is chosen does not affect this computation.

We shall now show that $\log f_1$ belongs to $\mathfrak{H}_{1/2}$. Since f_1 is bounded and bounded away from zero and $\|\operatorname{Arg} f_1\|_\infty < \pi/2$ its range lies in a compact set in the open right complex plane. Hence, there is a constant M so that for every $x, y \in R$,

$$|\operatorname{Log} f_1(x) - \operatorname{Log} f_1(y)| \leq M |f_1(x) - f_1(y)|.$$

The converse statement, (β) implies (α), is equally simple to prove. If we suppose that $\log f \in H_{1/2}$, then $\log f_1 \in \mathfrak{H}_{1/2}$. Since the range of $\log f_1$ lies in a compact set in the complex plane and $f_1 = \exp \operatorname{Log} f_1$, we find that there is a constant M so that for every $x, y \in R$,

$$|f_1(x) - f_1(y) \leq M |\operatorname{Log} f_1(x) - \operatorname{Log} f_1(y)|.$$

Since γ and $1/\gamma$ are bounded and $\gamma \in \mathfrak{H}_{1/2}$ it follows that $f = f_1/\gamma \in \mathfrak{H}_{1/2}$ and hence $k \in H_{1/2}$.

Let us now prove that (β) and (γ) are equivalent. Since $\log(1 + u) \in H^2(R)$ and $\log(1 + v) \in H^2(R)$, on taking Fourier transforms we find that

$$(\log f)^\wedge(t) = -(\log(1 + u))^\wedge(t), t > 0$$
$$(\log f)^\wedge(t) = -(\log(1 + v))^\wedge(t), t < 0. \tag{5.7}$$

Consequently, the equivalence of (β) and (γ) follows from (5.1) and (5.7).

Finally, let us show that (γ) and (δ) are equivalent. From (5.3′) we have

$$\|\log(1 + u)\|^2_{1/2} = \frac{1}{\pi} \iint_P \left|\frac{u'(z)}{1 + u(z)}\right|^2 dxdy. \tag{5.8}$$

Since $1/(1 + u) \in H^\infty(R)$ we have

$$\sup. \left\{\frac{1}{|1 + u(z)|} : \operatorname{Im} z > 0\right\} = \text{ess. sup.} \left\{\frac{1}{|1 + u(x)|} : x \in R\right\},$$

and therefore there is a constant M so that $1/|1 + u(z)| \leq M$. In the same way, since $u \in H^\infty(R)$ there is a constant $m > 0$ so that $1/|1 +$

$u(z)| \geq m$. Consequently, from (5.8) we get

$$m \| u \|_{1/2}^2 \leq \| \log(1 + u) \|_{1/2}^2 \leq M \| u \|_{1/2}^2.$$

This concludes the proof of the proposition.

PROPOSITION 5.4. Suppose f satisfies the hypotheses of Proposition 5.2 and moreover the argument of f can be chosen as a continuous function so that

$$\lim_{x \to \infty} \arg f(x) = \lim_{x \to -\infty} \arg f(x) = a,$$

where a is a finite number. Then there exists a function γ which will satisfy the hypotheses put on γ in Proposition 5.3.

Proof. Let us write

$$\log f = \log |f| + i \operatorname{Im} \log f,$$

where $\log f$ is defined by (4.25). Let $\arg f$ be the function described in the hypothesis, and let us set

$$\ln f = \log |f| + i \arg f.$$

Let V be the operator defined in (1.6) and set $\tilde{f} = V^{-1}f$. The function $\log |\tilde{f}|$ is bounded on the circle group T and $\arg \tilde{f}$ is continuous on T. According to a theorem of Zygmund ([**23**], p. 254) the function

$$\exp |K \arg \tilde{f}| \qquad (K = \text{conjugation operator})$$

belongs to $L^p(T)$, $1 \leq p < \infty$. Hence, if we set

$$\tilde{g} = \exp \frac{1}{2} \left\{ \ln \tilde{f} + i K \ln \tilde{f} \right\}$$

$$\tilde{h} = \exp \frac{1}{2} \left\{ \ln \tilde{f}^* + i K \ln \tilde{f}^* \right\}$$

it follows that $\tilde{g}$, $\tilde{h}$ and their inverses are outer factors in $H^p(T)$, $1 \leq p < \infty$. Moreover,

$$\tilde{f} = \tilde{g} \tilde{h}^*.$$

Since f satisfies the hypotheses of Proposition 5.3, the function $\tilde{f}$ also has a factorization of the form

$$\tilde{f} = \frac{1}{(1 + \tilde{u})(1 + \tilde{v})},$$

where $\tilde{u} = V^{-1}u$, $v = \tilde{V}^{-1}v$ and the functions $1/(1 + \tilde{u})$, $1/(1 + \tilde{v})^*$ and their inverses are in $H^q(T)$ for some $q > 2$. Using these two factorizations of $\tilde{f}$ we get

$$\frac{1}{\tilde{g}(1 + \tilde{u})} = (1 + \tilde{v})\tilde{h}^*.$$

The left side certainly belongs to $H^2(T)$ and hence both sides of this equality must be equal identically to a nonzero constant c. Hence

$$g = \frac{c}{1 + \tilde{u}}, \qquad \tilde{h}^* = \frac{1}{c(1 + \tilde{v})}.$$

If we set $g = V\tilde{g}$ and $h = V\tilde{h}$ we get

$$g = \exp \frac{1}{2} \left\{ \ln f + i\, C \ln f \right\}$$

$$h = \exp \frac{1}{2} \left\{ \ln f^* + i\, C \ln f^* \right\}$$

and

$$g = \frac{c}{1 + u}, h^* = \frac{1}{c(1 + v)}.$$

Now, by the manner in which logarithms of outer factors are defined we have

$$\log g = \frac{1}{2} \left\{ \ln f + i\, C \ln f \right\} = -\log (1 + u) + \log |c| + i\alpha$$

$$\log h^* = \frac{1}{2} \left\{ \ln f - i\, C \ln f \right\} = -\log (1 + v) - \log |c| + i\beta,$$

where α and β are real. It follows that

$$\log f + i(\alpha + \beta) = \ln f$$

and hence

$$\operatorname{Im} \log f + (\alpha + \beta) = \arg f.$$

Since $\log f \in L^2(R)$, there is a sequence $x_n \to \infty$ so that $\operatorname{Im} \log f(x_n) \to 0$. Consequently, $\alpha + \beta = a$ and clearly we can take a branch of $\arg f$ so that $a = 0$. Let us suppose we do this. It follows that $\arg f \in L^2(R)$.

Let us set

$$K_r(x) = \frac{2}{\pi r} \frac{\sin^2 rx/2}{x^2};$$

then

$$\int_{-r}^{r} \left(1 - \frac{|t|}{r}\right) e^{itx} (\arg f)^\wedge (t)\, dt = \int_{-\infty}^{\infty} K_r(x - y) \arg f(y) dy.$$

By the hypothesis on $\arg f$ it follows by Fejer's theorem for the line that there is a number r so that if we set $p(x) = K_r * \arg f(x)$, then

$$\| p - \arg f \|_\infty < \pi/2.$$

Let us set

$$q(x) = \int_0^r \left(1 - \frac{|t|}{r}\right) e^{itx} (\arg f)\hat{}\,(t)dt;$$

then clearly $q \in H^2(R) \cap H_{1/2}$ and moreover

$$p = q + q^*.$$

We shall set

$$\gamma = \exp - 2iq. \tag{5.9}$$

Clearly, γ and $1/\gamma$ are in $H^\infty(R)$ and $\log \gamma = -2iq \in H_{1/2}$. The fact that $\gamma \in \mathfrak{H}_{1/2}$ follows from the fact that q has its range in a compact set in the complex plane and hence there is a constant M so that

$$|\gamma(x) - \gamma(y)| \leq M\,|g(x) - g(y)|.$$

Finally, since $Re\, q = (q + q^*)/2 = p/2$, it follows from (5.9) that

$$\|\arg \gamma f\|_\infty = \|p - \arg f\|_\infty < \pi/2.$$

This completes the proof of the proposition.

We are now almost in a position to prove the main theorem of this section. However, before we do this it will be necessary to obtain an estimate on the rate of approach of $\hat{u}_r(0+)$ to $\hat{u}(0+)$ and $\hat{v}_r(0-)$ to $\hat{v}(0-)$. This is done in the next proposition.

PROPOSITION 5.5. Suppose f satisfies the conditions of Proposition 5.2 and moreover $1/(1 + u)$ and $1/(1 + v)$ are in $L^\infty(R)$. Then for all sufficiently large r,

$$\left.\begin{array}{l} |\hat{u}(0+) - \hat{u}_r(0+)| \\ |\hat{v}(0-) - \hat{v}_r(0-)| \end{array}\right\} \leq M\,\|u - u_r\|\;\|v - v_r\|. \tag{5.10}$$

Proof. We shall prove only the first inequality, the second following by similar reasoning. From equations (4.6), (4.11) and Parseval's theorem we get

$$\hat{u}(0+) - \hat{u}_r(0+) = \int_0^\infty \hat{k}(-t)[\hat{u}(t) - \hat{u}_r(t)]dt \tag{5.11}$$

$$= \frac{1}{2\pi}\int_{-\infty}^\infty k(x)[u(x) - u_r(x)]dx$$

Now,

$$k(x) = 1 - \frac{1}{(1 + u)(1 + v)} = \frac{u}{1 + u} + fv. \tag{5.12}$$

Since $1/(1+u) \in H^{\infty}(R)$ it follows that $u(u-u_r)/(1+u)$ belongs to $H^1(R)$ and hence

$$\int_{-\infty}^{\infty} \frac{u(x)[u(x) - u_r(x)]}{1 + u(x)}\, dx = 0.$$

Consequently, putting the right hand side of (5.12) into (5.11) we get

$$\hat{u}(0+) - \hat{u}_r(0+) = \frac{1}{2\pi} \int_{-\infty}^{\infty} [u(x) - u_r(x)]\, v(x) f(x)\, dx. \qquad (5.13)$$

From the proof of Theorem 4.1 we know that $P_r f(u_r - u) = 0$. Since $v^* \in H_r^2$ we get

$$\int_{-\infty}^{\infty} v_r(x)\, [u_r(x) - u(x)] f(x)\, dx = 0.$$

Using this fact in (5.13) we get

$$\hat{u}(0+) - \hat{u}_r(0+) = \frac{1}{2\pi} \int_{-\infty}^{\infty} [u(x) - u_r(x)][v(x) - v_r(x)] f(x)\, dx. \qquad (5.14)$$

Using the boundedness of f and the Schwarz inequality the first inequality of (5.10) is an immediate consequence of (5.14).

COROLLARY 5.6. If the hypotheses of proposition 5.3 are satisfied and $k \in H_{1/2}$, then

$$\left.\begin{array}{l} |\hat{u}(0+) - \hat{u}_r(0+)| \\ \\ |\hat{v}(0+) - \hat{v}_r(0+)| \end{array}\right\} = 0\left(\frac{1}{r}\right) \text{ as } r \longrightarrow \infty. \qquad (5.15)$$

Proof. From Proposition 5.3 it follows that $u, v \in H_{1/2}$. From Propositions 5.2 and 5.5 we get

$$\begin{aligned} |\hat{u}(0+) - \hat{u}_r(0+)| &= 0(\|u - u_r\| \, \|v - v_r\|) \\ &= 0\left(\frac{1}{r} \|u - s_r(u)\|_{1/2} \|v - s_r(v)\|_{1/2}\right). \end{aligned}$$

This proves the first equality and the second one follows by the same reasoning.

COROLLARY 5.7. If we set

$$\mu_r = \exp - \frac{1}{2} [\hat{u}_r(0+) + \hat{v}_r(0-)]$$

$$\mu = \exp - \frac{1}{2} [\hat{u}(0+) + \hat{v}(0-)], \qquad (5.16)$$

then

$$\left(\frac{\mu_r}{\mu}\right)^r \to 1 \qquad \text{as } r \to \infty. \tag{5.17}$$

Proof. An immediate consequence of the last corollary.

In order to describe the main theorem of this section it is necessary for us to introduce the Fredholm determinant

$$D_r = 1 + \sum_{n=1}^{\infty} \frac{(-1)^n}{n!} \int_0^r \cdots \int_0^r det[\hat{k}(t_i - t_j)]dt_1 \cdots dt_n.$$

It is a well known fact [**19**] that $W_r(f)$ is invertible if and only if $D_r \neq 0$. Hence, if $f = 1 - k$, $k \in L^2(R)$, and $D_r \neq 0$, then we can solve the Wiener-Hopf equation (4.4) for u_r. We think it is clear that $D_r \neq 0$ also implies that (4.4′) is solvable for v_r.

The functions u_r and v_r are clearly bounded continuous functions in $H_{1/2}$ which may be extended to entire functions on the complex plane. Indeed, let us set

$$1 + u_r(z) = 1 + \int_0^r e^{izt}\,\hat{u}_r(t)dt,$$

$$1 + v_r(z) = 1 + \int_{-r}^0 e^{izt}\,\hat{v}_r(t)dt.$$

The function $1 + u_r(z)$ is bounded in the closed half plane $\bar{P} = \{z\colon \text{Im } z \geq 0\}$ and the function $1 + v_r(z)$ is bounded in the half plane $\bar{Q} = \{z\colon \text{Im } z \leq 0\}$. If $1 + u_r(z) \neq 0$ in $\bar{P}$ then the reciprocal of this function is bounded and analytic in $\bar{P}$. The boundedness comes from the maximum modulus principle and the facts that $1 + u_r(x)$ never vanishes and $1 + u_r(x) \to 1$ as $x \to \pm\infty$. Hence, if $1 + u_r(z)$ does not vanish in $\bar{P}$, $1 + u_r(x)$ together with its reciprocal is an outer factor in $H^\infty(R)$. In the same way if $1 + v_r(z)$ does not vanish in $\bar{Q}$ we can prove that $1 + v_r{}^*(x)$ and its reciprocal are outer factors in $H^\infty(R)$. This being the case, the function $\log(1 + u_r)$ and $\log(1 + v_r{}^*)$ may be defined so as to be in $H^\infty(R)$. By exactly the same method used to prove that (δ) implies (γ) in Proposition 5.3 we can prove that $\log(1 + u_r)$ and $\log(1 + v_r{}^*)$ are in $H_{1/2}$.

According to a recent important result of I. I. Hirschman, Jr. [**13**], if $1 + u_r(z)$ does not vanish in the closed upper half plane $\bar{P}$ and if $1 + v_r(z)$ does not vanish in the closed lower half plane $\bar{Q}$, then

$$\frac{D_r}{\mu_r^r} = \exp \int_0^\infty t\,\widehat{\lambda u_r}(t)\,\widehat{\lambda v_r}(-t)dt, \tag{5.18}$$

where μ_r is defined by (5.16) and for the sake of simplicity we have set

$$\lambda u_r = \log(1 + u_r)$$
$$\lambda v_r = \log(1 + v_r).$$

Equation (5.18) will be essential in what follows.

THEOREM 5.7. Suppose k is a complex valued function defined on R which satisfies the following hypotheses:

1. $f = 1 - k$ is bounded, uniformly continuous and never vanishes,
2. $k \in H_{1/2}$,
3. $\Delta \arg f = \lim_{a,b \to \infty} \int_{-b}^{a} d \arg f = 0,$
4. C $\log f$ is bounded and uniformly continuous.

Then

$$\lim_{r \to \infty} \frac{D_r}{\mu^r} = \exp \int_0^\infty t\, \widehat{\lambda f}(t)\, \widehat{\lambda f}(-t) dt,$$

where μ is defined in (5.16) and $\lambda f = \log f$.

Proof. Before we actually begin the proof let us make some comments about the hypotheses of the theorem. Since k is bounded, uniformly continuous and in $L^2(R)$, it follows by Fejer's approximation theorem for the line that k can be uniformly approximated by functions which vanish at $\pm\infty$. Hence we must have $k(x) \to 0$ as $x \to \pm\infty$. Since we have assumed that $f = 1 - k$ never takes on the value zero, it follows that there is an $m > 0$ so that $|f| \geq m$ for all x.

Since f is continuous we may choose a continuous argument of f. The Condition 3 means that this argument function has finite and equal limits at $\pm\infty$. Hence, the argument function is uniformly continuous and we can choose it so that the limits at infinity are zero.

In Condition 4 and in the statement of the conclusion we are defining the logarithm function by

$$\log f = \log |f| + i \arg f.$$

It follows from Condition 4 that the outer factors

$$g = \exp \frac{1}{2} \{\log f + i\, C \log f\}$$
$$h = \exp \frac{1}{2} \{\log f^* + i\, C \log f^*\}$$

are uniformly continuous functions in $H^\infty(R)$. Moreover, their inverses also belong to $H^\infty(R)$ and

$$f = gh^*.$$

Let V be the map defined by (1.6) and set $\tilde{f} = V^{-1}f$, $\tilde{g} = V^{-1}g$ and $\tilde{h} = V^{-1}h$. The functions $\tilde{f}$, $\tilde{g}$ and $\tilde{h}$ are defined on the circle group T and moreover $\tilde{g}$, $\tilde{h}$, $1/\tilde{g}$ and $1/\tilde{h}$ are in $H^\infty(T)$ and

$$\tilde{f} = \tilde{g}\tilde{h}^*.$$

This means that the Toeplitz operator $T(\tilde{f})$ is invertible which in turn implies [**8**] that there is a function $\tilde{\gamma}$ defined on the circle group so that $\tilde{\gamma}$ and $1/\tilde{\gamma}$ are in $H^\infty(T)$ and $\|\operatorname{Arg} \tilde{\gamma}\tilde{f}\| < \pi/2$. The existence of a $\tilde{\gamma}$ which satisfies these properties can also be inferred from the fact that $V^{-1} \arg f$ is continuous on the circle group (see section 3).

If we set $\gamma = V\tilde{\gamma}$, then γ and $1/\gamma$ are in $H^\infty(R)$ and $\|\operatorname{Arg} \gamma f\| < \pi/2$. From Corollary 3.2 it follows that the conclusions of Theorem 3.1 are satisfied. Consequently, we may obtain the functions u and v and for all r sufficiently large we may obtain the functions u_r and v_r. The functions u, v, $1/(1 + u)$ and $1/(1 + v)$ are bounded and uniformly continuous, and indeed up to nonessential multiplicative constants the latter functions coincide with g and h^* respectively. The method of proof for this latter fact has already been given in the proof of Proposition 5.4. Also from the proof of that proposition we know that by taking $\arg f(x) \to 0$ as $x \to \infty$, the function $\log f$ as defined here coincides with the function defined by (4.25).

We are now in a position to finish off the proof of the theorem. From the hypotheses 1 and 3 and the results of the previous paragraph it follows that the hypothesis of Proposition 5.4 holds and hence also the conclusion. Using this and the results of the previous paragraph it follows that the hypotheses and conclusions of Proposition 5.3 are valid. In particular we have that u and v are bounded uniformly continuous functions in $H_{1/2}$. From the Fejer approximation theorem for the line we have

$$\|\sigma_r(u) - u\|_\infty + \|\sigma_r(v) - v\|_\infty \to 0 \qquad \text{as } r \to \infty.$$

Consequently, from Proposition 5.2 we get

$$\|u_r - u\|_\infty + \|v_r - v\|_\infty \to 0 \qquad \text{as } r \to \infty. \tag{5.19}$$

Notice that since $|u_r(x)| + |v_r(x)| \to 0$ as $x \to \pm\infty$ it follows that $|u(x)| + |v(x)| \to 0$ as $x \to \pm\infty$. From this it follows that $1 + V^{-1}u$ is continuous on the circle group and does not vanish anywhere. Since it is an outer factor its analytic extension into the disk does not vanish. It is a consequence of (5.19) that the analytic extension of $(1 + V^{-1}u_r)$ into the disk does not vanish on the closed unit disk for all sufficiently large r. Hence, the analytic extension of $1 + u_r$ into the upper half plane does not vanish for all sufficiently large r. In the same way we can show that the analytic extension of $1 + v_r$ into the lower half plane does not vanish for sufficiently large r. Consequently, Hirschman's formula (5.18) may be applied.

Recall that we had set $\lambda u_r = \log(1 + u_r)$, $\lambda v_r = \log(1 + v_r)$. We shall also set $\lambda u = \log(1 + u)$, $\lambda v = \log(1 + v)$ and $\lambda f = \log f$. We shall presently show that

$$\| \lambda u_r - \lambda u \|_{1/2} + \| \lambda v_r - \lambda v \|_{1/2} \rightarrow 0 \text{ as } r \rightarrow \infty .$$

From this it follows that

$$\int_0^\infty t\, \widehat{\lambda u_r}(t)\, \widehat{\lambda v_r}(-t)dt \rightarrow \int_0^\infty t\, \widehat{\lambda u}(t)\, \widehat{\lambda v}(-t)dt = \int_0^\infty t\, \widehat{\lambda f}(t)\, \widehat{\lambda f}(-t)dt.$$

Taken in conjunction with Hirschman's identity (5.18) this tells us that

$$\lim_{r\to\infty} \frac{D_r}{\mu_r^r} = \exp \int_0^\infty t\, \widehat{\lambda f}(t)\, \widehat{\lambda f}(-t)dt.$$

However, from Corollary 5.7 we know that $(\mu_r/\mu)^r \longrightarrow 1$ as $r \longrightarrow \infty$ and hence the proof of our theorem will be complete.

We shall now establish the fact that $\| \lambda u_r - \lambda u \|_{1/2} \longrightarrow 0$ as $r \longrightarrow \infty$. The fact that $\lambda v_r \longrightarrow \lambda v$ in $H_{1/2}$ has the same proof. First of all, using Proposition 5.2 we notice that

$$\begin{aligned} \| u_r - u \|_{1/2} &\le \| u_r - s_r(u) \|_{1/2} + \| s_r(u) - u \|_{1/2} \\ &= 0(\| s_r(u) - u \|_{1/2}) \longrightarrow 0 \text{ as } r \longrightarrow \infty . \end{aligned}$$

Next, for all sufficiently large r we may write

$$\begin{aligned} \| \lambda u_r - \lambda u \|_{1/2} &= \left[\frac{1}{\pi} \iint_P \left| \frac{u_r'(z)}{1 + u_r(z)} - \frac{u'(z)}{1 + u(z)} \right|^2 dxdy \right]^{1/2} \\ &\le \left[\frac{1}{\pi} \iint_P \left| \frac{u_r'(z)}{1 + u_r(z)} - \frac{u'(z)}{1 + u_r(z)} \right|^2 dxdy \right]^{1/2} \\ &+ \left[\frac{1}{\pi} \iint_P \left| \frac{u'(z)}{1 + u(z)} \right|^2 \left| \frac{1 + u(z)}{1 + u_r(z)} - 1 \right|^2 dxdy \right]^{1/2} . \end{aligned}$$

Since $1/(1 + u(x))$ is bounded on R and $u_r \longrightarrow u$ uniformly it follows that for all sufficiently large r, $1/(1 + u_r(x))$ is uniformly bounded. It follows from the maximum modulus principle that for all sufficiently large r that $1/(1 + u_r(z))$ is uniformly bounded in $\bar{P}$. Hence the first integral of the last sum is

$$0(\| u_r - u \|_{1/2})$$

which we have noted goes to zero as $r \to \infty$. Further, since $(1 + u(x))/(1 + u_r(x))$ goes to 1 uniformly on R, it follows from the maximum modulus principle that $(1 + u(z))/(1 + u_r(z)) \to 1$ uniformly on $\overline{P}$. Since $1/(1 + u(z))$ is bounded on $\overline{P}$ and $u \in H_{1/2}$ the second integral in the above sum goes to zero. This establishes that $\lambda u_r \to \lambda u$ in $H_{1/2}$ and we have completed the proof of the theorem.

REFERENCES

1. Achieser, N. I., Vorlesungen über Approximationstheorie, Berlin, 1953.
2. ———, The continuous analogue of some theorems on Toeplitz matrices, *Ukrainian Math. J.*, 16(1964), 445–462.
3. Baxter, Glen, Polynomials defined by a difference systems, *J. Math. Anal. and Appl.*, 2(1961), 223–263.
4. ———, A convergence equivalence related to polynomials on the unit circle, *Trans. Amer. Math. Soc.*, 99(1961), 471–487.
5. ———, A norm inequality for a 'finite section' Wiener-Hopf equation, *Illinois J. Math.*, 7(1963), 97–103.
6. Beurling, Arne, On two problems concerning linear transformations in Hilbert space, *Acta Math.*, 81(1949), 239–255.
7. Calderon, A., F. Spitzer and H. Widom, Inversion of Toeplitz matrices, *Illinois J. Math.*, 3(1959), 490–498.
8. Devinatz, Allen, Toeplitz operators on H^2 spaces, *Trans. Amer. Math. Soc.*, 112(1964), 304–317.
9. ———, An extension of a limit theorem of G. Szegö, *J. Math. Anal. and Appl.*, 14(1966), 499–510.
10. ———, The strong Szegö limit theorem, *Illinois J. Math.*, 11(1967), 160–175.
11. Hirschman, Jr., I. I., Finite sections of Wiener-Hopf equations and Szegö polynomials, *J. Math. Anal. and Appl.*, 11(1965), 290–320.
12. ———, On a theorem of Szegö, Kac and Baxter, *J. d'Analyse Math.*, 14(1965), 225–234.
13. ———, On a formula of Kac and Achiezer, to appear in *J. Math. and Mech.*
14. Kac, M., Toeplitz matrices, translation kernels and a related problem in probability theory, *Duke Math. J.* 21(1954), 501–509.
15. Krein, M. G., The continuous analogues of theorems on polynomials orthogonal on the unit circle, *Doklady Akad. Nauk*, SSSR, 105(1955), 637–640.
16. ———, Integral equations on the half line with kernels depending on the difference of the arguments, *Uspehi Math. Nauk*, vol. 13, No. 5(1958), 3–120.
17. Reich, E., On non-Hermitian Toeplitz matrices, *Math. Scand.*, 10(1962), 145–152.
18. Shinbrot, M., A class of difference kernels, *Proc. Amer. Math. Soc.* 13(1962), 399–406.
19. Smithies, F., Integral equations, Cambridge, 1958.
20. Szegö, G., Ein Grenzwertzatz über die Toeplitzschen Determinanten einer reelen positiven Funktion, *Math. Ann.*, 76(1915), 490–503.
21. ———, On certain Hermitian forms associated with the Fourier series of a positive function, *Festkrift Marcel Riesz, Lund* (1952), 228–238 (Comm. du Séminaire Math. de l'Univ. de Lund).
22. Widom, H., Inversion of Toeplitz matrices II, *Illinois J. Math.*, 4(1960), 88–99.
23. Zygmund, A., Trigonometric series, second edition, vol. I, Cambridge, 1959.

Scattering Theory for Transport Phenomena

P. D. LAX and R. S. PHILLIPS

1. INTRODUCTION

The streaming of particles reflected by an obstacle in an n-dimensional real Euclidean space is studied in this paper from the point of view of scattering theory. We assume that the particles are reflected according to the usual laws of reflection: the incident and reflected rays lie in one plane with the normal to the obstacle and make equal angles with the normal; and we show that this phenomenon fits into the framework of a general theory of scattering developed by the authors [**2, 3**] for the solution of the acoustic equation in an exterior domain.

We denote the domain exterior to the obstacle by G, the boundary of the obstacle by ∂G and assume that ∂G is bounded and twice continuously differentiable. All particles are assumed to travel with unit speed; therefore the appropriate phase space Ω_0 is the Cartesian product

$$\Omega_0 = G \times S_{n-1},$$

where S_{n-1} is the unit sphere in R_n. Finally we denote the elements of Ω_0 by $\omega = \{x, \theta\}$.

The trajectory $\tau_t(\omega)$ of a particle situated at the point ω is a straight line between reflections:

$$\tau_t(\omega) = \{x + t\theta, \theta\};$$

here $\omega = \{x, \theta\}$. We impose as measure m on Ω_0 the product of the Lebesgue measures on G and S_{n-1} and relative to this measure τ_t can be shown to be a measure preserving flow.

To proceed to the scattering theory formalism we make use of the Koopman representation for this flow:

$$[U(t)f](\omega) = f(\tau_{-t}(\omega)); \tag{1.1}$$

the operators $\{U(t)\}$ then define a strongly continuous one-parameter group of unitary operators on the Hilbert space $L_2(\Omega_0, m)$. If we denote the corresponding free space flow group by $\{U_0(t)\}$, then the wave operators are defined as

$$W_{\pm}f = \lim_{t\to\pm\infty} U(-t)U_0(t)f, \tag{1.2}$$

and the scattering operator is

$$S = W_{+}^{-1} W_{-}. \tag{1.3}$$

The wave operators are easily shown to be intertwining operators; that is,

$$U(t)W_{\pm} = W_{\pm} U_0(t); \tag{1.4}$$

and as a consequence S commutes with $U_0(t)$.

We are interested in S as an operator on the spectral representation of the unperturbed group; this is the so-called Heisenberg scattering matrix $\mathcal{S}$. The fact that S commutes with $U_0(t)$ can be used to prove that $\mathcal{S}$ is a multiplicative operator-valued function of frequency and as such has the possibility of having a holomorphic extension into the complex plane. Roughly speaking we show that when the sojourn-time of the trajectories in some ball containing the obstacle is bounded, then the scattering matrix can be extended to be entire; otherwise it has a holomorphic extension into the lower half-plane but the real axis is its natural boundary.

From the point of view of ergodic theory the scattering matrix represents another invariant of the flow. However we can also look upon this transport model as a crude approximation to geometrical optics in an exterior domain and as such it provides further insight into the corresponding acoustic problem.

2. PROPERTIES OF THE FLOW

We begin this study with an extension of Liouville's theorem. Although this is a fairly standard result, we include a sketch of the proof for the sake of completeness.

THEOREM 2.1. The flow τ_t on Ω_0 is measure preserving; that is, for every t and every measurable set Σ

$$m(\Sigma) = m(\tau_t(\Sigma)).$$

Proof. At a point of reflection a trajectory is discontinuous. However it is easy to show that for fixed t the discontinuities of $\tau_t(\omega)$ lie on a smooth hypersurface in Ω_0 and thus are of measure zero. Aside from these points the function $\tau_t(\omega)$ will be continuously differentiable for all ω for which the trajectory from ω to $\tau_t(\omega)$ is reflected only a finite number of times. We will show later on that this includes almost all ω and therefore it suffices to prove that the Jacobian of the transformation $\tau_t(\omega)$ is equal to one for just such trajectories.

We first consider a path segment from $\{x, \theta\}$ to $\tau_t(\{x, \theta\}) = \{x', \theta'\}$ containing but one reflection from ∂G, say at the point z where the unit inner normal to ∂G is n. Let $\sigma = |x - z|$. Then

$$x(z, \sigma, \theta) = z - \sigma\theta$$

$$x'(z, \sigma, \theta) = z + (t - \sigma)\theta'$$

where

$$\theta'(z, \theta) = \theta - 2(\theta \cdot n)n.$$

We then compute the Jacobians:

$$J_1 = \frac{\partial[x, \theta]}{\partial[z, \sigma, \theta]} \quad \text{and} \quad J_2 = \frac{\partial[x', \theta']}{\partial[z, \sigma, \theta]},$$

after suitably parameterizing z on ∂G. A straightforward calculation shows that

$$J_1 = -\theta \cdot n = J_2,$$

from which it follows that

$$\left|\frac{\partial[x', \theta']}{\partial[x, \theta]}\right| = \left|\frac{J_2}{J_1}\right| = 1, \tag{2.1}$$

provided that $\theta \cdot n < 0$.

This result can be applied successively to a chain of one-reflection segments along any trajectory. Thus (2.1) holds for any point ω such that the trajectory to $\tau_t(\omega)$ contains only a finite number of reflections at none of which does the trajectory approach ∂G in a tangential direction. There remain the paths for which there are an infinite number of reflections and those with some tangential approach to ∂G. We now show that for each t the set of such paths begin at an ω-set of measure zero.

Since ∂G is of class C^2, there will be a minimal radius of curvature on ∂G and therefore given $\delta > 0$, along any trajectory of length t for which $\theta \cdot n \leq -\delta$ at each point of reflection, there can be only a finite number of reflections. Let Σ_δ denote the set of all initial points ω for which $\theta \cdot n > -\delta$ at some point of reflection; then the set of points ω for which the Jacobain is possibly different from one is contained in the set $\Sigma_0 \equiv \bigcap \Sigma_\delta$. It suffices to prove that $m(\Sigma_0) = 0$.

For a path starting from an ω in Σ_δ, there will be a first reflection occurring, say at z, for which $\theta \cdot n > -\delta$. The Jacobian for the trajectory up to this point is one, and hence the measure of such points can be estimated as though there were no previous reflections and the paths lay in a section of the sphere of radius t and center z defined by $0 \geq \theta \cdot n > -\delta$. The measure of the points ω in this section reflected on a surface element dS of ∂G about z is readily seen to be of the order $\delta^2 t\, dS$, and integrating over ∂G we obtain the estimate

$$m(\Sigma_\delta) \leq C\delta^2 t \times (\text{area of } \partial G);$$

consequently $m(\Sigma_0) = 0$, as desired.

In what follows we shall denote the image of any set Σ under τ_t by $\Sigma(t)$. A point ω is called *free forward* if the trajectory through ω has no points of reflection for t large enough; *free backward* is defined similarly. A point not free forward is called *trapped forward*; and *trapped backward* is defined similarly. If a point is trapped both forward and backward we simply call it *trapped*. Trapped points play no role in scattering; we shall ignore them and deal exclusively with their complement, denoted by Ω.

THEOREM 2.2. The set of points trapped in one direction but not in the other has measure zero.

Proof. Denote by Ω_+ the set of points trapped backward but not forward, by Ω_- those trapped forward but not backward; then $\Omega \supset \Omega_+ \cup \Omega_-$. By definition, for any ω in Ω_+ there exists a largest time T such that $\tau_T(\omega)$ is a point of reflection; on the other hand there are arbitrarily large negative times for which $\tau_t(\omega)$ is a point of reflection. It follows from this that for $t < T$ the spatial part of every point of the trajectory $\tau_t(\omega)$ lies on a line segment whose end points belong to ∂G; thus all of these spatial parts lie in the convex hull of ∂G. Since ∂G was assumed to be bounded, all points $\tau_t(\omega)$ with $t < T$ lie in the bounded set B consisting of the product of the convex hull of ∂G and S_{n-1}.

Next let j be any integer and denote by Ω_j the set of all those points ω in Ω_+ for which T lies between j and $j + 1$. Clearly

$$\Omega_+ = \bigcup \Omega_j; \tag{2.2}$$

therefore if we show that all sets Ω_j have measure zero it will follow by countable additivity that Ω_+ is also of measure zero.

By construction, the set $\Omega_j(t)$ into which Ω_j is carried by the flow after time t belongs to B for $t \leq j$. In particular $\Omega_j(j)$ is a subset of B and it follows then that $\Omega_j(j + 1)$ is contained in $B(1)$ so that it is also bounded. Let d denote an upper bound on the diameter of $\Omega_j(j + 1)$; that is, the distance between the spatial parts of any two points of $\Omega_j(j + 1)$ is less than d. Now by definition, for $t > j + 1$ each points of $\Omega_j(t)$ is obtained by carrying the corresponding point of $\Omega_j(j+1)$ along a straight line for a distance of $t-(j+1)$. Since the distance between the spatial parts of any two points ω and ω' of $\Omega_j(j+1)$ is less than d, it follows that if t and t' differ by at least d and if both are greater than $j+1$, then $\tau_t(\omega)$ and $\tau_{t'}(\omega')$ are different; this means that the sets $\Omega_j(t)$ and $\Omega_j(t')$ are disjoint. In particular for any positive integer k the sets

$$\Omega_j(j+1+d), \Omega_j(j+1+2d), \ldots, \Omega_j(j+1+kd) \tag{2.3}$$

are pairwise disjoint. Since the flow is measure preserving, each of the sets (2.3) has the same measure, say m, as the set Ω_j, and since they are disjoint their union has measure km.

On the other hand since $\Omega_j(t)$ lies in B for $t < j$, it follows that each point of the sets (2.3) is carried into B by the flow after time $-(1+kd)$. Again using the measure-preserving character of the flow it follows that the measure of B is greater than km. Since B, being bounded, has finite measure and since k was an arbitrary positive integer, this can be so only if the measure m of Ω_j is zero. Combining this with (2.2) we see that $m(\Omega_+) = 0$. That $m(\Omega_-) = 0$ can be proved similarly; this completes the proof of Theorem 2.2.

Let ρ denote the radius of a ball around the origin which contains all points of ∂G. The point sets E_+ and E_- defined as

$$E_+ = [\{x, \theta\};\ \ x \cdot \theta \geq \rho], \tag{2.4$_+$}$$

$$E_- = [\{x, \theta\};\ \ x \cdot \theta \leq -\rho] \tag{2.4$_-$}$$

certainly have the property that E_+ is free forward and E_- is free backward. Further properties are summarized in

THEOREM 2.3.

i)$_+$ $E_+(t) \subset E_+$ for $t \geq 0$,
i)$_-$ $E_-(t) \subset E_-$ for $t \leq 0$,
ii)$_+$ $\bigcap E_+(t) = \emptyset$,
ii)$_-$ $\bigcap E_-(t) = \emptyset$,
iii) Both sets

$$\bigcup E_+(t) \quad \text{and} \quad \bigcup E_-(t)$$

are subsets of Ω which differ from Ω by a set of measure zero,

$$\text{iv)}\ \ E_+ \cap E_- = \emptyset$$

Proof. Properties (i)$_\pm$, (ii)$_\pm$ and (iv) follow directly from definition (2.4). It further follows from the definition that $\bigcup E_+(t)$ is the set of all points free in the forward direction and this shows that $\bigcup E_+(t)$ is contained in Ω. According to Theorem 2.2 almost all points of Ω are free forward and hence (iii)$_+$ holds. The proof of (iii)$_-$ is similar.

3. THE SCATTERING OPERATOR

We turn now to the Koopman representation of this flow; that is, we denote by H the Hilbert space $L_2(\Omega, m)$ and define the operators $\{U(t)\}$ by (1.1). Since the flow is one-to-one, onto and measure preserving, each operator $U(t)$ is a unitary map of H onto H; it is easy to show, in spite of the occasional discontinuity of the flow, that the $\{U(t)\}$ define a strongly continuous one-parameter group of operators.

Corresponding to the subsets $E_\pm$ we now define the following subspaces:

$$D_+ = [f;\ \operatorname{supp} f \subset E_+], \tag{3.1$_+$}$$

$$D_- = [f;\ \operatorname{supp} f \subset E_-]. \tag{3.1$_-$}$$

THEOREM 3.1. The subspaces D_- and D_+ satisfy the following properties:

i)$_-$ $U(t)\,D_- \subset D_-$ for $t \leq 0$,
i)$_+$ $U(t)\,D_+ \subset D_+$ for $t \geq 0$,
ii)$_-$ $\bigcap U(t)\,D_- = \{0\}$,
ii)$_+$ $\bigcap U(t)\,D_+ = \{0\}$,
iii)$_-$ $\bigcup U(t)\,D_-$ is dense in H,
iii)$_+$ $\bigcup U(t)\,D_+$ is dense in H,
iv) D_- is orthogonal to D_+.

Proof. Properties (i)$_\pm$, (ii)$_\pm$ and (iv) follow directly from the corresponding parts of Theorem 2.3. If (iii)$_+$ were not valid, then there would exist an f in H orthogonal to $\bigcup U(t)\,D_+$. We could infer from this that $U(t)f$ is orthogonal to D_+ for all t and this in turn requires, aside from a null set,[1] that

$$\tau_t(\operatorname{supp} f) \cap E_+ = \phi \tag{3.2}$$

for all t. According to property (iii) of Theorem 2.3, this can happen only if $m(\operatorname{supp} f) = 0$; that is, if f is the zero vector. Property (iii)$_-$ is proved similarly.

Subspaces D_- and D_+ satisfying properties (i), (ii), and (iii) are in the terminology of [**2, 3**] incoming and outgoing subspaces for the group $\{U(t)\}$. According to the general theory, associated with each incoming [outgoing] subspace there is a translation representation of $\{U(t)\}$ mapping H unitarily onto $L_2(-\infty, \infty; N)$, where N is an auxiliary Hilbert space,

[1]Since $E_+(t) \subset E_+$ for $t \geq 0$, the relation (3.2) holds for all t if it holds for all integral values of t and this requires throwing out only a denumerable number of null sets from the support of f.

sending $D_-[D_+]$ onto $L_2(-\infty, 0; N)$ [respectively $L_2(0, \infty; N)$] and the action of $U(t)$ into translation to the right by t units.

All of this applies in particular to the unperturbed problem for which there is no obstacle. In this case, the phase space is $\Omega_0 = R_n \times S_{n-1}$ and the corresponding flow is simply

$$\tau_t^0(\{x, \theta\}) = \{x + t\theta, \theta\}.$$

The unperturbed group of unitary operators defined on $H_0 = L_2(\Omega_0, m)$ is defined as

$$[U_0(t)f](\omega) = f(\tau_{-t}^0(\omega)).$$

It is convenient to replace $E_\pm$ by

$$E_-^0 = [\{x, \theta\}; \quad x \cdot \theta \leq 0] \quad \text{and} \quad E_+^0 = [\{x, \theta\}; \quad x \cdot \theta \geq 0];$$

and $D_\pm$ by

$$D_-^0 = [f; \operatorname{supp} f \subset E_-^0] \quad \text{and} \quad D_+^0 = [f; \operatorname{supp} f \subset E_+^0].$$

Denote by M the tangent manifold of the sphere S_{n-1} and by N the space $L_2(M)$ with respect to the usual measure in M. To each function f in $L_2(\Omega_0)$ we assign a function k_0 in $L_2(-\infty, \infty; N)$ as follows: Decompose x as

$$x = s\theta + \zeta, \qquad \zeta \text{ orthogonal to } \theta,$$

and set

$$k_0(s) = f(\{s\theta + \zeta, \theta\}). \tag{3.3}$$

It is not hard to verify that the mapping:

$$f \rightarrow k_0$$

given by (3.3) is a unitary translation representation for $\{U_0(t)\}$ which is both incoming and outgoing.

It is clear for f in D_+ and for $t \geq 0$ that $U(t)f = U_0(t)f$ and hence for such f the action of the wave operator [see (1.2)] is given by $W_+ f = f$. Moreover for any f with bounded spatial support, $U_0(t)f$ will lie in D_+ for t sufficiently large, say $t \geq T$, and hence for such an f, $W_+ f = U(-T) \cdot U_0(T)f$. Consequently W_+ exists and is isometric on a dense subset of H_0 and can therefore be defined by continuity on all of H_0; the resulting W_+ is again an isometry. Finally, the wave operator W_+ is an intertwining operator [see (1.4)]; and it follows from this together with property (iii)$_+$ of Theorem 3.1 that the range of W_+ is all of H. A similar argument applies to W_- and hence the scattering operator S given by (1.3) is well defined and unitary.

The perturbed incoming and outgoing translation representers k_- and k_+ of any f in H can be expressed in terms of the unperturbed representation in H_0 and the wave operators: For any f in H let $k_0(s)$ be the unperturbed translation representer of $W_+^{-1}f$; then

$$k_+(s) = k_0(s + \rho).$$

In fact it follows from the unitary and intertwining properties of the wave operator that this defines a translation representation of $\{U(t)\}$ onto $L_2(-\infty, \infty; N)$ and since D_+ maps onto $L_2(\rho, \infty; N)$ in the unperturbed representation it maps onto $L_2(0, \infty; N)$ in the above representation. Similarly if k_0 is the unperturbed translation representer of $W_-^{-1}f$ then the perturbed incoming translation representer of f is

$$k_-(s) = k_0(s - \rho).$$

Now for f in D_+, $W_+ f = f$; and hence in this case we can write, using the explicit expression (3.3) for the unperturbed representation, that

$$k_+(s; \zeta, \theta) = f(\{\zeta + (s + \rho)\theta, \theta\}) \qquad \text{for } f \text{ in } D_+; \tag{3.4$_+$}$$

similarly

$$k_-(s; \zeta, \theta) = f(\{\zeta + (s - \rho)\theta, \theta\}) \quad \text{for } f \text{ in } D_-, \tag{3.4$_-$}$$

where in both cases $\theta \cdot \zeta = 0$.

Next, for an f such that $U(T)f$ belongs to D_+ for some T, the outgoing translation representer of $U(T)f$ can be determined from $(3.4)_+$; that of f itself is obtained by translating backward by an amount T. This recipe can be put into the following more compact form:

$$k_+(s; \zeta, \theta) = f(p_+) \tag{3.5$_+$}$$

where the point $p_+ = p(s; \zeta, \theta)$ is

$$p_+ = \tau_s(\{\zeta + \rho\theta, \theta\}). \tag{3.6$_+$}$$

Similarly for an f such that $U(T)f$ belongs to D_- for some T

$$k_-(s; \zeta, \theta) = f(p_-) \tag{3.5$_-$}$$

where

$$p_- = \tau_s(\{\zeta - \rho\theta, \theta\}). \tag{3.6$_-$}$$

Since the set of f of the above kind is dense in H by property (iii) of Theorem 3.1, it follows by continuity that $(3.5)_\pm$ holds for all f in H.

As described in (3.6) the points p_+ and p_- are functions of s, ζ, θ; these relations can be inverted to give s_+, ζ_+, and θ_+ as functions of p, and similarly s_-, ζ_-, and θ_- can be obtained as functions of p. There is thus a well defined one-to-one correspondence between the triplets $\{s_-, \zeta_-, \theta_-\}$

and $\{s_+, \zeta_+, \theta_+\}$ corresponding to the same point p; and we can regard $\{s_-, \zeta_-, \theta_-\}$ as functions of $\{s_+, \zeta_+, \theta_+\}$. It is important to note that in this correspondence the difference $s_- - s_+$ is determined as a function of ζ_+ and θ_+ alone:

$$s_-(s_+, \zeta_+, \theta_+) - s_+ \equiv \ell(\zeta_+, \theta_+). \tag{3.7}$$

This is obvious since for any value of t the triplets $\{s_- + t, \zeta_-, \theta_-\}$ and $\{s_+ + t, \zeta_+, \theta_+\}$ both correspond to the point $p_t = \tau_t(p)$.

Comparing formulas $(3.5)_+$ and $(3.5)_-$ we conclude that

$$k_+(s_+; \zeta_+, \theta_+) = k_-(s_+ + \ell; \zeta_-, \theta_-);$$

we rewrite this by dropping the subscript $+$:

$$k_+(s; \zeta, \theta) = k_-(s + \ell; \zeta_-, \theta_-), \tag{3.8}$$

where ℓ, ζ_-, and θ_- are functions of ζ and θ.

These functions ℓ, ζ_-, and θ_- give the following interesting geometric description of the scattering process: A particle which is originally just about to leave E_- from the point $\zeta_- - \rho\theta_-$, traveling in the θ_- direction, will, after bouncing around for a time ℓ, enter E_+ at the point $\zeta + \rho\theta$ traveling in the direction θ. The quanity ℓ is called the *sojourn time*.

Now k_- and k_+ denote the incoming and outgoing translation representers, respectively, of a given f in H. Hence, neglecting a trivial shift of ρ, the free space translation representer of $W_-^{-1}f$ is k_- and that of

$$W_+^{-1}f = S[W_-^{-1}f]$$

is k_+. Thus the action of S on the free space translation representation is simply:

$$S\colon\ k_- \to k_+;$$

here we neglect a shift of 2ρ. The scattering matrix relates the corresponding spectral representers. Taking the Fourier transform of (3.8) we therefore obtain an explicit expression for $\mathcal{S}$:

$$\begin{aligned} \hat{k}_+(\sigma; \zeta, \theta) &= [\mathcal{S}(\sigma)\hat{k}_-(\sigma; \cdot, \cdot)](\zeta, \theta) \\ &= e^{-i\ell(\zeta,\theta)\sigma}\hat{k}_-(\sigma; \zeta_-, \theta_-). \end{aligned} \tag{3.9}$$

This shows that the action of the scattering matrix $\mathcal{S}(\sigma)$ is a point transformation in M followed by multiplication by $\exp(-i\ell\sigma)$.

We define the possibly infinite-valued domain functional $\ell(G)$ as follows:

$$\ell(G) = \sup \ell(\zeta, \theta). \tag{3.10}$$

From the explicit description (3.9) of $\mathcal{S}(\sigma)$ we deduce

THEOREM 3.2. If $\mathcal{L}(G)$ is finite then $\mathcal{S}(\sigma)$ can be extended as an analytic function to the whole complex σ-plane. If $\mathcal{L}(G) = \infty$ then $\mathcal{S}(\sigma)$ is analytic in the lower half-plane but the real axis is its natural boundary.

4. THE ASSOCIATED SEMI-GROUP

In the previous section the scattering operator was defined in terms of the subspaces D_- and D_+, and the group of operators $\{U(t)\}$. A dual object, namely the family of operators

$$Z(t) = P_+ U(t) P_-, \qquad t \geq 0, \tag{4.1}$$

where P_- and P_+ are orthogonal projections onto the orthogonal complements of D_- and D_+, respectively, is also defined in terms of these same ingredients; it is to be expected, therefore, that these two objects are intimately related.

It can be proved [**2,3**] that the $\{Z(t)\}$ form a strongly continuous semigroup of operators on $K = H - (D_- + D_+)$ and the spectral properties of its infinitesimal generator B are related to the singularities of the scattering matrix $\mathcal{S}(\sigma)$(cf. H. Helson [**1**]). In fact μ with $Re\ \mu < 0$ belongs to the resolvent set of B if and only if $\mathcal{S}(i\bar{\mu})$ is regular and a purely imaginary μ_0 belongs to the resolvent set of B if and only if $\mathcal{S}(\sigma)$ can be continued analytically across the real axis in some neighborhood of $i\bar{\mu}_0$; the so-continued operator-valued function is equal to $[\mathcal{S}^*(\sigma)]^{-1}$ in the part of its domain of holomorphicity which belongs to the upper half-plane.

In the present example it is easy to show that the domain K is $L_2(\Omega_\rho; m)$, where Ω_ρ is the set

$$\Omega_\rho = [\{x, \theta\};\ |x\cdot\theta| \leq \rho] \cap \Omega; \tag{4.2}$$

and that for every f in K

$$[Z(t)f](\omega) = \begin{cases} f(\tau_{-t}(\omega)) & \text{for } \omega \text{ in } \Omega_\rho, \\ 0 & \text{otherwise.} \end{cases} \tag{4.3}$$

Now a trajectory enters the set Ω_ρ at a point $\{x, \theta\}$ where $x\cdot\theta = -\rho$ and leaves it at a point x', θ' where $x'\cdot\theta' = \rho$. According to the geometrical characterization given above, the time spent by this trajectory in Ω_ρ is just $\mathcal{L}$; hence the name sojourn time. If the functional $\mathcal{L}(G)$ defined in (3.10) as the longest sojourn time is finite, then it follows from (4.2) and (4.3) that $Z(\mathcal{L}(G)) = 0$. In this case the spectrum of the infinitesimal generator B is empty and by the general theory the scattering matrix can be extended to be an entire function. This confirms what we found to be the case earlier by examining the scattering matrix directly. When $\mathcal{L}(G)$ is infinite the situation is somewhat more complicated; however, since

$\ell(\zeta, \theta)$ is continuous it will for arbitrary L in this case be greater than L on a subset of M of positive measure.

THEOREM 4.1. If $\ell(G)$ is infinite then B has a pure continuous spectrum, which fills out the entire left half-plane, $Re\, z \leq 0$.

Proof. Obviously $Z(t)$ is a contraction operator and hence the spectrum of B is contained in the left half-plane, $Re\, z \leq 0$. Our first step in characterizing the spectrum of B is to prove that the point spectrum of B is empty. Otherwise there would exist an f in K such that $Bf = \mu f$ and hence

$$f(\tau_{-t}(\omega)) = [Z(t)f](\omega) = e^{\mu t} f(\omega).$$

This means that the support of f, aside from a null set, is invariant in Ω_ρ under the action of τ_{-t} for all $t \geq 0$, contrary to property (iii) of Theorem 2.3.

The adjoint of B is the generator of the adjoint semigroup:

$$Z^*(t) = P_- U(-t) P_+, \qquad t \geq 0,$$

which can be obtained from $Z(t)$ by simply reversing the direction of time; this automatically interchanges D_- and D_+. Consequently B^* has no point spectrum and it follows from this that B has no residual spectrum.

Since B has neither point nor residual spectrum and since the spectrum is a closed point set, it suffices to prove that the continuous spectrum includes the open left half-plane. To this end choose $\Delta > 0$ so that the obstacle is contained in the ball $\{|x| < \rho - \Delta\}$ and let F_k consist of all trajectories[2] in Ω_ρ such that $(k-1)\Delta < \ell(\zeta, \theta) \leq k\Delta$. By assumption there is an infinite subsequence (we renumber for notational convenience) for which $m(F_k) > 0$.

Let $\chi_k(\omega)$ be the characteristic function of F_k and set

$$g_k = \chi_k + \mu \chi_k \int_0^\infty e^{\mu t} U(-t) \chi_k \, dt.$$

Starting at the end of a trajectory in Ω_ρ and measuring arc lengths in the negative direction, we see that $g_k = \exp(\mu s)\chi_k$. Thus at the beginning of a trajectory in F_k we have

$$e^{-\alpha k \Delta} \leq |g_k| \leq e^{-\alpha(k-1)\Delta},$$

where $\alpha = -Re\, \mu > 0$.

[2]It is easy to see that F_k is an m-measurable subset of Ω_ρ. In fact F_k is by definition measurable relative to a second measure m' obtained by parameterizing Ω in terms of trajectories and arc lengths along a trajectory starting from $\{\zeta - \rho\theta, \theta\}$, say as $\{\zeta, \theta, s\}$. It is clear that a subset F of E_- will be measurable relative to m if and only if it is measurable relative to m' and $m(F) = m'(F)$. On the other hand both measures are invariant under translation by τ_t. It therefore follows from property (iii) of Theorem 2.3 that the class of measurable subsets and their measures are the same for both measures.

Next choose $\zeta(\sigma)$ in C^∞ to be zero at $\sigma = 0$ and one for $\sigma \geq \Delta$ and set

$$f_k(\omega) = \zeta(x\cdot\theta + \rho)g_k(\omega).$$

Then an easy calculation shows that

$$|f_k|^2 \geq \frac{m(F_k)}{k\Delta}\,\frac{1 - e^{-2\alpha(k-1)\Delta}}{2\alpha}.$$

Moreover f_k belongs to the domain of B and

$$[Bf_k](\omega) = \mu f_k(\omega)$$

except in

$$[\{x,\theta\};\ -\rho \leq x\cdot\theta \leq -\rho + \Delta] \cap F_k$$

where it is equal to $\zeta' g_k$. Consequently

$$|B - \mu I)f_k|^2 \leq C\frac{m(F_k)}{(k-1)\Delta}e^{-2\alpha(k-1)\Delta}.$$

It follows that

$$\lim_{k\to\infty}\frac{|(B - \mu I)f_k|}{|f_k|} = 0$$

and this proves that μ belongs to the continuous spectrum of B.

Applying the general theory previously mentioned, we obtain

COROLLARY 4.1. If $\mathcal{L}(G)$ is infinite, then the maximal domain of holomorphicity for $\mathcal{S}(\sigma)$ is the lower half-plane, Im $\sigma < 0$, and for each σ in this half-plane $\mathcal{S}(\sigma)$ is a singular operator.

REFERENCES

1. Helson, Henry, *Lectures on Invariant Subspaces*, Academic Press, New York, 1964.
2. Lax, P. D. and R. S. Phillips, Scattering Theory, *Bull. Amer. Math. Soc.*, Vol 70, 1964, pp. 130–142.
3. Lax, P. D. and R. S. Phillips, Scattering Theory, Academic Press, New York, 1967.

On a Problem of Calkin

SHÔICHIRÔ SAKAI

1. INTRODUCTION

Let $\mathfrak{H}$ be a separable Hilbert space, $B(\mathfrak{H})$ the C^*-algebra of all bounded operators on $\mathfrak{H}$, $C(\mathfrak{H})$ the C^*-algebra of all compact operators on $\mathfrak{H}$. Calkin [**1**] studied the *-representations of the quotient C^*-algebra $B(\mathfrak{H})/C(\mathfrak{H})$, and raised a problem of whether or not there exists a type III-factor *-representation of $B(\mathfrak{H})/C(\mathfrak{H})$.

In the present paper, we shall show that this algebra has a type III-factor *-representation. The crucial tools in the proof of the theorem are the results of the author [**5**] and Schwartz [**7**].

Whether or not the C^*-algebra has a type II_∞-factor *-representation (even a global type II_∞ *-representation) is still an open question.

2. THE THEOREM

In this section, we shall show the following theorem.

THEOREM. The C^*-algebra $B(\mathfrak{H})/C(\mathfrak{H})$ has a type III-factor *-representation.

To prove the theorem, we shall proceed as follows. Schwartz [**7, 8**] showed that there is a type III-factor M in the Hilbert space $\mathfrak{H}$ satisfying the following: there is a linear projection P with norm 1 of $B(\mathfrak{H})$ onto M satisfying the conditions:

$$P(a^*) = P(a)^* \quad \text{for } a \in B(\mathfrak{H}); \tag{1}$$

$$P(h) \geq 0 \quad \text{if } h \geq 0 \text{ and } h \in B(\mathfrak{H}); \tag{2}$$

$$P(axb) = aP(x)b \quad \text{for } a, b \in M \text{ and } x \in B(\mathfrak{H}). \tag{3}$$

Moreover we can easily see that the projection P also satisfies the following condition:

$$P(x^*x) \geq P(x)^*P(x) \quad \text{for } x \in B(\mathfrak{H}). \tag{4}$$

Now let Ω be the set of all linear projections of $B(\mathfrak{H})$ onto M satisfying the conditions (1), (2), (3) and (4). Then every element Q of Ω is a bounded linear mapping of $B(\mathfrak{H})$ onto M and its norm on the self-adjoint portion of $B(\mathfrak{H})$ is one, in fact, let k be a self-adjoint element of $B(\mathfrak{H})$, then $\|k\| \cdot I \pm k \geqq 0$ and so $Q(\|k\| \cdot I \pm k) = \|k\| \cdot I \pm Q(k) \geqq 0$, where I is the identity operator on $\mathfrak{H}$; hence $\|Q(k)\| \leqq \|k\|$.

Let $\mathfrak{L}(B(\mathfrak{H}), M)$ be the Banach space of all bounded linear mappings of $B(\mathfrak{H})$ into M. Then it is the dual of the Banach space $B(\mathfrak{H}) \otimes_\gamma M_*$ (cf. [**3**]), where M_* is the associated space of M (namely, the dual of $M_* = M$) and γ is the greatest cross norm.

LEMMA 1. Ω is a $\sigma(\mathfrak{L}(B(\mathfrak{H}), M), B(\mathfrak{H}) \otimes_\gamma M_*)$—compact convex subset of $\mathfrak{L}(B(\mathfrak{H}), M)$.

Proof. It is clear that all elements of the closure $\bar{\Omega}$ of Ω are linear projections satisfying the conditions (1), (2), and (3).

Let $Q \in \bar{\Omega}$, then $\langle Q(x)^*Q(x), \varphi\rangle = \langle Q(x^*Q(x)), \varphi\rangle = \langle x^*Q(x), Q^*(\varphi)\rangle$ for $x \in M$ and $\varphi(\geqq 0) \in M_*$, where Q^* is the dual of Q and $\langle(\cdot), \varphi\rangle$ is the value of φ at the point $(\cdot)$. $Q^*(\varphi)$ is a positive linear functional on $B(\mathfrak{H})$, because $\langle h, Q^*(\varphi)\rangle = \langle Q(h), \varphi\rangle \geqq 0$ for all positive $h \in B(\mathfrak{H})$. Hence,

$$\langle x^*Q(x), \quad Q^*(\varphi)\rangle \leqq \langle x^*x, Q^*(\varphi)\rangle^{1/2}\langle Q(x)^*Q(x), Q^*(\varphi)\rangle^{1/2}.$$

Therefore, $\langle Q(x)^* \ Q(x), \ \varphi\rangle \leqq \langle Q(x^*x), \ \varphi\rangle$, because $\langle Q(x)^*Q(x), Q^*(\varphi)\rangle = \langle Q(Q(x)^*Q(x)), \ \varphi\rangle = \langle Q(x)^*Q(x), \ \varphi\rangle$; hence $Q(x)^*Q(x) \leqq Q(x^*x)$. The convexity of Ω is clear. This completes the Proof.

Let φ be a normal, faithful, positive linear functional on M (namely, $\varphi(a^*a) = 0$ implies $a = 0$ for $a \in M$ such that $\varphi(I) = 1$. For $Q \in \Omega$, we shall define a positive linear functional φ_Q on $B(\mathfrak{H})$ by $\varphi_Q(x) = \varphi(Q(x))$ for $x \in B(\mathfrak{H})$.

Let $\mathcal{E} = \{\varphi_Q \mid Q \in \Omega\}$, then we can easily see that $\mathcal{E}$ is a compact convex subset of the state space of $B(\mathfrak{H})$ with the topology $\sigma(B(\mathfrak{H})^*, B(\mathfrak{H}))$, where $B(\mathfrak{H})^*$ is the dual of $B(\mathfrak{H})$.

LEMMA 2. $Q(C(\mathfrak{H})) = 0$ for all $Q \in \Omega$.

Proof. Suppose that there are Q_0 in Ω and h_0 in $C(\mathfrak{H})$ such that $Q_0(h_0) \neq 0$. It is enough to assume that $h_0 > 0$. Then, $Q_0(h_0) > 0$; therefore we can choose a nonzero projection e in M such that $\lambda e \leqq Q_0(h_0)$ for some positive number λ and e commutes with $Q_0(h_0)$. Then $Q_0(Meh_0) = MeQ_0(h_0) \supset Me$; therefore $Q_0(Meh_0)$ is not uniformly separable. On the other hand, $Meh_0 \subset C(\mathfrak{H})$ and so it is uniformly separable and it is a contradiction. This completes the proof.

Let $\varphi_Q(Q \in \Omega)$ be an extreme point of $\mathcal{E}$, and let $\{\pi Q, \mathfrak{H} Q\}$ be the *-representation of $B(\mathfrak{H})$ on a Hilbert space $\mathfrak{H}_Q$ constructed via φ_Q. By

Lemma 2, $\varphi_Q(C(\mathfrak{H})) = 0$ and so $\{\pi_Q, \mathfrak{H}_Q\}$ can be canonically considered a *-representation of $B(\mathfrak{H})/C(\mathfrak{H})$.

Let N be the weak closure of $\pi_Q(B(\mathfrak{H}_Q))$ on $\mathfrak{H}_Q$. Then we shall define a linear mapping of N onto M in the following consideration.

Let N_* be the associated space of N. For $f \in M_*$, we define $F(\pi_Q(x)) = f(Q(x))$ for $x \in B(\mathfrak{H})$; then F is a bounded linear functional on the C^*-algebra $\pi_Q(B(\mathfrak{H}))$.

First of all, we shall show that F is strongly continuous on bounded spheres. Let $\{\pi_Q(x_\alpha) \mid x_\alpha \in B(\mathfrak{H}),\ \|x_\alpha\| \leqq 1\}$ be a directed set of elements in $\pi_Q(B(\mathfrak{H}))$ which converges strongly to 0, then $\varphi_Q(x_\alpha^* x_\alpha) = \varphi(Q(x_\alpha^* x_\alpha)) \Longrightarrow 0$; hence $\varphi(Q(x_\alpha^* x_\alpha)) \geqq \varphi(Q(x_\alpha)^* Q(x_\alpha)) \Longrightarrow 0$. Therefore, $\{Q(x_\alpha)\}$ converges strongly to 0 in the W^*-algebra M, because $\{Q(x_\alpha)\}$ is bounded and φ is normal, faithful; hence

$$f(Q(x_\alpha)) = F(\pi_Q(x_\alpha)) \Longrightarrow 0.$$

LEMMA 3. Let G be a bounded linear functional of $\pi_Q(B(\mathfrak{H}))$ which is strongly continuous on bounded spheres, then it can be uniquely extended to a normal linear functional $\overline{G}$ on N with $\|G\| = \|\overline{G}\|$.

Proof. Let $\pi_Q(B(\mathfrak{H}))^{**}$ be the second dual of the C^*-algebra $\pi_Q(B(\mathfrak{H}))$, then it is a W^*-algebra (cf. [**9**]). For $H \in N_*$, let $\tilde{H}$ be the restriction of H on $\pi_Q(B(\mathfrak{H}))$, then $\|\tilde{H}\| = \|H\|$ by the density theorem of Kaplansky (cf. [**2**]). Put $\tilde{N}_* = \{\tilde{H} \mid H \in N_*\}$, then $\tilde{N}_*$ is a closed subspace of the dual $\pi_Q(B(\mathfrak{H}))^*$ of $\pi_Q(B(\mathfrak{H}))$ and moreover it is invariant—namely $\tilde{H} \in \tilde{N}_*$ implies $L_a R_b \tilde{H} \in \tilde{N}_*$ for $a, b \in \pi_Q(B(\mathfrak{H}))$, where $L_a R_b \tilde{H}(x) = \tilde{H}(axb)$ for $x \in \pi_Q(B(\mathfrak{H}))$. Let $\tilde{N}_*^0$ be the polar of $\tilde{N}_*$ in $\pi_Q(B(\mathfrak{H}))^{**}$, then it is a σ-weakly closed ideal (cf. [**4**]); therefore, there is a central projection z of $\pi_Q(B(\mathfrak{H}))^{**}$ such that $\tilde{N}_*^0 = \pi_Q(B(\mathfrak{H}))^{**} z$. Moreover we can easily see that the W^*-algebra N (resp. the associated space N_*) can be canonically identified with $\pi_Q(B(\mathfrak{H}))^{**}(I - z)$ (resp. $\tilde{N}_*$).

Suppose that Lemma 3 is not true. Then there is no element $\overline{G}$ in N_* satisfying $G = \overline{G}$ on $\pi_Q(B(\mathfrak{H}))$; therefore $L_z G \neq 0$; hence there is an element a in $\pi_Q(B(\mathfrak{H}))^{**}$ such that $az = a$ and $G(a) \neq 0$.

Now, choose a bounded directed set (a_α) of elements in $\pi_Q(B(\mathfrak{H}))$ such that $a_\alpha \to a$ (strongly) in the W^*-algebra $\pi_Q(B(\mathfrak{H}))^{**}$, then $a_\alpha(I - z)$ converges strongly to $a(I - z) = 0$; hence by the assumption, $G(a_\alpha) \to 0$. On the other hand, $G(a_\alpha) \to G(a) \neq 0$. This is a contradiction. This completes the proof.

By Lemma 3, the F can be uniquely extended to an element $\overline{F}$ of N_* with $\|F\| = \|\overline{F}\|$. Put $T(f) = \overline{F}$ for $f \in M_*$, then T is a bounded linear mapping of M_* into N_*. Let T^* be the dual of T, then T^* is a continuous linear mapping of N with the topology $\sigma(N, N_*)$ into M with the topology $\sigma(M, M_*)$.

LEMMA 4. T^* satisfies the following conditions:

(1) $T^*(\pi_Q(x)) = Q(x)$ for $x \in B(\mathfrak{H})$,
(2) $T^*(y^*) = T^*(y)^*$ for $y \in N$,
(3) $T^*(h) \geqq 0$ for $h\,(\geqq 0) \in N$,
(4) $T^*(\pi_Q(a)y\pi_Q(b)) = aT^*(y)b$ for $a, b \in M$ and $y \in N$,
(5) $T^*(y^*y) \geqq T^*(y)^*\, T^*(y)$ for $y \in N$.

Proof

(1) $\langle T^*(\pi_Q(x)), f\rangle = \langle \pi_Q(x), T(f)\rangle = \langle Q(x), f\rangle$ for $f \in M_*$. Hence, $T^*(\pi_Q(x)) = Q(x)$.

(2) Let (x_α) be a bounded directed set of elements of $B(\mathfrak{H})$ such that $\pi_Q(x_\alpha) \to y$ (σ-weakly) in N, then $T^*(\pi_Q(x_\alpha)^*) = T^*(\pi_Q(x_\alpha^*)) = Q(x_\alpha^*) = Q(x_\alpha)^* = T^*(\pi_Q(x_\alpha))^* \to T^*(y)^*$ (σ-weakly) in M, and $T^*(\pi_Q(x_\alpha)^*) \to T^*(y^*))$ (σ-weakly) in M; hence $T^*(y)^* = T^*(y^*)$.

(3) The proof is analogous with (2).

(4) $T^*(\pi_Q(a)\,\pi_Q(x)\,\pi_Q(b)) = T^*(\pi_Q(axb)) = Q(axb) = aQ(x)b$ for a, $b \in M$ and $x \in B(\mathfrak{H})$. Therefore, by the σ-weak continuity of T^* and the density of $\pi_Q(B(\mathfrak{H}))$ in N, we can prove this easily.

(5) Let χ be a positive element of M_*, then

$$\langle T^*(y)^*\, T^*(y), \chi\rangle = \langle T^*(y^*\,\pi_Q(T^*(y)), \chi\rangle$$
$$= \langle y^*\,\pi_Q(T^*(y)), T(\chi)\rangle \leqq \langle y^*y, T(\chi)\rangle^{1/2}\langle \pi_Q(T^*(y)^*\pi_Q(T^*(y)), T(\chi)\rangle^{1/2}$$
$$= \langle y^*y, T(\chi)\rangle^{1/2}\langle T^*(y)^*\, T^*(y), \chi\rangle^{1/2},$$

because $\langle \pi_Q(h), T(\chi)\rangle = \langle Q(h), \chi\rangle$ for $h \in B(\mathfrak{H})$ and so $T(\chi) \geqq 0$; hence $T^*(y)^*\, T^*(y) \leqq T^*(y^*y)$. This completes the proof.

LEMMA 5. N is a factor.

Proof. Let Z_p be the set of all central projections of N. For $x \in Z_p$, $T^*(z)$ is a central element of M, because $T^*(z)a = T^*(z\pi_Q(a)) = T^*(\pi_Q(a)z) = aT^*(z)$ for $a \in M$. Therefore, $T^*(z) = \lambda(z)\, I$, where $\lambda(z)$ is a real number such that $0 \leqq \lambda(z) \leqq 1$.

Suppose that $0 < \lambda(z) < 1$, then we shall define two linear mappings Q_1 and Q_2 of $B(\mathfrak{H})$ into M as follows:

$$Q_1(x) = (1/\lambda(z))\cdot T^*(\pi_Q(x)z)$$

and

$$Q_2(x) = (1/1 - \lambda(z))\cdot T^*(\pi_Q(x)(I - z)) \text{ for } x \in B(\mathfrak{H}).$$

Then, Q_1 (resp, Q_2) is a projection of $B(\mathfrak{H})$ onto M, because $Q_1(a) = (1/\lambda(z))T^*(\pi_Q(a)z) = (1/\lambda(z))aT^*(z) = a$ for $a \in M$ (resp. $Q_2(a) = a$).

Moreover,

$$Q_1(x)^* = (1/\lambda(z))T^*(\pi_Q(x)z)^*$$
$$= (1/\lambda(z))T^*(\pi_Q(x^*)z) = Q_1(x^*) \quad \text{for } x \in B(\mathfrak{H});$$
$$Q_1(h) = (1/\lambda(z))T^*(\pi_Q(h)z) \geqq 0 \quad \text{for } h\,(\geqq 0) \in B(\mathfrak{H});$$
$$Q_1(axb) = (1/\lambda(z))\, T^*(\pi_Q(axb)z) = (1/\lambda(z))a\, T^*(\pi_Q(x)z)b = aQ_1(x)b$$

for $a, b \in M$ and $x \in B(\mathfrak{H})$. Therefore Q_1 and analogously Q_2 belong to $\underline{\Omega}$ (cf. the proof of Lemma 1). Then,

$$\langle x, \varphi_{Q_1}\rangle = \langle (1/\lambda(z))T^*(\pi_Q(x)z), \varphi\rangle$$
$$= (1/\lambda(z))\,\langle \pi_Q(x)z, T(\varphi)\rangle$$
$$= (1/\lambda(z))\langle \pi_Q(x)z, \overline{\varphi}_Q\rangle,$$

where $\overline{\varphi}_Q$ is the unique normal extension of $\underline{\varphi_Q}$ on N (cf. Lemma 3), because

$$\langle T^*(\pi_Q(x)), \varphi\rangle = \langle Q(x), \varphi\rangle = \langle x, \varphi_Q\rangle \quad \text{for } x \in B(\mathfrak{H}).$$

Analogously,

$$\langle x, \varphi_{Q_2}\rangle = (1/1 - \lambda(z))\langle \pi_Q(x)(I - z), \overline{\varphi}_Q\rangle.$$

Therefore, $\varphi_Q = \lambda(z)\varphi_{Q_1} + (1 - (z))\,\varphi_{Q_2}$; by the extremity of φ_Q, $\varphi_Q = \varphi_{Q_1} = \varphi_{Q_2}$ on $B(\mathfrak{H})$ and so $\overline{\varphi}_Q = \overline{\varphi}_{Q_1} = \overline{\varphi}_{Q_2}$ on N. This is a contradiction; hence $\lambda(z) = 0$ or 1.

Suppose that $\lambda(z) = 0$, then

$$\langle z, \varphi_Q\rangle = \langle z, T(\varphi)\rangle = \langle T^*(z), \varphi\rangle = \lambda(z) = 0.$$

Now consider the *-representation $\{\pi_Q, \mathfrak{H}_Q\}$ and let I_Q be the image of the identity in $\mathfrak{H}_Q$, then $0 = \langle z, \overline{\varphi}_Q\rangle = (zI_Q, I_Q)$, where $(\ ,\ )$ is the inner product of $\mathfrak{H}_Q$; hence $zI_Q = 0$ and so $\pi_Q(B(\mathfrak{H}))\ zI_Q = z\pi_Q(B(\mathfrak{H}))\, I_Q = 0$; hence $z = 0$. Therefore N is a factor. This completes the proof.

Now we shall prove the theorem.

PROOF OF THEOREM. Let $[\pi_Q(M)I_Q]$ be the closed subspace of $\mathfrak{H}_Q$ generated by $\pi_Q(M)I_Q$ and E' be the projection of $\mathfrak{H}_Q$ onto $[\pi_Q(M)I_Q]$, then E' belongs to the commutant of $\pi_Q(M)$.

$\pi_Q(M)E'$ is weakly closed, because φ_Q is normal on M; therefore, $E'\pi_Q(M)'E'$ is a type III-factor, where $\pi_Q(M)'$ is the commutant of $M\pi_Q(M)$.

Let F' be the central envelope of E' in $\pi_Q(M)'$, then $F'\pi_Q(M)'F'$ is a type III-factor. Therefore, there is a family of orthogonal, equivalent projections $\{E'_\alpha\}$ in $\pi_Q(M)'$ such that $\sum_\alpha \oplus E'_\alpha = F'$ and $E'_\alpha \sim E'$.

Now we shall show that $\pi_Q(M)F'$ is weakly closed on $\mathfrak{H}_Q$. Let $\{\pi_Q(a_\beta) \mid a_\beta \in M, \|a_\beta\| \leqq 1\}$ be a directed set such that σ-weak lim $\pi_Q(a_\beta)F' = A$ on $\mathfrak{H}_Q$. Then there is a subdirected set $\{a_{\beta\gamma}\}$ such that $a_{\beta\gamma} \to a$ (σ-weakly) in M for some $a \in M$; therefore, $\pi_Q(a_{\beta\gamma})E' \to \pi_Q(a)E'$ (σ-weakly) on $\mathfrak{H}_Q$. Then, $\pi_Q(a_{\beta\gamma}) E'_\alpha = \pi_Q(a_{\beta\gamma}) V'^*_\alpha E' V'_\alpha = V'^*_\alpha \pi_Q(a_{\beta\gamma})E'V'_\alpha \to V'^*_\alpha \pi_Q(a) \quad E'V'_\alpha = \pi_Q(a) E'_\alpha$ (σ-weakly) on $\mathfrak{H}_Q$, where V'_α is a partial isometry such that $V'^*_\alpha V'_\alpha = E'_\alpha$ and $V'_\alpha V'^*_\alpha = E'$. Therefore, $\sum_\alpha \oplus \pi_Q(a_{\beta\gamma})E'_\alpha = \pi_Q(a_{\beta\gamma})F' \to \sum_\alpha \oplus \pi_Q(a) \quad E'_\alpha = \pi_Q(a)F'$ (σ-weakly) on $\mathfrak{H}_Q$; hence $\pi_Q(a)F' = A$ and so $\pi_Q(M)F'$ is weakly closed.

Now we shall prove that N is of type III. The proof is quite similar with the case of [**5**].

Suppose that N is semi-finite, then there is a semi-finite, faithful, normal trace τ on N (cf. [**2**]). Put $N_0 = \{e \mid \tau(e) < +\infty, e \text{ projection in } N\}$. F' belongs to $\pi_Q(M)'' \subset N$; $T^*(F') \neq 0$, because $\langle T^*(F'), \varphi\rangle = \langle F', \bar{\varphi}_Q\rangle = (F'I_Q, I_Q)$ and so $T^*(F') = 0$ implies $F'I_Q = 0$, but $I_Q \in E'\mathfrak{H}_Q \subset F'\mathfrak{H}_Q$. Therefore, there is a nonzero $e_0 \in N_0$ such that $e_0 \leqq F'$ and $T^*(e_0) \neq 0$, and so there is a non-zero projection p in M such that $\lambda p \leqq T^*(e_0)$ for some positive number λ.

Suppose that a directed set $(a_\alpha)(\|a_\alpha\| \leqq 1, a_\alpha \in pMp)$ is strongly convergent to 0 in M, then $\pi_Q(a_\alpha)F'$ is strongly convergent to 0 on $\mathfrak{H}_Q$, because $\pi_Q(M)F'$ is weakly closed and so the mapping $a \to \pi_Q(a)F'$ ($a \in M$) is a W^*-representation; hence $\pi_Q(a_\alpha)e_0$ converges to 0 strongly on $\mathfrak{H}_Q$; by the finiteness of e_0, $\{e_0\pi_Q(a_\alpha)^*\}$ is strongly convergent to 0 (cf. [**5**], [**6**]).
Then,

$$T^*((e_0\pi_Q(a_\alpha)^*)^*(e_0\pi_Q(a_\alpha)^*))$$
$$\geqq T^*(e_0\pi_Q(a_\alpha)^*)^* T^*(e_0\pi_Q(a_\alpha)^*) \to 0 \quad (\sigma\text{-weakly})$$

in M; hence $\{T^*(e_0\pi_Q(a_\alpha)^*)\}$ converges strongly to 0 in M. Therefore,

$$\begin{aligned} &\{pT^*(e_0)p + (I-p)\}^{-1} p\, T^*(e_0\pi_Q(a_\alpha)^*) \\ &= \{pT^*(e_0)p + (I-p)\}^{-1} p\, T^*(e_0)a_\alpha^* \\ &= a_\alpha^* \to 0 \quad \text{(strongly) in } M. \end{aligned}$$

Hence, the *-operation is strongly continuous on bounded spheres of pMp, but pMp is of type III. This is a contradiction (cf. [**5**], [**6**]). This completes the proof of the theorem.

REMARK. The discussions which are used in the proof of the theorem are applicable to more general situation. Using those discussions and the result of Glimm concerning separable type I C^*-algebras, we can show that every C^*-algebra containing a nontype I separable C^*-subalgebra has a type III-factor *-representation. This will be proved in the next paper.

REFERENCES

1. Calkin, J. W., Two sided ideals and congruences in the ring of bounded operators in Hilbert space, *Ann. Math. Vol.* 42(1941) pp. 839–873.
2. Dixmier, J., Les algèbras d'operateurs dans l'espace hilbertien, Gauthier-Villars, Paris, 1957.
3. Grothendieck, A., Produit tensoriels topologiques et espaces nucléaires, *Memoirs of Amer. Math. Soc.*, 16.
4. Sakai, S., On the σ-weak topology of W^*-algebras, *Proc. Japan Acad.*, 32 (1956), pp. 329–332.
5. ———, On topological properties of W^*-algebras, *Proc. Japan Acad.*, 33(1957), pp. 439–444.
6. ———, The theory of W^*-algebras, Lecture notes, Yale University, 1962.
7. Schwartz, J., Two finite, non-hyperfinite, non-isomorphic factors, *Comm. Pure Appl. Math.*, Vol. 16, (1963), pp. 19–26.
8. ———, Non-isomorphism of a pari of factors of type III, *Comm. Pure. Appl. Math.*, Vol. 16, (1963), pp. 111–120.
9. Takeda, Z., Conjugate spaces of operator algebras, *Proc. Japan Acad.*, 30(1954), pp. 90–95.
10. Tomiyama, J., On the projection of norm one in W^*-algebras, *Proc. Japan Acad.* 33(1957), 608–612.

On a Characterization of Type I C*-Algebras*

SHÔICHIRÔ SAKAI

1. INTRODUCTION

Recently, establishing a conjecture of Calkin [**1**], the author [**7**] showed the following result: Let $\mathfrak{H}$ be a separable Hilbert space, $B(\mathfrak{H})$ the C^*-algebra of all bounded operators on $\mathfrak{H}$, $C(\mathfrak{H})$ the C^*-algebra of all compact operators on $\mathfrak{H}$, then the quotient C^*-algebra $B(\mathfrak{H})/C(\mathfrak{H})$ has a type III-factor *-representation. The discussions used in the proof of this result are applicable to more general situations.

In the present paper, by using those discussions and the result of Glimm [**3**], we shall give the characterization of type I C^*-algebras without the assumption of separability as follows:

MAIN THEOREM. Let A be a C^*-algebra. Then the following conditions are equivalent.

(1) A is a G C R algebra
(2) A is of type I
(3) A has no type III-factor *-representation.

2. THEOREMS

First of all we shall state a generalization of the result that was crucial in the proof of Calkin's conjecture.

THEOREM 1. Let A be a C^*-algebra with unit I, B a C^*-subalgebra containing I of A and M a type III-factor on a separable Hilbert space. Suppose that there is a linear mapping P of A into M satisfying the following conditions:

(1) $P(x^*) = P(x)^*$ for $x \in A$
(2) $P(h) \geqq 0$ for $h(\geqq 0) \in A$

*This paper written with partial support from ONR contract ONR NR-551(57).

(3) $P(axb) = P(a)P(x)P(b)$ for $a,b \in B$ and $x \in A$

(4) $P(B)$ is σ-weakly dense in M.

Then A has a type III-factor *-representation.

The proof of this theorem is quite similar to the one in [7]. Here we shall sketch the proof.

Let Ω be the set of all linear mappings Q of A into M satisfying the conditions (1), (2), (3) and $Q(a) = P(a)$ for $a \in B$. Let $\mathcal{L}(A, M)$ be the Banach space of all bounded linear mappings of A into M. Then it is the dual of a Banach space $A \otimes_\gamma M_*$, where M_* is the associated space (namely, the dual of $M_* = M$) and γ is the greatest cross norm.

LEMMA 1. Ω is a $\sigma(\mathcal{L}(A, M), A \otimes_\gamma M_*)$-compact convex subset of $\mathcal{L}(A, M)$ and each $Q \in \Omega$ satisfies $Q(x^*x) \geqq Q(x)^*Q(x)$ for $x \in A$.

The first part of Lemma 1 is clear. For the last part, by the assumptions (1), (3) and (4), and the density theorem of Kaplansky, there is a directed set (a_α) in B such that $\|a_\alpha\| \leqq \|Q(x)\|$ and $Q(a_\alpha) \to Q(x)$ (strongly) in M. Then, for $\varphi(\geqq 0) \in M_*$,

$$\langle Q(x)^*Q(x),\varphi\rangle = \lim_\alpha \langle Q(x)^*Q(a_\alpha),\varphi\rangle$$

$$= \lim_\alpha \langle Q(x^*a_\alpha),\varphi\rangle = \lim_\alpha \langle x^*a_\alpha, Q^*(\varphi)\rangle$$

$$\leqq \limsup_\alpha \langle x^*x, Q^*(\varphi)\rangle^{1/2}\langle a_\alpha^*a_\alpha, Q^*(\varphi)\rangle^{1/2} \text{ (because } Q^*(\varphi) \geqq 0)$$

$$= \limsup_\alpha \langle Q(x^*x),\varphi\rangle^{1/2}\langle Q(a_\alpha)^*Q(a_\alpha),\varphi\rangle^{1/2}.$$

Hence $Q(x)^*Q(x) \leqq Q(x^*x)$ for $x \in A$. This completes the proof.

Let φ be a normal, faithful state on M. For $Q \in \Omega$, we shall define a state φ_Q on A by $\varphi_Q(x) = \varphi(Q(x))$ for $x \in A$. Let $\mathcal{E} = \{\varphi_Q \mid Q \in \Omega\}$, then by Lemma 1, we can easily show that $\mathcal{E}$ is a compact convex subset of the state space of A. Let $\varphi_Q(Q \in \Omega)$ be an extreme point of $\mathcal{E}$, and let $\{\pi_Q, \mathfrak{H}_Q\}$ be the *-representation of A on a Hilbert space $\mathfrak{H}_Q$ constructed via φ_Q.

Let N be the weak closure of $\pi_Q(A)$ on $\mathfrak{H}_Q$. Then we shall define a linear mapping of N onto M in the following.

For $f \in M_*$, we define $F(\pi_Q(x)) = f(Q(x))$ for $x \in A$. This is well defined, because $\pi_Q(x) = 0$ implies $\varphi_Q(x^*x) = \varphi(Q(x^*x)) = 0$ and so $Q(x^*x) \geqq Q(x)^*Q(x) = 0$, so that $Q(x) = 0$.

Then, F is strongly continuous on bounded spheres [cf. (7)] and so by Lemma 3 in [7], the F can be uniquely extended to an element $\bar{F}$ of N_*, where N_* is the associated space of N with $\|F\| = \|\bar{F}\|$.

Put $T(f) = \bar{F}$ for $f \in M_*$, then T is a bounded linear mapping of M_* into N_*. Let T^* be the dual of T, then T^* is a continuous linear mapping of N with the topology $\sigma(N, N_*)$ into M with the topology $\sigma(M, M_*)$.

LEMMA 2. T^* satisfies the following conditions:

(1) $T^*(\pi_Q(x)) = Q(x)$ for $x \in A$

(2) $T^*(y^*) = T^*(y)^*$ for $y \in N$

(3) $T^*(h) \geqq 0$ for $h\,(\geqq 0) \in N$

(4) $T^*(uyv) = T^*(u)T^*(y)T^*(v)$

for $u, v \in$ the σ-weak closure of $\pi_Q(B)$ in N and $y \in N$

(5) $T^*(y^*y) \geqq T^*(y)^*T^*(y)$ for $y \in N$.

The proofs of the equalities (1–4) are quite similar with the corresponding proofs in Lemma 4 in [7].

The proof of (5). Let χ be a positive element of M_* and let (a_α) be a bounded directed set of B such that $Q(a_\alpha) \to T^*(y)$ (strongly) in M, then

$$\langle T^*(y)^*T^*(y), \chi\rangle = \lim_\alpha \langle T^*(y)^*Q(a_\alpha), \chi\rangle$$

$$= \lim_\alpha \langle T^*(y^*\pi_Q(a_\alpha)), \chi\rangle$$

$$= \lim_\alpha \langle y^*\pi_Q(a_\alpha), T(\chi)\rangle$$

$$\leqq \limsup_\alpha \langle y^*y, T(\chi)\rangle^{1/2} \langle \pi_Q(a_\alpha^*a_\alpha), T(\chi)\rangle^{1/2}$$

$$= \limsup_\alpha \langle T^*(y^*y), \chi\rangle^{1/2} \langle Q(a_\alpha^*a_\alpha)\ \chi\rangle^{1/2}$$

$$= \langle T^*(y^*y), \chi\rangle^{1/2} \langle T^*(y)^*T^*(y), \chi\rangle^{1/2}.$$

Hence, $T^*(y)^*T^*(y) \leqq T^*(y^*y)$. This completes the proof.

LEMMA 3. N is a factor.

The proof is quite similar with the proof of Lemma 5 in [7].

Now we shall prove Theorem 1.

Proof of Theorem 1. Let $[\pi_Q(B)I_Q]$ be the closed subspace of $\mathfrak{H}_Q$ generated by $\pi_Q(B)I_Q$, where I_Q is the image of I in $\mathfrak{H}_Q$ and E' be the projection of $\mathfrak{H}_Q$ onto $[\pi_Q(B)I_Q]$, then E' belongs to $\pi_Q(B)'$.

$$\varphi_Q(a^*bc) = \varphi(Q^*(abc)) = \varphi(Q(a)^*Q(b)^*Q(c))$$

for $a, b, c \in B$ and $Q(B)$ is σ-weakly dense in M, and so the *-isomorphism $\pi_Q(b)E' \to Q(b)$ of $\pi_Q(B)E'$ into M can be uniquely extended to a *-isomorphism ρ of a W^*-algebra $\{\pi_Q(B)''E'\}$ onto M; therefore $\pi_Q(B)''E'$ and $E'\pi_Q(B)'E'$ are type III-factors. Let F' be the central envelope of E' in $\{\pi_Q(B)\}'$, then F' belongs to $\pi_Q(B)''$. The mapping $\eta{:}xF' \to xE'$ $(x \in \pi_Q(B)'')$ of $\pi_Q(B)''F'$ onto $\pi_Q(B)''E'$ is a *-isomorphism. Therefore, the mapping $\rho\cdot\eta$ of $\pi_Q(B)''F'$ onto M is a *-isomorphism. Now suppose that N is semifinite, then there is a normal semifinite, faithful trace τ on N.

Put $N_0 = \{e \mid \tau(e) < +\infty,\ e \text{ projection in } N\}$. $F' \in \pi_Q(B)''$ and $T^*(F') \neq 0$, because $\langle T^*(F'), \varphi\rangle = \langle F', Q(\varphi)\rangle = (F'I_Q, I_Q)$ and $I_Q \in E'\mathfrak{H}_Q$. Therefore, there is a non-zero $e_0 \in N_0$ such that $e_0 \leqq F'$ and $T^*(e_0) \neq 0$, and so there is a nonzero projection p in M such that $\lambda p \leqq T^*(e_0)$ for some positive number λ.

Suppose that a directed set $(a_\alpha)(\|a_\alpha\| \leqq 1,\ a_\alpha \in pMp)$ converges strongly to 0 in M, then $\{\eta^{-1}\rho^{-1}(a_\alpha)\}$ converges strongly to 0 on $\mathfrak{H}_Q$ and so $\{\eta^{-1}\rho^{-1}(a_\alpha)e_0\}$ converges strongly to 0; by the finiteness of e_0, $\{e_0(\eta^{-1}\rho^{-1}(a_\alpha))^*\}$ converges strongly to 0 (cf. [**5**], [**6**]).

Then,

$$T^*((e_0(\eta^{-1}\rho^{-1}(a_\alpha))^*)^*(e_0(\eta^{-1}\rho^{-1}(a_\alpha))^*))$$
$$\geqq T^*(e_0(\eta^{-1}\rho^{-1}(a_\alpha))^*)^*T^*(e_0(\eta^{-1}\rho^{-1}(a_\alpha))^*) \to 0\ (\sigma\text{-weakly})$$

in M; hence $T^*(e_0(\eta^{-1}\rho^{-1}(a_\alpha))^*)$ converges strongly to 0 in M.

$\eta^{-1}\rho^{-1}(Q(b)) = \eta^{-1}\pi_Q(b)E' = \pi_Q(b)F'$ for $b \in B$ and $\pi_Q(B)$ (resp. $Q(B)$) is σ-weakly dense in $\pi_Q(B)''$ (resp. M).

Let $\{Q(b_\beta)\}$ be a bounded directed set in M such that $b_\beta \in B$ and $Q(b_\beta) \to a$ (σ-weakly) in M for some $a \in M$, then $\eta^{-1}\rho^{-1}(Q(b_\beta)) = \pi_Q(b_\beta)F' \to \eta^{-1}\rho^{-1}(a)$ (σ-weakly) in $\pi_Q(B)''$; $T^*(\eta^{-1}\rho^{-1}(Q(b_\beta)) = T^*(\pi_Q(b_\beta)F') = T^*(\pi_Q(b_\beta))T^*(F') = Q(b_\beta)T^*(F') \to aT^*(F')$ (σ-weakly) in M; hence $aT^*(F') = T^*(\eta^{-1}\rho^{-1}(a))$ for all $a \in M$.

Therefore,

$$\{pT^*(e_0)p + (I-p)\}^{-1}pT^*(e_0(\eta^{-1}\rho^{-1}(a_\alpha))^*)$$
$$= \{pT^*(e_0)p + (I-p)\}^{-1}pT^*(e_0)T^*(\eta^{-1}\rho^{-1}(a_\alpha))^*$$

((because $\eta^{-1}\rho^{-1}(a_\alpha) \in \pi_Q(B)''$, and $T^*(e_0)T^*(F') = T^*(e_0F') = T^*(e_0)$) $= \{pT^*(e_0)p + (I-p)\}^{-1}pT^*(e_0)a_\alpha^* = a_\alpha^* \to 0$ (strongly) in M. Hence, the *-operation is strongly continuous on bounded spheres of pMp, but pMp is of type III. This is a contradiction (cf. [**5**], [**6**]). This completes the proof.

Now we shall show

THEOREM 2. Let A be a C^*-algebra. Then the following conditions are equivalent:

(1) A is G C R

(2) A is of type I

(3) A has no type III-factor *-representation.

Proof. (1) $\Longrightarrow$ (2) is Theorem 6 of Kaplansky [**4**]. (2) $\Longrightarrow$ (3) is clear from the definition of type I. Now we shall show that (3) $\Longrightarrow$ (1).

Suppose that A is not G C R. Let ϑ be the maximum G C R ideal of A ([**4**]), then the quotient algebra A/ϑ has no non-zero G C R ideals.

If we can show that A/ϑ has a type III-factor *-representation, then A has a type III-factor *-representation. Therefore we can assume that $\vartheta = (0)$, and moreover A has the unit I.

Then by the results of Glimm (Lemmas 4 and 5 and the proof of (b1) $\Longrightarrow$ (b2); (b1) $\Longrightarrow$ (b3) of Theorem 1 in [**3**]), A contains a non-type I separable C^*-subalgebra B.

Then by the results of Glimm (pp. 588–589 in [**3**]) and Schwartz [**9**], B has a type III-factor *-representation $\{\pi, \mathfrak{H}\}$ on a separable Hilbert space $\mathfrak{H}$ such that $\pi(B)'$ has the property P in the sense of Schwartz [**8**] and so there is a linear mapping R of the C^*-algebras $B(\mathfrak{H})$ of all bounded operators on $\mathfrak{H}$ onto $\pi(B)''$ satisfying the conditions (1) $R(x^*) = R(x)^*$ for $x \in B(\mathfrak{H})$, (2) $R(h) \geqq 0$ for $h(\geqq 0) \in B(\mathfrak{H})$, (3) $R(axb) = aR(x)b$ for $a,b \in \pi(B)''$ and $x \in B(\mathfrak{H})$.

Now let ξ ($\|\xi\| = 1$) be a separating and generating vector of $\pi(B)''$ in $\mathfrak{H}$ (cf. (2)) and put $\chi_1(a) = (\pi(a)\xi\cdot\xi)$ for $a \in B$.

Let χ be an extended state of χ_1 on A and let $\{\pi_\chi, \mathfrak{H}_\chi\}$ be the *-representation of A constructed via χ.

Let $[\pi_\chi(B)I_\chi]$ be the closed subspace of $\mathfrak{H}_\chi$ generated by $\pi_\chi(B)I_\chi$ and E' be the projection of $\mathfrak{H}_\chi$ onto $[\pi_\chi(B)I_\chi]$, then the representation $b \to \pi(b)$ of B can be identified with the representation $b \to \pi_\chi(b)E'$ of B.

Then, R is a linear mapping of the C^*-algebra $B(E'\mathfrak{H}_\chi)$ all bounded operators on the Hilbert space $E'\mathfrak{H}_\chi$ onto $\pi_\chi(B)''E'$.

Now we shall define a linear mapping P of $\pi_\chi(A)$ into the type III-factor $\pi_\chi(B)''E'$ as follows:

$$P(\pi_\chi(A)) = R(E'\pi_\chi(A)E') \quad \text{for } x \in A.$$

Then

$$P(\pi_\chi(x)^*) = P(\pi_\chi(x))^* \text{ for } \pi_\chi(x) \in \pi_\chi(A)$$

$$P(\pi_\chi(h)) \geqq 0 \text{ for } \pi_\chi(h)\,(\geqq 0) \in \pi_\chi(A).$$

$$P(\pi_\chi(a)\pi_\chi(x)\pi_\chi(b)) = R(E'\pi_\chi(a)\pi_\chi(x)\pi_\chi(b)E') = E$$

$$= R(\pi_\chi(a)E'E'\pi_\chi(x)E'\pi_\chi(b)E')$$

$$= R(E'\pi_\chi(a)E')R(E'\pi_\chi(x)E')R(E'\pi_\chi(b)E')$$

$$= P(\pi_\chi(a))\,P(\pi_\chi(x))\,P(\pi_\chi(b))$$

for $a,b \in B$ and $x \in A$. $P(\pi_\chi(B)) = \pi_\chi(B)E'$ is σ-dense in $\pi_\chi(B)''E$,

Therefore P satisfies the conditions of Theorems 1.

Hence, the C^*-algebra $\pi_\chi(A)$, and so the C^*-algebra A, has a type III-factor *-representation.

This completes the proof.

REFERENCES

1. Calkin, J. W., Two sided ideals and congruences in the ring of bounded operators in Hilbert space, *Ann. Math.*, v. 42(1941), pp. 839–873.
2. Dixmier, J., Les algebres d'operateurs dans l'espace hilbertien, Gauthier-Villars, Paris, 1957.
3. Glimm, J., Type I C^*-algebras, *Ann. Math.*, v. 73(1961), pp. 572–612.
4. Kaplansky, I., The structure of certain operator algebras, *Trans. Amer. Math. Soc.*, 70(1951), pp. 219–255.
5. Sakai, S., On topological properties of W^*-algebras, *Proc. Japan Acad.*, 33(1957), pp. 439–444.
6. ———, The theory of W^*-algebras, Lecture note, Yale University, 1962.
7. ———, On a problem of Calkin, to appear.
8. Schwartz, J., Two finite, nonhyper-finite, non-isomorphic factors, *Comm. Pure Appl. Math.*, 16(1963), pp. 19–26.
9. Schwartz, J., Nonisomorphism of a pair of factors type III, *Comm. Pure Appl. Math.*, 16(1963), pp. 111–120.

III

BANACH ALGEBRAS

Extensions of Interpolation Sets

by
WILLIAM G. BADE

INTRODUCTION

Let Ω be a compact Hausdorff space and Q be a closed set in Ω. A linear subspace X (not necessarily closed) of $C(\Omega)$ is said to *interpolate* $C(Q)$ if $X \mid Q = C(Q)$. More briefly, we call Q an *interpolation set for* X. In this paper we investigate a class of theorems which state for appropriate Ω, Q and X that if X interpolates $C(Q)$, or even comes close to doing so, then X interpolates $C(V)$ for some closed neighborhood V of Q.

Two examples will illustrate the sort of theorems we prove. Let $m(N)$ be the space of all bounded complex sequences identified with $C(\beta(N))$, where $\beta(N)$ is the Stone-Cech compactification of the set N of positive integers. Let Q be the closed set $\beta(N) \sim N$. Note that any closed neighborhood of $\beta(N) \sim N$ has the form $V = \beta(N) \sim F$, where F is a finite set of integers, and $C(\beta(N) \sim F) = m(N \sim F)$.

THEOREM A. Let X be a closed linear subspace of $m(N)$ such that $X \mid \beta(N) \sim N = C(\beta(N) \sim N)$. Then there exists a finite set F of integers such that $X \mid \beta(N) \sim F = m(N \sim F)$. Moreover, X has finite codimension in $m(N)$.

THEOREM B. Let A be a subalgebra of $m(N)$ containing the constants which is a Banach algebra under some norm. If $A \mid \beta(N) \sim N$ is dense in $C(\beta(N) \sim N)$, then there exists a finite set F of integers such that $A \mid \beta(N) \sim F = m(N \sim F)$. Moreover A is sup norm closed, self-adjoint, and has finite codimension in $m(N)$.

Despite the similarity in the statements of Theorems A and B they have very different proofs. They both have generalizations in three different directions, which reflect different ways of looking at $\beta(N)$. In Section 1 we suppose Ω is a locally compact and σ-compact Hausdorff

This research was supported by the Miller Institute for Basic Research in Science, and by the National Science Foundation under Grant GP-5138.

space. It is shown that if a closed linear subspace X of $C(\beta(\Omega))$, the bounded continuous functions on Ω, satisfies $X \mid \beta(\Omega) \sim \Omega = C(\beta(\Omega) \sim \Omega)$ then there is a closed neighborhood V of $\beta(\Omega) \sim \Omega$ such that $X \mid V = C(V)$. A similar analogue of Theorem B is proved by Banach subalgebras of $C(\beta(\Omega))$. In Section 2 we prove Theorems A and B with N replaced by any discrete set. In the final section the theorems generalize the role of $\beta(N) \sim N$ as a closed G_δ set in the extremely disconnected space $\beta(N)$. We obtain analogues of the theorems of Section 1 when Q is any closed G_δ set in a compact space which is an F-space in the sense of Gillman and Henriksen. (The defining condition for an F-space is that disjoint open F_σ sets shall have disjoint closures. These spaces are discussed in [**6**], Chapter 14.) In each section various weaker results are obtained under weaker hypotheses.

Our theorems for closed subspaces X have application to show that certain subspaces of continuous functions are not complemented. Clearly Theorem A implies the result of Phillips [**18**] that $c_0(N)$ is not complemented in $m(N)$, since any complement X to $c_0(N)$ would have to have finite codimension in $m(N)$. We prove in Section 3 that if Q is a closed G_δ set in a compact F-space, the subspace $Z(Q)$ of functions vanishing on Q is uncomplemented unless Q is open as well as closed.

Throughout this paper we shall rely heavily on results in a recent paper [**1**] with P. C. Curtis Jr. The method of proof of Theorem B and its generalizations is an extension of the methods of that paper. The proofs of theorems of the type of Theorem A depend on properties of convergent sequences of measures.

THE BOUNDED CONTINUOUS FUNCTIONS ON A LOCALLY COMPACT SPACE

In this section Ω is a locally compact and σ-compact Hausdorff space, and $\beta(\Omega)$ denotes its Stone-Cech compactification. It follows that Ω is normal ([**6**], page 49) and that $\beta(\Omega) \sim \Omega$ is a closed G_δ set in $\beta(\Omega)$. In its relative topology $\beta(\Omega) \sim \Omega$ is a compact F-space ([**6**], page 210). We denote points of either Ω or $\beta(\Omega) \sim \Omega$ by ω. Note that open neighborhoods of $\beta(\Omega) \sim \Omega$ in $\beta(\Omega)$ have the form $\beta(\Omega) \sim F$, where F is a compact set in Ω.

For any compact Hausdorff space Φ and closed linear subspace X of $C(\Phi)$ the closed sets Q of Φ that are interpolation sets for X are characterized by the following important result of Glicksberg [7] (see also [**5**]): One has $X \mid Q = C(Q)$ if and only if there exists a constant t, $0 < t \leq 1$, such that

$$|\mu|(\Phi \sim Q) \geq t \|\mu\|$$

for all measures μ in $X^\perp$. Here $|\mu|(E)$ denotes the total variation of μ on E and $\|\mu\| = |\mu|(\Phi)$. This characterization is basic to our first theorem.

1.1 THEOREM. Let Ω be locally compact and σ-compact. Let X be a closed linear subspace of $C(\beta(\Omega))$ such that

$$X \mid \beta(\Omega) \sim \Omega = C(\beta(\Omega) \sim \Omega).$$

Then there exists a closed neighborhood V of $\beta(\Omega) \sim \Omega$ in $\beta(\Omega)$ such that $X \mid V = C(V)$.

Proof. Write $Q = \beta(\Omega) \sim \Omega$. Then we can find open sets W_n in $\beta(\Omega)$ such that $Q = \bigcap W_n$, $\overline{W}_{n+1} \subseteq W_n$. Moreover, since $X \mid Q = C(Q)$, there exists t, $0 < t \leq 1$ such that

$$|\mu|(\Omega) = |\mu|(Q') \geq t\|\mu\|, \quad \mu \in X^\perp.$$

Suppose the theorem is false. Then if V is any closed neighborhood of Q, we have $X \mid V \neq C(V)$. Hence by Glicksberg's theorem again, for each $\epsilon > 0$ there exists $\mu \in X^\perp$, $\|\mu\| = 1$, with

$$|\mu|(V') < \epsilon.$$

Set $V_0 = \beta(\Omega)$, let V_1 be any closed neighborhood of Q with $V_1 \subseteq W_1$, and choose $\mu_1 \in X^\perp$, $\|\mu_1\| = 1$ such that

$$|\mu_1|(V_1') < \frac{t}{2}.$$

Then

$$|\mu_1|(V_1 \sim Q) = |\mu_1|(Q') - |\mu_1|(V_1') > t - \frac{t}{2} = \frac{t}{2}.$$

Pick a closed neighborhood V_2 of Q, $V_2 \subseteq W_2 \cap \operatorname{int}(V_1)$, such that

$$|\mu_1|(V_2 \sim Q) < \frac{t}{2^2}.$$

Hence

$$|\mu_1|(V_1 \sim V_2) = |\mu_1|(V_1 \sim Q) - |\mu_1|(V_2 \sim Q) > \frac{t}{2} - \frac{t}{4} = \frac{t}{4}.$$

Select $\mu_2 \in X^\perp$, $\|\mu_2\| = 1$, such that

$$|\mu_2|(V_2') < \frac{t}{2^2}.$$

Continuing inductively, construct sequences $\{\mu_n\}$, $\{V_n\}$ such that $\mu_n \in X^\perp$, $\|\mu_n\| = 1$, V_n is a closed neighborhood of Q with

$$V_{n+1} \subseteq W_{n+1} \cap \operatorname{int}(V_n),$$

$$|\mu_n|(V_n') < \frac{t}{2^n},$$

$$|\mu_n|(V_n \sim V_{n+1}) > \frac{t}{4}.$$

Now choose K_n compact, $K_n \subseteq V_n \sim V_{n+1}$ such that

$$|\mu_n(K_n)| > \frac{t}{16}, \quad n = 1, 2, \cdots,$$

and let U_n be disjoint open sets such that

$$K_n \subseteq U_n, \quad U_n \subseteq V_{n-1} \sim V_{n+1}, \quad n = 1, 2, \cdots,$$

$$|\mu_n|(U_n \sim K_n) < \frac{t}{32}.$$

Select $y_n \in C_0(\Omega)$ with $0 \leq y_n \leq 1$,

$$y_n(K_n) = 1, \quad y_n(U_n') = 0.$$

We now use the y_n to define a subspace W of $C(\beta(\Omega))$ isometric to $m(N)$. If $\{\alpha_n\}$ is a bounded complex sequence, define the bounded continuous function z on Ω by

$$z(\omega) = \alpha_n y_n(\omega), \quad \omega \in U_n$$

$$z(\omega) = 0, \quad \omega \in \Omega \sim \bigcup_{n=1}^{\infty} U_n.$$

Then z has a unique continuous extension w defined on $\beta(\Omega)$. The map T: $\{\alpha_n\} \to w$ is linear and isometric. Let W be the range of T.

Let $f \in W$. Since $X \mid Q = C(Q)$, we may write $f = g + h$ where g vanishes at infinity on Ω and $h \in X$. Thus

$$\left| \int_{\beta(\Omega)} f(\omega)\mu_n(d\omega) \right| = \left| \int_{\Omega} g(\omega)\mu_n(d\omega) \right|$$

$$\leq \left| \int_{V_n'} g(\omega)\mu_n(d\omega) \right| + \left| \int_{V_n \sim Q} g(\omega)\mu_n(d\omega) \right|$$

$$\leq \|g\|_\infty |\mu_n|(V_n') + \sup_{\omega \in V_n \sim Q} |g(\omega)|$$

$$\leq \frac{t\|g\|_\infty}{2^n} + \sup_{\omega \in W_n} |g(\omega)| \to 0.$$

It follows from the Lemma of Phillips ([**18**], page 525, or [**3**], page 32) that

$$\lim_{n\to\infty} \mu_n(y_n) = 0$$

However,

$$\begin{aligned} |\mu_n(y_n)| &\geq |\mu_n(K_n)| - |\mu_n(y_n) - \mu_n(K_n)| \\ &\geq |\mu_n(K_n)| - |\mu_n|(U_n \sim K_n) \\ &> \frac{t}{32}, \quad n = 1, 2, \ldots. \end{aligned}$$

This contradiction completes the proof.

1.2 COROLLARY. Let Ω be locally compact and σ-compact. The subspace $C_0(\Omega)$ of functions vanishing at infinity on Ω is not complemented in $C(\beta(\Omega))$.

Proof. Let X be a closed subspace complementary to $C_0(\Omega)$. Then $X \mid \beta(\Omega) \sim \Omega = C(\beta(\Omega) \sim \Omega)$. By Theorem 1.1 there exists a closed neighborhood V of $\beta(\Omega) \sim \Omega$ such that $X \mid V = C(V)$. However, then X must contain nonzero functions which vanish on $\beta(\Omega) \sim \Omega$, i.e. elements of $C_0(\Omega)$.

This corollary also follows from of an important result of J. B. Conway [**2**]. He proves that if Ω is locally compact and $C_0(\Omega)$ is complemented in $C(\beta(\Omega))$, then Ω must be pseudocompact.

For the next theorem we need the following elementary lemmas.

1.3 LEMMA. Let $\{V_n\}$ be a sequence of open sets in Ω with

$$\overline{V}_{n+1} \subseteq V_n, \quad n = 1, 2, \ldots; \qquad \bigcap_{n=1}^{\infty} V_n = \phi.$$

Let $\{K_n\}$ be a sequence of closed sets with $K_n \subseteq V_n$. Then $\bigcup_{n=1}^{\infty} K_n$ is closed.

1.4 LEMMA. Let $\{H_n\}$ be a sequence of G_δ sets in Ω, and let $\{U_n\}$ be open sets such that

$$U_m \cap U_n = \phi, \quad m \neq n; \qquad H_n \subseteq U_n, \quad n = 1, 2, \ldots.$$

Then $\bigcup_{n=1}^{\infty} H_n$ is a G_δ set.

The next lemma is the main tool of the proof.

1.5. LEMMA. Let $\omega_0 \in \beta(\Omega) \sim \Omega$ and let ν be a function defined on ordered pairs $[F_1, F_2]$ of disjoint compact subsets of $\beta(\Omega) \sim \{\omega_0\}$, with values in $[0, \infty)$. Suppose ν is monotone, i.e.

$$\nu(E_1, E_2) \leq \nu(F_1, F_2) \quad \text{if} \quad E_1 \subseteq F_1, E_2 \subseteq F_2.$$

Then there exists an open neighborhood W of ω_0 in $\beta(\Omega)$ such that

$$\sup \nu(F_1, F_2) < \infty$$

for all pairs F_1, F_2 of disjoint compact subsets of $W \sim \{\omega_0\}$.

Proof. Let $\{G_n\}$ be a sequence of open sets in $\beta(\Omega)$ such that $G_n \supseteq \overline{G}_{n+1}$, and $\bigcap_{n=1}^{\infty} G_n = \beta(\Omega) \sim \Omega$. Suppose the lemma is false and let W_1 be any open neighborhood of ω_0 in $\beta(\Omega)$ with $\overline{W}_1 \subseteq G_1$. There exist disjoint compact sets F_{11}, $F_{12} \subseteq W_1 \sim \{\omega_0\}$ for which $\nu(F_{11}, F_{12}) \geq 1$. Let W_2 be an open neighborhood of ω_0 such that

$$\overline{W}_2 \subseteq G_2 \cap [W_1 \sim (F_{11} \cup F_{12})].$$

There exist disjoint compact sets $F_{21}, F_{22} \subseteq W_2 \sim \{\omega_0\}$ for which $\nu(F_{21}, F_{22}) \geq 2$. Continuing inductively, we construct sequences $\{W_k\}$ of open sets and $\{F_{k1}, F_{k2}\}$ of disjoint compact sets such that

$$\omega_0 \in W_k; \qquad F_{k1}, F_{k2} \subseteq W_k \sim \{\omega_0\}$$

$$\overline{W}_{k+1} \subseteq G_{k+1} \cap \left[W_k \sim \bigcup_{i=1}^{k} (F_{i1} \cup F_{i2}) \right]$$

$$\nu(F_{k1}, F_{k2}) \geq k.$$

To obtain the necessary contradiction we are going to construct a pair R_1, R_2 of disjoint compact sets in $\beta(\Omega) \sim \{\omega_0\}$ for which $\nu(R_1, R_2) \geq k$, $k = 1, 2, \ldots$. The sets will have the form

$$R_1 = \overline{\bigcup_{j=1}^{\infty} F_{k_j 1}}, \quad R_2 = \overline{\bigcup_{j=1}^{\infty} F_{k_j 2}}$$

for an appropriate subsequence $\{k_j\}$.

Select open sets B_{ki}, compact G_δ sets C_{ki} and open sets D_{ki} in $\beta(\Omega)$ such that

$$F_{ki} \subseteq B_{ki} \subseteq C_{ki} \subseteq D_{ki} \subseteq W_k \sim \overline{W}_{k+1}, k = 1, 2, \ldots, \quad i = 1, 2.$$

$$D_{k1} \cap D_{k2} = \phi, \quad k = 1, 2, \ldots.$$

Thus the open sets D_{ki} are all disjoint, $k = 1, 2, \ldots, i = 1, 2$.

Define

$$K_{ki} = C_{ki} \cap \Omega.$$

Then K_{ki} is a closed G_δ set in Ω. Moreover,

$$K_{ki} \subseteq D_{ki} \cap \Omega \subseteq W_k \cap \Omega \subseteq G_k \cap \Omega.$$

Since $\bigcap_{k=1}^{\infty} (G_k \cap \Omega) = \phi$, it follows from Lemmas 1.2 and 1.3 that $\bigcup_{k=1}^{\infty} K_{k1}$ and $\bigcup_{k=1}^{\infty} K_{k2}$ are disjoint closed G_δ sets in Ω. Since Ω is normal, these sets are zero sets of continuous functions on Ω, and hence

$$\overline{\bigcup_{k=1}^{\infty} K_{k1}} \cap \overline{\bigcup_{k=1}^{\infty} K_{k2}} = \phi,$$

where the closure is in $\beta(\Omega)$ (cf. [**6**] pages 49 and 86). We note that if B is open in $\beta(\Omega)$ then $\overline{B \cap \Omega} = \overline{B}$. Thus

$$\overline{\bigcup_{k=1}^{\infty} F_{ki}} \subseteq \overline{\bigcup_{k=1}^{\infty} B_{ki}} = \overline{\bigcup_{k=1}^{\infty} (B_{ki} \cap \Omega)}$$

$$\subseteq \overline{\bigcup_{k=1}^{\infty} (C_{ki} \cap \Omega)} = \overline{\bigcup_{k=1}^{\infty} K_{ki}}, \quad i = 1, 2.$$

Thus writing $M_i = \bigcup_{k=1}^{\infty} F_{ki}$, $i = 1,2$ we have $\overline{M_1} \cap \overline{M_2} = \phi$. The point ω_0 can belong to at most one of $\overline{M_1}$ and $\overline{M_2}$. Suppose $\omega_0 \in \overline{M_1}$. Write

$$N_1 = \bigcup_{k=1}^{\infty} F_{(2k)1}, \quad N_2 = \bigcup_{k=1}^{\infty} F_{(2k+1)1}.$$

Exactly the same argument shows $\overline{N_1} \cap \overline{N_2} = \phi$. Thus there exists a subsequence $\{k_j\}$ such that

$$R_1 = \overline{\bigcup_{j=1}^{\infty} F_{k_j1}}, \qquad R_2 = \overline{\bigcup_{j=1}^{\infty} F_{k_j2}}$$

are disjoint compact sets in $\beta(\Omega) \sim \{\omega_0\}$. Since ν is monotone, $\nu(R_1, R_2) \geq k$, $k = 1, 2, \ldots$.

1.6 LEMMA. Let Ω be a locally compact and σ-compact Hausdorff space and let X be a linear subspace of $C(\beta(\Omega))$ which is a Banach space under a norm $\|\cdot\|$ such that the natural imbedding of X into $C(\beta(\Omega))$ is continuous. Let $\omega_0 \in \beta(\Omega) \sim \Omega$, and suppose there exists a closed neighborhood V of ω_0 in $\beta(\Omega)$ such that

$$X \mid V \cap (\beta(\Omega) \sim \Omega) = C(V \cap (\beta(\Omega) \sim \Omega)).$$

Then there exists a closed neighborhood U of ω_0 in $\beta(\Omega)$ such that

$$X \mid U = C(U).$$

Proof. Since V contains a closed neighborhood of ω_0 which is a G_δ, we may assume without loss of generality that V is a compact G_δ. Hence

$V \cap Q$ is a compact G_δ, since $Q = \beta(\Omega) \sim \Omega$ is a G_δ in $\beta(\Omega)$. Let $\{S_n\}$ be a sequence of open sets in $\beta(\Omega)$ such that

$$S_n \supseteq \overline{S}_{n+1}, \qquad V \cap Q = \bigcap_{n=1}^{\infty} S_n.$$

We now define an integer-valued function ν of pairs of disjoint compact sets in $\beta(\Omega) \sim \{\omega_0\}$ as follows: By the closed graph theorem there exists a constant M such that if $f \in C(\beta(\Omega))$, there exists $x \in X$ with

$$x(\omega) = f(\omega), \quad \omega \in V \cap Q$$

$$\|x\| \leq M \sup_{\omega \in V \cap Q} |f(\omega)|.$$

Let F_1, F_2 be disjoint compact sets in $\beta(\Omega) \sim \{\omega_0\}$. We can find an $f \in C(\beta(\Omega))$ satisfying

$$f(F_1) = 1, \quad f(F_2) = 0, \quad f(\omega_0) = 0, \quad \|f\|_\infty = 1. \tag{1}$$

There will be an $x \in X$ and an integer n such that

$$\text{(2)} \qquad \begin{cases} |f(\omega) - x(\omega)| \leq \dfrac{1}{8}, & \omega \in S_n, \\ x(\omega_0) = 0, & \|x\| \leq M. \end{cases}$$

Define $\nu(F_1, F_2)$ to be the smallest integer n obtained for all choices of $f \in C(\beta(\Omega))$ satisfying (1) and $x \in X$ satisfying (2). It is clear that ν is monotone. Thus by Lemma 1.5 there exists an integer k_0 and an open neighborhood W of ω_0 in $\beta(\Omega)$ such that

$$\nu(F_1, F_2) \leq k_0$$

for all pairs F_1, F_2 of disjoint compact sets contained in $W \sim \{\omega_0\}$. Let U be a compact neighborhood of ω_0 in $\beta(\Omega)$ such that

$$U \subseteq S_{k_0} \cap W.$$

It follows that if F_1, F_2 are disjoint compact sets in $U \sim \{\omega_0\}$, there is an $x \in X$ with

$$\|x\| \leq M, \quad x(\omega_0) = 0$$

$$|x(F_1) - 1| \leq \frac{1}{8}, \quad |x(F_2)| \leq \frac{1}{8}.$$

Let $X_0 = \{x \in X \mid x(\omega_0) = 0\}$. Theorem 1.5 of [1] shows that

$$X_0 \mid U \sim \{\omega_0\} = \{f \in C(U) \mid f(\omega_0) = 0\}.$$

Since X contains a function not vanishing at ω_0, $X \mid U = C(U)$.

1.7 THEOREM. Let Ω be locally compact and σ-compact and let X be a subspace of $C(\beta(\Omega))$ which is a Banach space under a norm such that the natural imbedding of X into $C(\beta(\Omega))$ is continuous. Suppose $X \mid \beta(\Omega) \sim \Omega$ is dense in $C(\beta(\Omega) \sim \Omega)$. Then there exists a finite covering $U_1, \ldots, U_n$ of $\beta(\Omega) \sim \Omega$ by open sets in $\beta(\Omega)$ such that

$$X \mid \overline{U}_i = C(\overline{U}_i), \quad i = 1, \ldots, n.$$

Proof. By [**1**], Theorem 3.2, there is a finite covering $W_1, \ldots, W_m$ of $Q = \beta(\Omega) \sim \Omega$ by open sets such that

$$X \mid \overline{W}_i \cap Q = C(\overline{W}_i \cap Q), \quad i = 1, \ldots, m.$$

By Lemma 1.6 and compactness we get the required cover $U_1, \ldots, U_n$.

We next consider the case of a Banach subalgebra of $C(\beta(\Omega))$. The added algebraic structure leads to a much stronger result.

1.8 THEOREM. Let Ω be locally compact and σ-compact. Let A be a subalgebra of $C(\beta(\Omega))$ which contains the constants and is a Banach algebra under some norm. Suppose $A \mid \beta(\Omega) \sim \Omega$ is dense in $C(\beta(\Omega) \sim \Omega)$. Then there exists a closed neighborhood V of $\beta(\Omega) \sim \Omega$ in $\beta(\Omega)$ such that $A \mid V = C(V)$.

Proof. Since $\beta(\Omega) \sim \Omega$ is an F-space, we know from [**1**], Theorem 3.3, that $A \mid Q = C(Q)$, $Q = \beta(\Omega) \sim \Omega$. Since the natural imbedding of A into $C(\beta(\Omega))$ is continuous, by Theorem 1.7 there exists a covering $U_1, \ldots, U_n$ of Q by open sets such that

$$A \mid \overline{U}_i = C(\overline{U}_i), \quad i = 1, \ldots, n.$$

Let$K \geq 1$ be a constant such that for $i = 1, \ldots, n$, if $f \in C(\overline{U}_i)$ there exists an $x \in A$ with

$$x(\omega) = f(\omega), \quad \omega \in \overline{U}_i; \qquad \|x\| \leq K \sup_{\omega \in U_i} |f(\omega)|.$$

Let $H_i = Q \cap U_i, i = 1, \ldots, n$, and let $x_1, \ldots, x_n$ be elements of A which on Q form a partition of unity subordinate to the covering $H_1, \ldots, H_n$.

Choose $\epsilon < (6Kn)^{-1}$. Since $x_i(\omega) = 0$ for $\omega \in Q \sim H_i = Q \sim U_i$, we can find a closed neighborhood V of Q such that

$$Q \subseteq V \subseteq \bigcup_{i=1}^{n} U_i,$$

$$|x_i(\omega)| < \epsilon, \omega \in V \sim U_i, i = 1, \ldots, n,$$

$$\left| 1 - \sum_{i=1}^{n} x_i(\omega) \right| < \epsilon, \omega \in V.$$

Let $f \in C(V)$ with $\|f\|_\infty = 1$. There exist $y_1, \ldots, y_n \in A$ such that

$$y_i(\omega) = f(\omega), \quad \omega \in V \cap \overline{U}_i, \quad \|y_i\| \le K.$$

Consider $z = \Sigma_{i=1}^n x_i y_i$. Then $z \in A$. If $\omega \in V$ then

$$\begin{aligned} |z(\omega) - f(\omega)| &= \left|\sum_{i=1}^n x_i(\omega) y_i(\omega) - f(\omega)\right| \\ &\le \left|\sum_{i=1}^n x_i(\omega)[y_i(\omega) - f(\omega)]\right| \\ &\quad + \left|f(\omega)\left[\sum_{i=1}^n x_i(\omega) - 1\right]\right| \\ &\le \left|\sum_{i=1}^n x_i(\omega)[y_i(\omega) - f(\omega)]\right| + \epsilon \end{aligned}$$

The point ω will belong to some of the sets $\overline{U}_i$ but not to others. Suppose they have been renumbered so $\omega \in \overline{U}_1, \ldots, \overline{U}_k$ but $\omega \notin \overline{U}_{k+1}, \ldots, \overline{U}_n$. Then

$$\begin{aligned} \left|\sum_{i=1}^n x_i(\omega)[y_i(\omega) - f(\omega)]\right| &= \left|\sum_{i=k+1}^n x_i(\omega)[y_i(\omega) - f(\omega)]\right| \\ &\le (K+1) \sum_{i=k+1}^n |x_i(\omega)| \le 2Kn\epsilon. \end{aligned}$$

Thus

$$\|z - f\|_\infty \le 3Kn\epsilon \le \frac{1}{2}$$

while

$$\|z\| \le nK \max \|x_i\|.$$

It follows from [**1**], Theorem 1.2, that $A \mid V = C(V)$.

1.9 COROLLARY. Let A be a subalgebra of $C(\beta(\Omega))$ which is normal on Ω. If A is a Banach algebra under some norm, then there exists a closed neighborhood V of $\beta(\Omega) \sim \Omega$ such that $A \mid V = C(V)$.

Proof. Clearly $A \mid \beta(\Omega) \sim \Omega$ is normal on $\beta(\Omega) \sim \Omega$. Since $\beta(\Omega) - \Omega$ is a compact F-space, $A \mid \beta(\Omega) \sim \Omega = C(\beta(\Omega) \sim \Omega)$ ([**1**], Theorem 3.3), so Theorem 1.8 applies.

2. THE BOUNDED FUNCTIONS ON A DISCRETE SET

Let S be any discrete set and $m(S)$ denote the bounded complex functions on S. We may identify $m(S)$ with $C(\beta(S))$. The compact set $\beta(S) \sim S$ will be a G_δ if and only if S is countable. None the less we can prove analogues of the results of Section 1 for arbitrary S by suitably modifying the arguments. Here the feature that replaces the G_δ requirement in the proofs is the property that a neighborhood of $\beta(S) \sim S$ is the complement in $\beta(S)$ of a finite set in S.

2.1 THEOREM. Let S be any set and let X be a closed linear subspace of $m(S)$ such that

$$X \mid \beta(S) \sim S = C(\beta(S) \sim S).$$

Then X has finite codimension in $m(S)$. There exists a finite set $F \subseteq S$ such that

$$X \mid S \sim F = m(S \sim F).$$

Proof. Suppose X has infinite codimension. Then for any finite set $F \subseteq S$ we can find a nonzero measure $\mu \in X^\perp$ such that $|\mu|(F) = 0$. Construct inductively sequences $\{F_n\}$ of disjoint finite subsets of S and $\{\mu_n\}$ of measures in $X^\perp$ such that $\|\mu_n\| = 1$ and

$$|\mu_n|\left(\bigcup_{i=1}^{n-1} F_i\right) = 0, \quad |\mu_n|(S \sim F_n) < \frac{1}{2^n}, \quad n = 1, 2, \ldots.$$

If $f \in m(S)$ then we can find $g \in c_0(S)$ and $h \in X$ such that $f = g + h$. Hence

$$\mu_n(f) = \mu_n(g) = \int_{F_n} g\,d\mu_n + \int_{S \sim F_n} g\,d\mu_n,$$

so

$$|\mu_n(f)| \le \sup_{F_n} |g(s)| + \frac{\|g\|_\infty}{2^n} \to 0, \quad f \in m(S).$$

Thus $\mu_n \to 0$ weak star in $m(S)^*$. Hence by a theorem of Grothendieck [**8**], page 168, $\mu_n \to 0$ weakly. Writing $\nu_n = \mu_n \mid S$, we see $\nu_n \to 0$ weakly in $\ell_1(S)$. Hence $\|\nu_n\|_1 \to 0$ ([**4**], page 295). However by Glicksberg's theorem there exists t, $0 < t \le 1$, such that

$$\|\nu_n\| = |\mu_n|(S) \ge t, \quad n = 1, 2, \ldots.$$

This contradiction shows X has finite codimension.

Let $y_1, \ldots, y_n$ span a finite-dimensional subspace Y of $m(S)$ complementary to X. We can find $x_1, \ldots, x_n$ in X such that $y_i(s) = x_i(s)$, $s \in \beta(S) \sim S$, $i = 1, \ldots, n$. Let $z_i = y_i - x_i$. Then the z_i are linearly independent elements of $c_0(S)$. Let F be a finite set in S such that $v_i = z_i \cdot k_F$ are linearly independent and such that the subspace V they span does not meet X. Then V is a complement to X and $X \mid S \sim F = m(S \sim F)$.

2.2 COROLLARY. No infinite dimensional closed linear subspace of $c_0(S)$ is complemented in $m(S)$.

Proof. Let Y be a subspace of $c_0(S)$ with complement X in m(S). Since $X \mid \beta(X) \sim S = C(\beta(S) \sim S)$, X has finite codimension.

It is known from the theorem of Conway [**2**] and the work of Pelczynski and Sudakov [**17**] that $c_0(S)$ is not complemented in $m(S)$. Corollary 2.2 sharpens this theorem. It is known when S is countable that no separable subspace of $m(S)$ is complemented in $m(S)$ ([**8**], page 169). There are further theorems in the paper of Pelczynski and Sudakov which we cannot obtain by our methods. For example, they prove for uncountable S that the subspace of functions that vanish except on countable sets is not complemented in $m(S)$.

By using results of [**1**] we are able to give a short proof of the following analogue of Theorem 1.8. Again the result is much stronger, as we are able to characterize all Banach subalgebras A of $m(S)$ for which $A \mid \beta(S) \sim S$ is dense in $C(\beta(S) \sim S)$.

2.3 THEOREM. Let A be a subalgebra of $m(S)$, containing the constants, which is a Banach algebra under some norm. Suppose $A \mid \beta(S) \sim S$ is dense in $C(\beta(S) \sim S)$. Then A is closed in $m(S)$, self adjoint, and has finite codimension. There exists a finite set $K_0 \subseteq \beta(S)$ and a partition $K_0 = \bigcup_{i=1}^{m} K_i$ of K_0 such that

$$A = \{f \in m(S) \mid f \text{ is constant on each } K_i\}.$$

Moreover, each K_i contains at most one point of $\beta(S) \sim S$, and we have

$$A \mid S \sim K_0 = m(S \sim K_0).$$

Proof. By [**1**], Theorem 3.3, $A \mid \beta(S) \sim S = C(\beta(S) \sim S)$. Applying Theorem 2.1 to the uniform closure B of A in $m(S)$, we get a finite set $F \subseteq S$ such that

$$B \mid \beta(S) \sim F = C(\beta(S) \sim F).$$

Since $A \mid \beta(S) \sim F$ is dense in $B \mid \beta(S) \sim F$, Theorem 3.3 of [**1**] shows

$$A \mid \beta(S) \sim F = C(\beta(S) \sim F).$$

It follows easily that A is closed in $m(S)$ and has finite codimension.

The remaining statements follow from the next lemma, whose brief proof is due to Donald Sarason.

2.4 LEMMA. Let Ω be a compact Hausdorff space and let A be a closed subalgebra of $C(\Omega)$ containing the constants and having finite codimension. Then there exists a finite set $K_0 \subseteq \Omega$ and a partition $K_0 = \bigcup_{i=1}^m K_i$ such that each K_i contains at least two points and

$$A = \{f \in C(\Omega) \mid f \text{ is constant on each } K_i\}.$$

Proof. We show each measure in $A^\perp$ has finite support. If $\nu \in A^\perp$ let J_ν be the ideal of all functions in $C(\Omega)$ which vanish on the support of ν. Then $J_\nu \cap A$ is the kernel of the map of A into $A^\perp$ which sends f into $fd\nu$. Since $\dim A^\perp < \infty$, $J_\nu \cap A$ has finite codimension in A, so J_ν has finite codimension in $C(\Omega)$. Hence J_ν consists of all functions vanishing on a finite set.

The union K of all supports of measures in $A^\perp$ is finite, and we need only establish the conclusion of the lemma for the finite dimensional algebra $A \mid K$. However, this is easily done.

We next prove an analogue of the "local" result (Theorem 1.7) for Banach subspaces. To prove it we shall need a form of Lemma 2.5. We shall prove this lemma as a statement about F-spaces so as to be able to use it also in the next section.

2.5 LEMMA. Let Ω be a compact F-space and let $\omega_0 \in \Omega$. Let ν be a function defined for ordered pairs $[F_1, F_2]$ of disjoint compact subsets of $\Omega \sim \{\omega_0\}$ with values in $[0, \infty)$. Suppose ν is monotone, i.e. $E_1 \subseteq F_1$, $E_2 \subseteq F_2$ implies

$$\nu(E_1, E_2) \leq \nu(F_1, F_2).$$

Then there exists an open neighborhood W of ω_0 such that

$$\sup \nu(F_1, F_2) < \infty$$

for all F_1, F_2 disjoint compact subsets of $W \sim \{\omega_0\}$.

Proof. If the lemma is false we may construct inductively sequences $\{W_k\}$ of open sets, $\{F_{k1}, F_{k2}\}$ of disjoint compact sets such that

$$\omega_0 \in W_k; \qquad F_{k1}, F_{k2} \subseteq W_k \sim \{\omega_0\}$$

$$\overline{W}_{k+1} \subseteq W_k \sim \bigcup_{i=1}^{k} (F_{i1} \cup F_{i2})$$

$$\nu(F_{k1}, F_{k2}) \geq k.$$

Select open F_σ sets B_{k1}, B_{k2} such that

$$F_{ki} \subseteq B_{ki} \subseteq W_k \sim \overline{W}_{k+1}, \quad B_{k1} \cap B_{k2} = \phi.$$

Let $M_i = \bigcup_{k=1}^{\infty} F_{ki}$, $i = 1, 2$. Then

$$M_1 \cap M_2 \subseteq \overline{\left(\bigcup_{k=1}^{\infty} B_{k1}\right)} \cap \overline{\left(\bigcup_{k=1}^{\infty} B_{k2}\right)} = \phi,$$

since disjoint open F_σ sets in an F-space have disjoint closures. Thus ω_0 belongs to at most one of the sets M_1, M_2. Since we can drop to subsequences k even or k odd we can ssume $\omega_0 \notin M_1 \cup M_2$. Then $\nu(M_1, M_2) \geq k, k = 1, 2, \ldots$.

2.6 THEOREM. Let $X \subset m(S)$ be a linear subspace which is a Banach space under a norm $\|\cdot\|$ such that the natural imbedding of X into $m(S)$ is continuous. Suppose $X \mid \beta(S) \sim S$ is dense in $C(\beta(S) \sim S)$. Then there exists a covering $U_1, \ldots, U_n$ of $\beta(S) \sim S$ by open and closed sets in $\beta(S)$ such that

$$X \mid U_i = C(U_i), \qquad i = 1, \ldots, n.$$

Proof. Note that $\beta(S) \sim S$ is an F-space, since it is a closed subset of the Stonian space $\beta(S)$. Hence by Theorem 3.2 of [**1**], each point $\omega_0 \in \beta(S) \sim S$ has an open and closed neighborhood V in $\beta(S) \sim S$ such that $X \mid V = C(V)$. Now $V = U \cap (\beta(S) \sim S)$ where U is open and closed in $\beta(S)$. Moreover, U is the closure of a subset S_0 of S, $U = \beta(S_0)$, and $V = \beta(S_0) \sim S_0$. Thus by compactness of $\beta(S) \sim S$ it suffices to prove the theorem under the stronger assumption that $X \mid \beta(S) \sim S = C(\beta(S) \sim S)$.

By the closed graph theorem there exists a constant M such that if $g \in m(S)$, there exists an $x \in X$ with

$$x(\omega) = g(\omega), \qquad \omega \in \beta(S) \sim S$$

$$\|x\| \leq M \sup_{\omega \in \beta(S) \sim S} |g(\omega)|.$$

Let $\omega_0 \in \beta(S) \sim S$. Let F_1, F_2 be disjoint compact sets in $\beta(S) \sim \{\omega_0\}$. There always exists a neighborhood V of $\beta(S) \sim S$ and an $x \in X$ with $\|x\| \leq M$ such that

$$\begin{cases} |x(F_1 \cap V) - 1| \leq \dfrac{1}{8} \\[2ex] |x(F_2 \cap V)| \leq \dfrac{1}{8} \\[2ex] x(\omega_0) = 0 \end{cases} \tag{*}$$

Such V is the complement in $\beta(S)$ of a finite set in S. Define $\nu(F_1, F_2)$ to be the minimum cardinality of $S \sim V$ for all V such that there exists an x satisfying (*) above. Since ν is monotone, Lemma 2.5 shows there exists an open and closed neighborhood W of ω_0 and integer k_0 such that

$$\nu(F_1, F_2) \leq k_0, \qquad \text{for } F_1, F_2 \subseteq W \sim \{\omega_0\}.$$

We must eliminate the possibility that our sets V might have $(S \sim V) \cap W \neq \phi$. For F_1, F_2 disjoint compact subsets of $W \sim \{\omega_0\}$, let $n(F_1, F_2)$ be the smallest integer n such that there exists an $x \in X$ with $\|x\| \leq M$, $x(\omega_0) = 0$, and

$$|x(\omega) - 1| \leq \frac{1}{8}, \qquad \omega \in F_1 \sim A$$

$$|x(\omega)| \leq \frac{1}{8}, \qquad \omega \in F_2 \sim A,$$

where A is a finite subset of $F_1 \cup F_2$ of cardinality n. Clearly $n(F_1, F_2) \leq k_0$. If $n(F_1, F_2) = 0$ for all $F_1, F_2 \subseteq W \sim \{\omega_0\}$, we conclude from [**1**], Theorem 1.2, that $X \mid W = C(W)$. Suppose we can find a pair of disjoint compact sets $G_1, G_2 \subseteq W \sim \{\omega_0\}$ with

$$0 < n(G_1, G_2) \leq k_0.$$

If $F_1, F_2 \subseteq W \sim [G_1 \cup G_2 \cup \{\omega_0\}]$ then

$$n(G_1 \cup F_1, G_2 \cup F_2) \leq k_0,$$

and any x which competes for this, also competes for $n(G_1, G_2)$. Thus

$$n(F_1, F_2) \leq k_0 - n(G_1, G_2).$$

We see in this way that there exists a compact and open set $K \subseteq W \sim \{\omega_0\}$ such that $n(F_1, F_2) = 0$ if $F_1, F_2 \subseteq W \sim (K \cup \{\omega_0\})$. Thus if $U = W \sim K$, we have $\omega_0 \in U$, and $X \mid U = C(U)$. A covering argument completes the proof.

There are several questions associated with Theorems 2.1 and 2.6.

QUESTION 1. Can one prove Theorem 2.1 under the weaker hypothesis that $X \mid \beta(S) \sim S$ is dense in $C(\beta(S) \sim S)$?

A positive solution to Question 1 would settle an old problem in Banach space theory. Let F be a closed subspace of a Banach space E. A closed subspace G of E is called a quasicomplement to F if $F \cap G = (0)$ and $F \oplus G$ is dense in E. When E is separable, each closed subspace of E has a quasicomplement (Mackey [**13**], Murray [**14**]). This result has very recently been extended to nonseparable reflexive spaces by J. Lindenstrauss [**12**]. However, it is not known if it holds for every non-separable Banach space. If Question 1 has an affirmative answer then $c_0(N)$ has no quasicomplement in $m(N)$. For any quasicomplement X of $c_0(N)$ would have the property that $X \mid \beta(N) \sim N$ is dense in $C(\beta(N) \sim N)$. It would follow that X had finite codimension in $m(N)$.

As a small contribution to this problem we have the following facts suggested by work of Grothendieck [**8**].

2.7 THEOREM. Let X be a closed linear subspace of $m(N)$ such that $X \mid \beta(N) \sim N$ is dense in $C(\beta(N) \sim N)$. Then

(a) The quotient space $m(N)/X$ is separable and reflexive.

(b) The natural map $T{:}c_0(N) \to m(N)/X$ defined by $Tz = z + X$, $z \in c_0(N)$, is compact.

Proof. Since $X \mid \beta(N) \sim N$ is dense in $C(\beta(N) \sim N)$, $c_0(N) + X$ is dense in $m(N)$, so $m(N)/X$ is separable. Hence by a result of Grothendieck ([**8**], page 160) the quotient map of $m(N)$ onto $m(N)/X$ must be weakly compact. It follows that $m(N)/X$ is reflexive. Thus $X^{\perp} = [m(N)/X]^*$ is separable andd reflexive, and T^*: $X^{\perp} \to \ell_1(N)$ maps the unit ball of $X^{\perp}$ into a weakly, and hence norm, compact subset of $\ell_1(N)$. Therefore T^*, and hence T, are compact maps.

QUESTION 2. Under what additional conditions can the finitely many interpolation sets $U_1, \ldots, U_n$ in the conclusion of Theorem 2.6 be replaced by a single neighborhood of $\beta(S) \sim S$?

In [**1**] there is an example due to J. Lindenstrauss of a Banach space X which is continuously and densely imbedded as a proper subspace of $L_\infty(0, 1)$. By a result of Pelczynski [**16**], $L_\infty(0, 1)$ is isomorphic to $m(N)$, so we may also obtain an example of such a subspace X in $m(N)$. Clearly $X \mid \beta(N) \sim N$ is dense in $\beta(N) \sim N$. If there were a neighborhood U of $\beta(N) \sim N$ such that $X \mid U = C(U)$ it would follow that X was sup norm closed in $m(N)$. Thus Question 2 has a negative solution in general.

Question 2 has a positive answer when X is a conjugate space and the imbedding of X into $m(S)$ is continuous for the weak star topologies of X and $m(S)$. This is equivalent to the following situation which is more convenient for applications. Let T be a continuous linear map of $\ell_1(S)$ into a Banach space Y, so T^*: $Y^* \to m(S)$. If $T^*Y^* \mid \beta(S) \sim S$ is dense in $C(\beta(S) \sim S)$, then we shall prove $T^*Y^* \mid S \sim F = m(S \sim F)$ for some finite set F. Actually we can get by with a formally weaker hypothesis than the density above. This theorem was proved by Helson and Kahane ([**9**], page 249) in the case that $S = N$ and Y and Y^* were certain spaces of continuous functions and measures. Our proof is an abstract version of theirs.

2.8 THEOREM. Let T be a continuous linear map of $\ell_1(S)$ into a Banach space Y, so T^*: $Y^* \to m(S)$. We suppose that for each $h \in m(S)$ with $|h(S)| \equiv 1$ there exists a $y^* \in Y^*$ such that

$$\sup_{\omega \in \beta(S) \sim S} |h(\omega) - (T^*y^*)(\omega)| < 1$$

Then T^*Y^* is closed in $m(S)$ and has finite codimension. There exists a finite subset F of S such that

$$T^*Y^* \mid S \sim F = m(S \sim F)$$

Proof. We prove the last conclusion and show it implies the others. Note that if G is any finite set in S, we have $T^*Y^* \mid S \sim G = m(S \sim G)$ if and only if $T \mid Z(G)$ is a linear homeomorphism into Y, where $Z(G) = \{f \in \ell_1(S) \mid f(G) = 0\}$. Suppose $T \mid Z(G)$ fails to be a linear homeomorphism for every finite set G. Then inductively we may construct a sequence $\{G_n\}$ of disjoint finite sets in S and a sequence $\{f_n\}$ of unit vectors in $\ell_1(S)$ such that f_n is carried on G_n, and $\| Tf_n \| \to 0$ in Y. Define

$$\begin{aligned} h(s) &= \frac{|f_n(s)|}{f_n(s)}, \qquad s \in G_n \\ &= 1, \qquad s \in S \sim \bigcup_{n=1}^{\infty} G_n. \end{aligned}$$

Then there exists a finite set F_0, an element y^* of Y^*, and a $\delta > 0$ such that

$$|h(s) - (T^*y^*)(s)| \leq 1 - \delta, s \in S \sim F_0.$$

If $G_n \cap F_0 = \phi$ we have

$$\begin{aligned} 1 = \|f_n\|_1 &= \langle f_n, h \rangle = \langle f_n, h - T^*y^* \rangle + \langle f_n, T^*y^* \rangle \\ &\leqq 1 - \delta + |y^*Tf_n| \end{aligned}$$

Clearly we have a contradiction for large values of n. Thus there exists a finite set F such that $T^*Y^* \mid S \sim F = m(S \sim F)$.

Since T is a linear homeomorphism on $Z(F)$, and $Z(F)$ has finite codimension, T has closed range. Its null space $n(T)$ has finite dimension since $n(T) \cap Z(F) = (0)$. Thus $T^*Y^* = n(T)^\perp$ ([**4**], page 487).

2.9 COROLLARY (Helson-Kahane). Let K be a compact subset of the reals and let $n_1 < n_2 < \cdots$ be positive integers. For complex Borel measures μ on K we form the sequences

$$\hat{\mu}(n_j) = \int_K e^{in_jt} \mu(dt), \qquad j = 1, 2, \ldots.$$

Suppose that for each element d of $m(N)$ with $|d(N)| \equiv 1$ there exists a measure μ on K such that

$$\overline{\lim_{j \to \infty}} |d(j) - \hat{\mu}(n_j)| < 1.$$

Then there exists an integer k_0 such that for every $b \in m(N)$ there exists μ such that

$$b(j) = \hat{\mu}(n_j), \qquad \text{for all } j \geq k_0.$$

Proof. Let $Y = C(K)$ and define T: $\ell_1(N) \to Y$ by $Tb = \Sigma_{j=1}^{\infty} b(j)e^{in_jt}$, $b \in \ell_1(N)$, $t \in K$. Then $T^*\mu$ is the sequence $\{\hat{\mu}(n_j)\}$, and Theorem 2.6 applies.

We shall give another application to the algebra H^∞ of bounded analytic functions in the unit disc. A sequence $D = \{z_n\}$, $|z_n| < 1$, is called an *interpolating sequence* for H^∞ if for each element a of $m(N)$ there exists an f in H^∞ such that

$$f(z_n) = a(n), \qquad n = 1, 2, \ldots.$$

The geometric structure of interpolating sequences is known from the work of L. Carleson and D. J. Newman (cf. [**10**], Chapter 10). The following result may be compared with a theorem of Hayman ([**10**], page 205; see also [**1**], Corollary 3.5).

2.10 COROLLARY. Let $D = \{z_n\}$ be a sequence in the open disc. Suppose that for each $a \in m(N)$ with $|a(n)| \equiv 1$ there exists an $f \in H^\infty$ such that

$$\overline{\lim_{n\to\infty}} |f(z_n) - a(n)| < 1$$

Then D is an interpolating sequence for H^∞.

Proof. Let T: $\ell_1(N) \to L_1(0, 2\pi)/H^1$ be the map taking b in $\ell_1(N)$ into the residue class of the function

$$\frac{b(1)}{z - z_1} + \frac{b(2)}{z - z_2} + \cdots.$$

Since $[L_1(0, 2\pi)/H^1]^* = H^\infty$, T^*: $H^\infty \to m(N)$. One checks easily that $T^*f = \{f(z_1), f(z_2), \ldots\}$ for $f \in H^\infty$ (cf. Newman, [**15**]). It follows from Theorem 2.8 that there is an integer k_0 such that $\{z_{k_0}, z_{k_0+1}, \ldots\}$ is an interpolating sequence. Hence D itself is an interpolating sequence.

3 CLOSED G_δ SETS IN *F*-SPACES

There is a further setting in which one has analogues of the theorems of Section 1. This is where Q is a closed G_δ set in a compact F-space. For the first theorem one may assume a somewhat less restrictive condition on the underlying space.

3.1 DEFINITION. A compact Hausdorff space Ω is a *G-space* if weak star and weak convergence coincide for sequences in $C(\Omega)^*$; i.e. if $\mu_n(f) \to \mu(f)$ for all $f \in C(\Omega)$ implies that $\mu_n \to \mu$ weakly.

A. Grothendieck established this property for extremely disconnected spaces in [**8**], page 168. G-spaces have been studied by Seever [**19**] and Semadeni [**20**]. Seever proved that every F-space is a G-space, but that there are G-spaces which are not F-spaces. It is not known how to characterize G-spaces in terms of their topology.

3.2 THEOREM. Let Q be a closed G_δ set in a compact G-space Ω, and let X be a closed linear subspace of $C(\Omega)$ such that $X \mid Q = C(Q)$. Then there exists a closed neighborhood V of Q such that $X \mid V = C(V)$.

Proof. If the theorem is false, then following the proof of Theorem 1.1 we can construct a sequence $\{V_n\}$ of closed neighborhoods of Q and a sequence $\{\mu_n\}$ of measures in $X^\perp$ of norm one such that

$$\bigcap_{n=1}^{\infty} V_n = Q, \quad V_{n+1} \subseteq \operatorname{int}(V_n). \tag{1}$$

$$|\mu_n|(V_n') < \frac{1}{2^n} \tag{2}$$

$$|\mu_n|(V_n \sim \overline{V}_{n+1}) > \delta > 0, \qquad n = 1, 2, \ldots. \tag{3}$$

If $f \in C(\Omega)$, then $f = g + h$, where $g(Q) = 0$, and $h \in X$. Therefore

$$|\mu_n(f)| = |\mu_n(g)| \leq \left| \int_{V_n'} g d\mu_n \right| + \left| \int_{V_n \sim Q} g d\mu_n \right|$$

$$\leq \|g\|_\infty |\mu_n|(V_n') + \sup_{\omega \in V_n \sim Q} |g(\omega)| \to 0.$$

Thus $\mu_n \to 0$ weak star, so $\mu_n \to 0$ weakly. However, because of (2) the sequence $\{\mu_n\}$ can not be weakly relatively compact (cf. [**8**], page 146).

3.3 COROLLARY. Let Q be a closed G_δ set in a compact G-space Ω and let $Z(Q)$ denote the functions in $C(\Omega)$ vanishing in Q. Then $Z(Q)$ is complemented in $C(\Omega)$ if and only if Q is both open and closed.

Proof. Suppose $Z(Q)$ is complemented by X. Then there exists a closed neighborhood V of Q such that $X \mid V = C(V)$. If Q is not open, then $V \sim Q \neq \phi$, so there are nonzero functions in X which vanish on Q. Thus $X \cap Z(Q) \neq (0)$. The converse is clear.

Remark. Suppose Ω is a compact F-space and Q is a closed nowhere dense G_δ in Ω. Then $\Omega = \overline{\Omega \sim Q} = \beta(\Omega \sim Q)$, since $\Omega \sim Q$ is C^* imbedded in Ω ([**6**], page 208). Thus we can obtain Theorem 3.2 for this special case from Theorem 1.1.

Suppose hereafter that Ω is a compact F-space, and Q is a closed G_δ. One can prove the exact analogues of Lemma 1.6, Theorem 1.7 and Theorem 1.8 with $\beta(\Omega) \sim \Omega$ replaced by Q. The proofs are the same, only one uses Lemma 2.5 in place of Lemma 1.5. We shall omit the details and state only the analogue of Theorem 1.8. It can be proved very briefly from Theorem 3.2 in the same way that Theorem 2.3 was obtained from Theorem 2.1 and the results of [**1**].

3.4 THEOREM. Let Q be a closed G_δ in a compact F-space. Let A be a subalgebra of $C(\Omega)$ containing the constants which is a Banach algebra under some norm. If $A \mid Q$ is dense in $C(Q)$, then there exists a closed neighborhood V of Q such that $A \mid V = C(V)$.

We close with an application to H^∞. We may identify H^∞ with a closed subalgebra $\hat{H}^\infty$ of $C(\Phi)$, where Φ is its Silov boundary. It is known that Φ is the maximal ideal space of $L_\infty(0, 2\pi)$, and hence is extremely disconnected (cf. [**10**], Chapter 10). We wish to show that if Q is a closed subset of Φ such that $\hat{H}^\infty \mid Q = C(Q)$, then Q *cannot contain a closed* G_δ. This fact was noted without proof in the paper [**11**] of Hoffman and Ramsay. It follows from Theorem 3.2 that if Q contained a closed G_δ, then there would be an open and closed set K in Φ such that $\hat{H}^\infty \mid K = C(K)$. Since K corresponds to a set $\tilde{K}$ of positive measure on the unit circle, the boundary values of H^∞ functions on $\tilde{K}$ would include all bounded measurable functions on $\tilde{K}$. This would contradict the known boundary behavior of functions in H^∞.

REFERENCES

1. Bade, W. G. and P. C. Curtis Jr., Embedding theorems for commutative Banach algebras, *Pacific J. Math.* **18** (1966) p. 391–409.
2. Conway, J. B. Projections and retractions, *Proc. Amer. Math. Soc.* **17** (1966) p. 843–847.
3. Day, M. M., *Normed linear spaces*, Berlin 1958.
4. Dunford, N. and J. T. Schwartz, *Linear Operators: General Theory*, New York 1958.
5. Gamelin, T. W., Restrictions of subspaces of $C(X)$, *Trans. Amer. Math. Soc.* **112** (1964), pp. 278–286.
6. Gillman, L. and M. Jerison, *Rings of continuous functions*, New York 1960.
7. Glicksberg, I., Measures orthogonal to algebras and sets of antisymmetry, *Trans. Amer. Math. Soc.* **105** (1962) pp. 415–435.
8. Grothendieck, A., Sur les applications linéaires faiblement compacte d'espaces du type $C(K)$, *Canadian J. Math* **5** (1953) pp. 129–173.
9. Helson H. and J.-P. Kahane, A Fourier method in diophantine problems, *Jour. d'Analyse Math.* **15** (1965), pp. 245–262.
10. Hoffman, K., *Banach spaces of analytic functions*, Englewood Cliffs, 1962.
11. Hoffman, K. and A. Ramsay, Algebras of bounded sequences, *Pacific J. Math.* **15** (1965) pp. 1239–1248.
12. Lindenstrauss, J., On a theorem of Murray and Mackey, *Anais de Acad. Brasileira Cien* (to appear).
13. Mackey, G., Note on a theorem of Murray, *Bull. Amer. Math. Soc.* **52** (1946), pp. 322–325.
14. Murray, F. J., Quasicomplements and closed projections in reflexive Banach spaces, *Trans. Amer. Math. Soc.* **58** (1945), pp. 77-95.

15. Newman, D. J., Interpolation in H^∞, *Trans. Amer. Math. Soc.* **92** (1959), pp. 501–507.
16. Pelczynski, A., On the isomorphism of the spaces m and M, *Bull. de l'Acad. Polon. Sci. ser. sci., math. et phys.* **6** (1958), pp. 695–696.
17. Pelczynski, A. and V. N. Sudakov, Remarks on noncomplemented subspaces of the space $m(S)$, *Colloquium Math.* **9** (1962), pp. 85–88.
18. Phillips, R. S., On linear transformations, *Trans. Amer. Math. Soc.* **48** (1940), pp. 516–541.
19. Seever, G. L., *Measures on F-spaces*, Thesis, University of California, Berkeley, 1963.
20. Semadeni, Z., On weak convergence of measures and σ-complete Boolean algebras, *Colloquium Math.* **12** (1964), pp. 229–233.

Rings of Germs of Continuous Functions[1]

MEYER JERISON

INTRODUCTION

Let p be a point in a topological space X. We denote by $C(X)$ the ring of all continuous real-valued functions on X and $\mathbf{O}_p$ the ideal of all functions in $C(X)$ that vanish in a neighborhood of p. The *germ* of a function at p is its residue-class modulo the ideal $\mathbf{O}_p$. The present paper deals with the following question which was raised by J.-P. Kahane: To what extent does the algebraic structure of the ring of germs $C(X)/\mathbf{O}_p$ determine the topology of X in a neighborhood of p?

It is easy to construct examples of essentially different spaces, even compact Hausdorff spaces, that have isomorphic rings of germs. We can extract enough information about the local topology of a space from the ring of germs, however, to be able to assert that if X is a Euclidean space then $C(X)/\mathbf{O}_p$ determines the dimension of X.

In the outline of this paper that appeared in [**5**], the proof of the main theorem was based upon the detailed knowledge of all the prime ideals in a ring $C(X)$, as developed by C. W. Kohls [**7**]. Here, the topological space of minimal prime ideals [**4**] is used instead. The advantage of the latter method is that it is applicable to rings of functions other than $C(X)$, where we know less about all the prime ideals. In particular, it was applied in [**6**] to the ring of functions on a locally compact abelian group that are Fourier transforms of integrable functions on the dual group. In fact, this is the ring that really interested Kahane.

1. THE MAIN THEOREM

The force of the restrictions that are placed on the space X and the point p will be discussed in section 3 in connection with the examples.

[1]This research was supported by the National Science Foundation under grant NSF-GP-3515.

1.1. THEOREM. Let X be a compact space and $p \in X$, with $\{p\}$ a G_δ. The algebraic structure of the ring $C(X)/\mathbf{O}_p$ determines the space

$$E = \beta(X - \{p\}) - (X - \{p\}),$$

where $\beta(\cdots)$ denotes the Stone-Čech compactification.

The trivial situation of an isolated point p is handled quickly. In that case, E is void, and $C(X)/\mathbf{O}_p$ is isomorphic with the real field. Conversely, if $C(X)/\mathbf{O}_p$ is isomorphic with the real field, then p must be isolated because $\{p\}$ is a G_δ.

When p is not isolated, we construct a sequence of spaces, each a continuous image of its predecessor, and end with the space E. These spaces are:

A. The space of minimal prime ideals of $C(X)/\mathbf{O}_p$.

B. The space of minimal prime ideals of $C(X)$ that contain the ideal $\mathbf{O}_p$.

C. The space of minimal prime z-filters on X that converge to p.

D. The space of z-ultrafilters on $X' = X - \{p\}$ that converge to p.

E. The space $\beta X' - X'$.

The topology of a space of minimal prime ideals [**4**] is the hull-kernel (Stone) topology. In a space of z-filters, the set of all z-filters that contain a given zero-set is a closed set by definition, and the family of all such sets is a base for the closed sets [**3**, p. 87].

1.2. LEMMA. The spaces A and B are homeomorphic under the natural mapping $\tau_1 : B \to A$ defined by $\tau_1(P) = P/\mathbf{O}_p$, $P \in B$.

Proof. By virtue of [**4**; Theorem 2.1] we only have to prove that τ_1 is surjective. Now, any minimal prime ideal in $C(X)/\mathbf{O}_p$ has the form $P/\mathbf{O}_p$, where P is a prime ideal in $C(X)$. To show that P is minimal, consider any prime ideal P_0 contained in P. Then P_0 contains $\mathbf{O}_p$ [**3**; p. 107, Theorem 7.15], so that $P_0/\mathbf{O}_p$ is a prime ideal in $C(X)/\mathbf{O}_p$ which is contained in $P/\mathbf{O}_p$. Since the latter is minimal, we have $P_0/\mathbf{O}_p = P/\mathbf{O}_p$, whence $P_0 = P$.

1.3. LEMMA. The spaces B and C are homeomorphic under the mapping $\tau_2 : B \to C$ defined by $\tau_2(P) = \{f^{-1}(0) : f \in P\}$, $P \in B$.

We shall omit the proof which is routine.

1.4. LEMMA. The mapping τ_3 which assigns to each minimal prime z-filter $\mathfrak{F} \in C$ the unique z-ultrafilter on X' that contains the trace of $\mathfrak{F}$ on X' is a continuous mapping of C onto D.

Proof. The hypothesis that $\{p\}$ be a G_δ in X implies that a set Z is a zero-set in X if and only if $Z' = Z \cap X'$ is a zero-set in X' [**3**; p. 48, 3C]. This fact is central to the proof of the lemma.

We prove first that for every $\mathfrak{F} \in C$, its trace $\mathfrak{F}'$ on X' is a minimal prime z-filter on X'. It follows immediately from the remark in the preceding paragraph that the operation of taking the trace on X' provided a one-to-one inclusion-preserving mapping of the set of all z-filters on X each of whose members meet X' onto the set of all z-filters on X'. Besides, prime z-filters on X map into prime z-filters on X'. We have left only to show that every member of a minimal prime z-filter meets X'; in other words, that $\{p\}$ belongs to no minimal prime z-filter. But $\{p\}$ belongs only to the z-ultrafilter that corresponds to the maximal ideal $\mathbf{M}_p = \{f: f(p) = 0\}$. Since p is not an isolated point although there is a function in $C(X)$ that vanishes only at p, $\mathbf{M}_p \neq \mathbf{O}_p$. The ideal $\mathbf{O}_p$ is an intersection of prime ideals, however [**3**; p. 27, Theorem 2.8], all of which are contained in $\mathbf{M}_p$. Therefore, $\mathbf{M}_p$ is not a minimal prime ideal, so that the only z-filter containing $\{p\}$ is not minimal.

The mapping τ_3 is now well defined by the statement of the lemma. That it is continuous is essentially the same as [**4**; Theorem 5.3(a)]. If $\mathcal{G}$ is any member of D, then the family of zero-sets on X

$$\{Z: Z \cap X' \in \mathcal{G}\}$$

is a prime z-filter on X which converges to p. It contains a minimal prime z-filter whose image under τ_3 is evidently $\mathcal{G}$. Thus, τ_3 is surjective.

1.5. LEMMA. The mapping τ_4 that assigns to each z-ultrafilter that belongs to D its limit in the space $\beta X'$ is a homeomorphism of D onto E.

This is evident from the construction of the Stone-Čech compactification in [**3**; p. 86–88].

Now let us consider the continuous mapping $\psi = \tau_4 \circ \tau_3 \circ \tau_2 \circ \tau_1^{-1}$ of A onto E. In order to complete the proof of the theorem, we must show that the algebraic structure alone of the ring $C(X)/\mathbf{O}_p$ determines the mapping ψ as well as the topology of E.

1.6. LEMMA. For $P_1, P_2 \in A$, $\psi(P_1) = \psi(P_2)$ if and only if the ideal $P_1 + P_2$ in $C(X)/\mathbf{O}_p$ is not maximal.

Proof. If $\psi(P_1) = \psi(P_2)$, let $\mathcal{U}$ be the unique z-ultrafilter on X' that converges to $\psi(P_1)$. Then the set

$$I = \{f \in C(X): f^{-1}(0) \cap X' \in \mathcal{U}\}$$

is a prime ideal in $C(X)$ which is not the maximal ideal $\mathbf{M}_p$. And $I/\mathbf{O}_p$ is an ideal in $C(X)/\mathbf{O}_p$ which is not maximal but contains $P_1 + P_2$.

The opposite situation, $\psi(P_1) \neq \psi(P_2)$, means that the smallest z-filter on X containing the z-filters $\tau_2 \circ \tau_1^{-1}(P_1)$ and $\tau_2 \circ \tau_1^{-1}(P_2)$ is the z-ultrafilter of all zero-sets that contain p. But this implies that the smallest ideal in $C(X)$ containing the ideals $\tau_1^{-1}(P_1)$ and $\tau_1^{-1}(P_2)$ is the maximal ideal $\mathbf{M}_p$ [**3**; p. 198, Lemma 14.8]. Therefore, the smallest ideal in $C(X)/\mathbf{O}_p$ containing P_1 and P_2 is the maximal ideal $\mathbf{M}_p/\mathbf{O}_p$.

1.7. LEMMA. A point $q \in E$ belongs to the closure of a set $H \subset E$ if and only if there is a nonmaximal prime ideal P in $C(X)/\mathbf{O}_p$ that contains all the members of $\psi^{-1}(q)$ as well as the intersection of all the members of $\psi^{-1}(H)$.

Proof. If q belongs to the closure of H, then according to the definition of the topology in the space D, the z-ultrafilter $\tau_4^{-1}(q)$ contains the intersection of all the z-ultrafilters in $\tau_4^{-1}(H)$. The ideal $I = \{f \in C(X): f^{-1}(0) \cap X' \in \tau_4^{-1}(q)\}$ is a prime ideal in $C(X)$, and $P = I/\mathbf{O}_p$ has the required properties.

Suppose, now, that q does not belong to the closure of H and that P is any nonmaximal prime ideal in $C(X)/\mathbf{O}_p$ containing all of the members of $\psi^{-1}(q)$. Let I be the inverse image of P under the canonical homomorphism of $C(X)$ onto $C(X)/\mathbf{O}_p$, so that I is a prime ideal which is contained properly in $\mathbf{M}_p$. Let $g \geq 0$ be a function in $\mathbf{M}_p$ that is not in I, and choose $\varphi \in C(\beta X')$, $0 \leq \varphi \leq 2$, so that $\varphi(q) = 2$ and φ vanishes on a neighborhood of H. Define

$$f(x) = \begin{cases} g(x)\varphi(x) & \text{if } x \in X' \\ 0 & x = p. \end{cases}$$

The function f belongs to $C(X)$ because φ is bounded while $g(p) = 0$. Furthermore, the zero-set of f belongs to every z-filter in $(\tau_4 \circ \tau_3)^{-1}(H)$, because each of these z-filters has a trace on X' which converges to some point of H in $\beta X'$, and so contains the intersection with X' of every zero-set-neighborhood of H. Consequently $f + \mathbf{O}_p$, the germ of f, belongs to every member of $\psi^{-1}(H)$. We show, however, that $f + \mathbf{O}_p$ does not belong to P. Let I_0 be any minimal prime ideal of $C(X)$ such that $\psi(I_0/\mathbf{O}_p) = q$; necessarily, $I_0 \subset I$. Since $\varphi(q) = 2$, the set

$$Z = \{p\} \cup \{x \in X' : \varphi(x) \geq 1\},$$

which is a zero-set in X, belongs to the prime z-filter $\tau_2(I_0)$ by the same argument as above. For all $x \in Z$, we have $f(x) \geq g(x)$, and this implies that in the natural order of $C(X)/I_0$[**3**; p. 68, 5.4(a)], $f + I_0 \geq g + I_0$. Now, the prime ideal I/I_0 is a symmetric interval in the totally ordered ring $C(X)/I_0$[**3**; p. 195]. Thus, $g + I_0 \notin I/I_0$ implies $f + I_0 \notin I/I_0$. Therefore, $f \notin I$, and so $f + \mathbf{O}_p \notin P$.

Theorem 1.1 follows directly from the lemmas.

Remark. Continuity of the mappings τ_i is not needed in the proof of the theorem, for Lemma 1.7 says directly that the ring $C(X)/\mathbf{O}_p$ determines the correct topology for the space. It should be noted, however, that in the context of [**6**] continuity of the composite mapping ψ makes Lemma 1.7 unnecessary. There, X is a locally compact abelian group, and the hypothesis that $\{p\}$ is a G_δ makes the group metrizable. As a consequence, the space A is compact, something which is not true in the general case, and E is then obtained as the quotient space of A under the identification specified in Lemma 1.6.

2. EUCLIDEAN SPACES

In this section we shall show how Theorem 1.1 leads to a proof that the dimension of a space $\mathbf{R}^n$ is determined by the ring $C(\mathbf{R}^n)/\mathbf{O}_p$, for any $p \in \mathbf{R}^n$. If X is the closed unit ball in $\mathbf{R}^n$ and p is the origin, then the ring $C(X)/\mathbf{O}_p$ is obviously isomorphic with $C(\mathbf{R}^n)/\mathbf{O}_p$. By the theorem, this ring determines the space $\beta(X - \{p\}) - (X - \{p\})$. But $X - \{p\}$ is homeomorphic with $\mathbf{R}^n$ − int X, and it is easy to see that $\beta(\mathbf{R}^n - \text{int } X) - (\mathbf{R}^n - \text{int } X)$ is homeomorphic with $\beta\mathbf{R}^n - \mathbf{R}^n$. It remains for us to show that the space $\beta\mathbf{R}^n - \mathbf{R}^n$ determines the number n.

The following theorem, which settles the matter, seems to have been published for the first time in [**5**], although it was certainly known long before then. Indeed, Ju. M. Smirnov [**8**] described a closed discrete subset of $\mathbf{R}^n$ whose closure in $\beta\mathbf{R}^n$ is n-dimensional.

2.1. THEOREM $\dim(\beta\mathbf{R}^n - \mathbf{R}^n) = n$.

Proof. The symbol dim refers, as usual, to the Lebesgue (covering) dimension. It is known that

$$\dim(\beta\mathbf{R}^n - \mathbf{R}^n) \leq \dim \beta\mathbf{R}^n = \dim \mathbf{R}^n = n.$$

To reverse the inequality it suffices, according to a theorem of P. S. Aleksandrov [**1**], to produce an *essential* mapping $\varphi{:}\beta\mathbf{R}^n - \mathbf{R}^n \to [-1, 1]^n$ in the sense that any mapping of $\beta\mathbf{R}^n - \mathbf{R}^n$ into the cube $[-1, 1]^n$ that agrees with φ on those points which φ sends into the boundary of the cube must be surjective. We define a mapping $f{:}\mathbf{R}^n \to [-1, 1]^n$ in terms of coordinates by the formula $f(x_1, \ldots, x_n) = (\cos \pi x_1, \ldots, \cos \pi x_n)$. Let f^* be the continuous extension of f to all of $\beta\mathbf{R}^n$, and φ, the restriction of f^* to $\beta\mathbf{R}^n - \mathbf{R}^n$. We want to prove that φ is essential.

Let Y be the inverse image of the boundary of the cube under the mapping f, that is, Y is the set of points in $\mathbf{R}^n$ having at least one coordinate an integer, and let Y' be the inverse image of the boundary of the cube under the mapping φ. Since f^* is a continuous mapping, every limit point of Y that is in $\beta\mathbf{R}^n - \mathbf{R}^n$ belongs to the set Y'. As a consequence, every neighborhood of Y' in the space $\beta\mathbf{R}^n$ includes all but a compact subset of Y.

Consider any mapping $g^*{:}\beta\mathbf{R}^n \to [-1, 1]^n$ that agrees with φ on all of Y'. Then $|f^*(q) - g^*(q)| = 0$ for all $q \in Y'$, where $|f^*(q) - g^*(q)|$ denotes the maximum of the absolute values of the differences of corresponding coordinates of $f^*(q)$ and $g^*(q)$. For any $\epsilon > 0$, the set

$$N_\epsilon = \{q \in \beta\mathbf{R}^n{:}\, |f^*(q) - g^*(q)| < \epsilon\}$$

is a neighborhood of Y', and so it contains all but a compact subset of Y. This means that the boundaries of all but a finite number of unit cubes whose vertices have integer coordinates are contained in N_ϵ. By [**2**; p. 374,

Hilfssatz], the image of every such unit cube under the mapping g^* includes the cube $[-1 + 2\epsilon, 1 - 2\epsilon]^n$. Thus, for each point $\xi \in [-1 + 2\epsilon, 1 - 2\epsilon]^n$, the set $\mathbf{R}^n \cap g^{*-1}(\xi)$ is noncompact so that its closure in $\beta\mathbf{R}^n$ meets $\beta\mathbf{R}^n - \mathbf{R}^n$, that is, $\xi \in g^*[\beta\mathbf{R}^n - \mathbf{R}^n]$. Since ϵ is arbitrary, $g^*[\beta\mathbf{R}^n - \mathbf{R}^n]$ includes the whole interior of $[-1, 1]^n$. Now, every mapping of $\beta\mathbf{R}^n - \mathbf{R}^n$ into $[-1, 1]^n$ that agrees with φ on Y' has a continuous extension $g^*:\beta\mathbf{R}^n \to [-1, 1]^n$. Therefore, φ is essential.

2.2. COROLLARY. If $C(\mathbf{R}^n)/\mathbf{O}_{\text{origin}}$ is isomorphic with $C(\mathbf{R}^m)/\mathbf{O}_{\text{origin}}$, then $m = n$.

3. EXAMPLES AND COMMENTS

The hypothesis that X be compact is used in the proof of Theorem 1.1 only in passing from the space D to the space E. If that hypothesis were omitted, the only difference in the entire development would be to make the mapping τ_4 a homeomorphism of D onto a subspace of $\beta X' - X'$ instead of all of $\beta X' - X'$.

On the other hand, the condition that $\{p\}$ be a G_δ is essential. Consider the space $\mathbf{W}$ of all countable ordinal numbers in the order topology [**3**; p. 72–76]. Let X_n be the one-point-compactification of the topological sum of n copies of $\mathbf{W}$ and p the point at infinity in X_n. Then it is easy to see that every continuous function on X_n is constant in a neighborhood of p so that $C(X_n)/\mathbf{O}_p$ is isomorphic with the real field, just as if p were an isolated point. The space $\beta(X_n - \{p\}) - (X_n - \{p\})$, however, consists of n points.

The possibility of getting information about the topology of a space X in the neighborhood of a point p from the space $\beta(X - \{p\}) - (X - \{p\})$ as was done in Corollary 2.2 is also weakened if $\{p\}$ is not a G_δ in X. For example, let $L^* = L \cup \{\infty\}$ be the one-point compactification of the "long line" L described in [**3**; p. 262, 16H]. Let B^n denote the closed unit ball in $\mathbf{R}^n$ and 0, the origin. Finally, let $X = L^* \times B^n$ and $p = (\infty, 0) \in X$. Then $\beta(X - \{p\}) - (X - \{p\})$ is homeomorphic with $\beta(B^n - \{0\}) - (B^n - \{0\})$ although the dimension of any neighborhood of p in X is $n + 1$.

We close with an example where the space A of minimal prime ideals of $C(X)/\mathbf{O}_p$ is not compact. In [**4**; 5.7] a compact space Γ is given which may be described as follows: Adjoin a countable closed discrete set of points to the space $\mathbf{W}$ and then compactify by adjoining one more point, ω_1. Now take the topological sum of countably many copies $\Gamma_1, \Gamma_2, \ldots$ of Γ and form X by adjoining one point p to this sum to compactify it. Since $\{p\}$ is the complement of a countable union of compact sets in X, it is a G_δ. Let f be any function in $C(X)$ that vanishes on all the copies of $\mathbf{W} \cup \{\omega_1\}$ in X, at the point p, and nowhere else. Such a function is easy to construct because its specified zero-set is the complement of a countable set of isolated points, in particular, a compact G_δ. If the space A were compact, then according to [**4**; 3.4] there would exist $g \in C(X)$ such that the product of the germs $(f + \mathbf{O}_p)\cdot(g + \mathbf{O}_p) = 0$, while 0 is the only element in $C(X)/\mathbf{O}_p$ that annihilates both $f + \mathbf{O}_p$ and $g + \mathbf{O}_p$. We shall show that no such function exists.

Consider any $g \in C(X)$ such that $(f + \mathbf{O}_p)\cdot(g + \mathbf{O}_p) = 0$. This means that there is a neighborhood N of p in X such that $f(x)\cdot g(x) = 0$ for all $x \in N$. Now, any neighborhood of p contains all but a finite number of the sets Γ_n, because a set that consists of one point from each of an infinite number of the sets Γ_n has no limit point in $X - \{p\}$ and so must have p in its closure. Suppose, then, that $\Gamma_n \subset N$ for all $n \geq m$. Since g vanishes on the set $N \sim f^{-1}(0)$, it must also vanish on the copy of the point ω_1 in each Γ_n for $n \geq m$. It therefore vanishes on all ordinals greater than some countable ordinal α_n in each Γ_n, $n \geq m$. The supremum of the ordinals α_n is again a countable ordinal α, and g vanishes on all ordinals greater than α in all Γ_n with $n \geq m$. Define $h \in C(X)$ as the function that assumes the value $1/n$ at the ordinal $\alpha + 1$ in the set Γ_n, $n \geq m$, and vanishes elsewhere on X. Then $hf = hg = 0$, while $h^{-1}(0)$ is not a neighborhood of p. Thus, $h + \mathbf{O}_p$ is a nonzero element of $C(X)/\mathbf{O}_p$ that annihilates both $f + \mathbf{O}_p$ and $g + \mathbf{O}_p$.

REFERENCES

1. Alexandroff, P., On the dimension of normal spaces, *Proc. Roy. Soc. London Ser.* A, 189(1947), 11–39.
2. Alexandroff, P. und H. Hopf, Topologie I, Springer, 1935.
3. Gillman, L. and M. Jerison, Rings of Continuous Functions, D. Van Nostrand, 1960.
4. Henriksen, M. and M. Jerison, The space of minimal prime ideals of a commutative ring, *Trans. Amer. Math. Soc.*, 115(1965), 110–130.
5. Jerison, M., Sur l'anneau des germes des fonctions continues, *C.R. Acad. Sci.* Paris, 260(1965), 6507–6509.
6. Jerison, M., Algebras of germs of Fourier transforms, Second Symposium on General Topology, Prague, 1966, to appear.
7. Kohls, C. W., Prime ideals in rings of continuous functions, *Illinois J. Math.*, 2(1958), 505–536; II, Duke Math. J., 25(1958), 447–458.
8. Smirnov, Ju. M., On the dimension of proximity spaces, *Mat. Sb.* 38(1956), 283–302. AMS Translations Ser. 2, 21(1962), 1–20.

Algebras of Kernels

by

JESÚS GIL DE LAMADRID

1. INTRODUCTION

In Hilbert space H one knows that (1) the class of all compact operators, (2) the class of all Hilbert-Schmidt operators and (3) the trace class of operators are two-sided ideals (hence subalgebras) of the algebra $\mathcal{L}(H)$ of all bounded operators on H. It is actually possible to define norms on these algebras, with respect to which they become Banach algebras with involution. For (1), it is the operator norm, for (2) it is the Hilbert-space norm given by the inner product $(T_1, T_2) = tr\ T_1^* T_2$, for (3) it is the trace norm $tr \sqrt{T^*T}$.

It turns out that each one of these algebras can be identified with a tensor product, (1) with $H \otimes_\lambda H$, where λ is the operator norm or so-called least cross norm, (2) with $H \otimes_\sigma H$, where σ is the Schmidt norm and (3) with $H \otimes_\gamma H$, where γ is the trace or greatest cross norm. These algebras have rather interesting properties. For instance, they are all semisimple and topologically simple [**4**, appendix]. Their duals (conjugate) spaces are also algebras of operators, and there are close connections between the duality theory of elements of a pair of one of these algebras and its dual, on the one hand, and the structure of the algebras on the other. The dual $(H \otimes_\lambda H)'$ of $H \otimes_\lambda H$ is $H \otimes_\gamma H$, $(H \otimes_\sigma H)' = H \otimes_\sigma H$ (of course) and $(H \otimes_\gamma H)' = \mathcal{L}(H)$. For these relations, see [**5**, pp 110–115].

2. TENSOR PRODUCTS

In attempting to generalize the above theory to arbitrary Banach spaces, one is led to the consideration of the algebraic tensor product

The present is a summary of results in Sections 8 and 9 of [1]. Support of the present work by National Science Foundation research grants (NSF G-19752 and NSF G-24295) is gratefully acknowledged.

$E' \otimes E$ of a Banach space E by its dual space E'. We shall limit our considerations to complex spaces. The action of an $x \in E$ and an $x' \in E'$ on each other will be denoted by $\langle x, x' \rangle$. The tensor product $E' \otimes E$ is the vector space of all objects

$$\supset = \sum_{i=1}^{n} x_i' \otimes x_i, \tag{1}$$

each of which is to be interpreted as an operator $T_{\supset}$ of finite rank, given by

$$T_{\supset} x = \sum_{i=1}^{n} \langle x, x_i' \rangle x_i. \tag{2}$$

The algebraic operations on $E' \otimes E$ are the usual algebraic operations on operators. The trace $tr \supset$ of a tensor $\supset$ in (1) is defined [**2**, p. 78] as

$$tr \supset = \sum_{i=1}^{n} \langle x_i, x_i' \rangle. \tag{3}$$

One shows that (3) is independent of the particular representation (1) of $\supset$. The greatest cross norm $\gamma(\supset)$ is defined [**5**, p. 38] as

$$\gamma(\supset) = \inf \sum_{i=1}^{n} \|x_i'\| \, \|x_i\|, \tag{4}$$

where the inf is taken over all possible representations of $\supset$ of the form (1). We consider on $E' \otimes E$ a norm α which is majorized by γ, and denote the associated complete space by $E' \otimes_\alpha E$. For such a norm α, the typical element U of $(E' \otimes_\alpha E)'$ is given by an operator (which we continue to denote by U) of $\mathfrak{L}(E')$, determined by the relation

$$\langle x, Ux' \rangle = \langle x' \otimes x, U \rangle. \tag{5}$$

In this way we can identify the dual $(E' \otimes_\alpha E)'$ with a vector subspace of $\mathfrak{L}(E')$. We shall say that α is *strongly modular* if $(E' \otimes_\alpha E)'$ is a two-sided ideal of $\mathfrak{L}(E')$. We emphasize at the moment the purely algebraic nature of the definition of the concept of strong modularity. The rest of this exposition concerns its topological implications.

3. ALGEBRAS OF KERNELS

In what remains of this work α will denote a strongly modular norm of $E' \otimes E$. One can show, as a first topological consequence of the definition, that α majorizes the operator norm, i.e., the mapping $\mathfrak{D} \to T_{\mathfrak{D}}$ in (2) is continuous with respect to the α-topology of $E' \otimes E$ and the operator norm topology of $\mathcal{L}(E)$, hence can be extended to a continuous representation $\mathfrak{D} \to T_{\mathfrak{D}}$ of $E' \otimes_{\alpha} E$ into $\mathcal{L}(E)$. We shall denote this representation by $\pi_0 : E' \otimes_{\alpha} E \to \mathcal{L}(E)$. Little is known about this mapping; in particular, it is not known if it is always isomorphic. We shall say that $\mathfrak{D}$ is a kernel of $T_{\mathfrak{D}}$ and shall refer to each $\mathfrak{D} \in E' \otimes_{\alpha} E$ as a kernel of type α. The mapping $\mathfrak{D} \to T_{\mathfrak{D}}$ is, however, isomorphic on $E' \otimes E \subset E' \otimes_{\alpha} E$, and maps $E' \otimes E$ onto the space of all bounded operators on E of finite rank. Since these operators form a subalgebra (indeed, a two-sided ideal) of the algebra $\mathcal{L}(E)$, a multiplication of kernels is defined on $E' \otimes E$, turning $E' \otimes E$ into a complex algebra, in such a way that the restriction of π_0 to $E' \otimes E$ is an isomorphism of the resulting algebra onto the algebra of all bounded operators on E of finite rank. Actually, the multiplication on $E' \otimes E$ is obtained by extending linearly, the product

$$(x_1' \otimes x_1)(x_2' \otimes x_2) = \langle x_2, x_1' \rangle \, x_2' \otimes x_1 \tag{6}$$

of decomposable tensors. One shows that the product of kernels is continuous with respect to α, hence, can be extended to $E' \otimes_{\alpha} E$, which then becomes a Banach algebra under an equivalent strongly modular norm. We shall assume, without loss of generality, that α is already such a norm. A Banach algebra $E' \otimes_{\alpha} E$ obtained by means of the above construction is called an *algebra of kernels* and its elements *kernels*.

The null space η_{α} of π_0 is the left anihilator and the right anihilator of $E' \otimes_{\alpha} E$. For the case $\alpha = \gamma$, this result is due to Grothendieck [**3**, Lemme, p. 350]. The space η_{α} is also the Jacobson radical of $E' \otimes_{\alpha} E$ (Rickart, [**4**, Theorem 2.8.21, p. 103]). Furthermore, one can show that η_{α} is the only proper closed maximal two-sided ideal of $E' \otimes_{\alpha} E$. It follows from these facts that the algebra of kernel $E' \otimes_{\alpha} E$ is semi-simple if and only if it is topologically simple (has only the obvious closed two-sided ideals), if and only if $\eta_{\alpha} = \{0\}$. We also have that the set of all closed two-sided ideals of $E' \otimes_{\alpha} E$ coincides with the lattice of all closed vector sub-spaces of η_{α}.

An algebra of operators on a discrete vector space is said to be *strictly irreducible* if the only vector subspaces which it leaves invariant are $\{0\}$ and the entire vector space [**4**, p. 48]. A representation of an algebra as an algebra of operators is said to be strictly irreducible if the representing algebra of operators is strictly irreducible.

THEOREM 1. The representation $\pi_0 : E' \otimes_{\alpha} E \to \mathcal{L}(E)$ is strictly irreducible. Furthermore, every continuous strictly irreducible representation $\pi : E' \otimes_{\alpha} E \to \mathcal{L}(F)$, where F is a Banach space, is of the form $\pi = \chi \circ \pi_0$, where χ is an isomorphism of the image $\pi_0(E' \otimes_{\alpha} E)$ into $\mathcal{L}(F)$.

4. DUALITY OF ALGEBRAS OF KERNELS

Let us first consider the Banach space $(E' \otimes_\alpha E)'$. By the definition of strong modularity we have that $(E' \otimes_\alpha E)'$ is a two-sided ideal, hence a subalgebra, of $\mathcal{L}(E')$. A simple application of the uniform boundedness theorem shows that composition of operators is actually continuous with respect to the natural norm of $(E' \otimes_\alpha E)'$ as the dual space of $E' \otimes_\alpha E$. Hence $(E' \otimes_\alpha E)'$ is a Banach algebra under a norm equivalent to its natural norm α'. We thus have the two Banach algebras $E' \otimes_\alpha E$ and $(E' \otimes_\alpha E)'$ in duality, the latter being an algebra of operators on E'. We are going to study the relation between this duality and the ideal structure of the algebras.

It also follows from the fact that $(E' \otimes_\alpha E)'$ is a two-sided ideal of $\mathcal{L}(E')$ that $(E' \otimes_\alpha E)'$ contains the two-sided ideal consisting of all operators on E' of finite rank, whose closure with respect to α', is denoted by $\mathcal{G}_\alpha$. From this we easily get the following theorem.

THEOREM 2. The algebra $(E' \otimes_\alpha E)'$ is a strictly irreduicible algebra of operators.

In studying the relation between the ideal structure of an algebra of kernels and its dual algebra one relies heavily on the existence of pairings $U \times \mathfrak{D}$ and $\mathfrak{D} \times U$ of kernels and dual kernels, with values in the tensor products $E' \otimes_\gamma E''$ and $E' \otimes_\gamma E$, respectively. They are defined as follows, for decomposable tensors.

$$U \times (x' \otimes x) = x' \otimes U'x \qquad (x' \otimes x) \times U = Ux' \otimes x. \tag{7}$$

In (7), U is an element of $\mathcal{L}(E')$ and $U' \in \mathcal{L}(E'')$ stands for its transposed operator.

THEOREM 3. The pairings in (7) can be extended by linearity and by passing to the limit to pairings $U \times \mathfrak{D} \in E' \otimes_\gamma E''$ and $\mathfrak{D} \times U \in E' \otimes_\gamma E$, for every $\mathfrak{D} \in E' \otimes_\alpha E$ and $U \in (E' \otimes_\alpha E)'$, such that

$$\gamma(U \times \mathfrak{D}) \leqq \alpha'(U)\alpha(\mathfrak{D}) \geqq \gamma(\mathfrak{D} \times U) \qquad \text{and} \tag{8}$$

$$\langle \mathfrak{D}, U \rangle = \operatorname{tr}(U \times \mathfrak{D}) = \operatorname{tr}(\mathfrak{D} \times U). \tag{9}$$

The fact that the traces involved in (9) are well-defined is a result of Grothendieck [**2**, p. 78].

In studying the theory of ideals, let us begin with the radical $\mathfrak{N}_\alpha$ of $E' \otimes_\alpha E$. By the *polar* K° of a subset $K \subset E' \otimes_\alpha E$ we mean the set of all U's, such that $| < \mathfrak{D}, U > | \leqq 1$, for every $\mathfrak{D} \in K$. If K is a vector space we may use 0 in the place of 1 in the definition of K°. The polar C° in $E' \otimes_\alpha E$ of a subset $C \subset (E' \otimes_\alpha E)'$, is defined similarly.

THEOREM 4. The polar of $\mathfrak{N}_\alpha$ is the weak* closure of $\mathcal{G}_\alpha$.

COROLLARY 1. $E' \otimes_\alpha E$ is semisimple if and only if $\mathcal{G}_\alpha$ is weakly* dense in $(E' \otimes_\alpha E)'$.

THEOREM 5. We shall say that E satisfies the *condition of approximation* of Grothendieck [**2**, Definition 9, p. 167] if every compact operator of E is the limit, with respect to the operator norm of operators of finite rank.

THEOREM 6. Suppose that E satisfies the condition of approximation of Grothendieck. Then the polar set of a left ideal in $E' \otimes_\alpha E$ is its right anihilator with respect to the pairing $\mathfrak{D} \times U$. The polar set in $E' \otimes_\alpha E$ of a right ideal in $(E' \otimes_\alpha E)'$ is its left anihilator under the pairing $\mathfrak{D} \times U$.

THEOREM 7. If E satisfies the condition of approximation of Grothendieck, then the polar set of a left ideal of $E' \otimes_\alpha E$ is a weakly* closed right ideal of $(E' \otimes_\alpha E)'$. The polar set in $E' \otimes_\alpha E$ of a right ideal of $(E' \otimes_\alpha E)'$ is a closed left ideal of $E' \otimes_\alpha E$.

Hence the operation of taking polars establishes a 1-1 correspondence between the closed left ideals of $E' \otimes_\alpha E$ and the weakly* closed right ideals of $(E' \otimes_\alpha E)'$. The following theorems are valid for more general spaces, but, for the sake of simplicity, we restrict ourselves to reflexive spaces.

THEOREM 8. If E is reflexive and satisfies the condition of approximation of Grothendieck, then the polar set of a right ideal of $E' \otimes_\alpha E$ is its left anihilator with respect to the pairing $U \times \mathfrak{D}$, and the polar set in $E' \otimes_\alpha E$ of a left ideal of $(E' \otimes_\alpha E)'$ is its right anihilator with respect to the pairing $U \times \mathfrak{D}$.

Theorem 8 yields now an analogue of Theorem 7 (which we omit) for right ideals of $E' \otimes_\alpha E$ and left ideals of $(E' \otimes_\alpha E)'$. Combining all these results we now obtain the following theorem.

THEOREM 9. If E is reflexive and satisfies the condition of approximation of Grothendieck, then the polar set of a vector subspace of $\mathfrak{N}_\alpha$ is a weakly* closed two-sided ideal of $(E' \otimes_\alpha E)'$. The polar set of a non-trivial two-sided ideal of $(E' \otimes_\alpha E)'$ is a closed vector subspace of $\mathfrak{N}_\alpha$.

We have thus established a 1-1 correspondence between the closed vector subspaces of $\mathfrak{N}_\alpha$ and the non-trivial weakly* closed two-sided ideals of $(E' \otimes_\alpha E)'$.

BIBLIOGRAPHY

1. Gil de Lamadrid, J., Topological modules: Banach algebras, tensor products, algebras of kernels, *Trans. Amer. Math Soc.*, Vol. 126, pp. 361–419.
2. Grothendieck, A., Produits tensoriels topologiques et espaces nucléaires, *Amer. Math. Soc.*, No. 16, 1955.

3. Grothendieck, A., La théorie de Fredholm, *Bul. Soc. Math. France* 84 (1956), pp. 319–384.
4. Rickart, C. E., General theory of Banach algebras, Van Nostrand, New York, 1960.
5. Schatten, R., A theory of cross spaces, *Ann. Math. Studies* No. 26, Princeton University Press, Princeton, 1950.

Ergodic Flows and Functional Analysis

LEON W. GREEN

At the conference I outlined a procedure for applying standard function-analytic techniques to the question of ergodicity of certain flows on manifolds. Since the results announced at that time are to appear elsewhere, I shall here merely sketch the basic approach, and use it to prove a new theorem on strong mixing which clarifies the role the horocycles play in E. Hopf's classical treatment of manifolds with constant negative curvature [**3**]. Only Hilbert space methods will be used here; the verification of the hypotheses for specific flows on manifolds can be very difficult and is in many cases open.

1. ROOT OPERATORS

Let $\{X_t\}$, be a one-parameter group of unitary operators in the Hilbert space $\mathcal{H}$. Denote by X its infinitesimal generator; it is well known that this is a closed, densely defined operator.

DEFINITION: The closed, densely defined operator H is a root operator for $\{X_t\}$ if there exist a dense linear subspace D of $\mathcal{H}$ and a bounded operator B such that

(i) $X_t D = D$ for all t,

and (ii) $XH - HX = BH$ on D.

In particular, condition (ii) requires that D be contained in the domains of H, X, XH, and HX. The operator B will be called the root of X corresponding to H.

THEOREM 1.1. Let the root B of X corresponding to H be positive definite. Then

$$\lim_{t\to\infty} HX_t\varphi = 0$$

strongly in $\mathcal{H}$, for every $\varphi \in D$.

Proof. For every $\varphi \in D$,

$$\frac{d}{dt}(X_{-t}HX_t\varphi) = -X_{-t}[X, H]X_t\varphi = -X_{-t}BHX_t\varphi = -B_tX_{-t}HX_t\varphi,$$

where $B_t = X_{-t}BX_t$. Set $\psi(t) = X_{-t}HX_t\varphi$ and suppose that $(B\xi, \xi) \geq c\|\xi\|^2$ for some $c > o$. Then

$$\frac{d}{dt}\|\psi(t)\|^2 = 2\,Re\left(\frac{d}{dt}\psi(t), \psi(t)\right) = -2(B_t\psi, \psi) \leq -2c\|\psi\|^2.$$

By integration, this inequality implies that

$$\|HX_t\varphi\|^2 = \|X_{-t}HX_t\varphi\|^2 \leq e^{-2ct}\|H\varphi\|^2,$$

which immediately leads to the conclusion of the theorem.

COROLLARY 1.2. If B, H, and X are as above, and H is the infinitesimal generator of the one-parameter group of bounded operators $\{H_s\}$, then, for each s,

$$\lim_{t\to\infty} X_{-t}H_sX_t = I$$

strongly on all of $\mathcal{H}$.

Proof. It is known that

$$H_s\xi - \xi = \int_o^s H_\sigma H\xi\, d\sigma,$$

for all $\xi \in D$. Set $\xi = X_t\varphi$, and apply the theorem as follows:

$$\|X_{-t}H_sX_t\varphi - \varphi\| \leq \left(\int_o^s \|X_{-t}H_\sigma\|\, d\sigma\right)\|HX_t\varphi\| \to 0,$$

since the integral, which equals $\int_o^s \|H_\sigma\|\, d\sigma$, is bounded for each fixed s. The proof of the corollary follows by a density argument, since the operators in question are uniformly bounded when s is fixed.

The applications to geodesic flows should be mentioned. In, say, the case of two-dimensional compact manifolds with negative curvature, $\{X_t\}$ is the geodesic flow in the unit tangent bundle and $\{H_s\}$ is the horocycle flow. The operator B turns out to be multiplication by a real function which is bounded away from zero (the geodesic curvature of the horocycles). It follows from the corollary that any eigenfunction of the geodesic flow is an invariant function of the horocycle flow. The horocycle flow is not in general measure preserving, so the group $\{H_s\}$ is not usually unitary. (Corollary 1.2 is what was called "Mautner's Lemma" in [**1**] and [**2**].)

2. SPECIAL TYPES OF GROUPS

Let $\mathcal{C}$ be a closed linear manifold of $\mathcal{H}$. A one-parameter group of operators in $\mathcal{H}$ will be called $\mathcal{C}$-*ergodic* if its set of invariant vectors (= null space of its infinitesimal generator) is precisely $\mathcal{C}$. A one-parameter unitary group $\{X_t\}$ will be called *weakly* $\mathcal{C}$*-mixing* if it is $\mathcal{C}$-ergodic and the restriction of the group to $\mathcal{C}^{\perp}$, the orthogonal complement of $\mathcal{C}$, has only continuous spectrum. A $\mathcal{C}$-ergodic unitary group $\{X_t\}$ will be called *strongly* $\mathcal{C}$*-mixing* if, for any φ, $\psi \in \mathcal{C}^{\perp}$, $\lim_{t\to\infty} (X_t\varphi, \psi) = 0$. For dynamical systems in spaces of finite measure, $\mathcal{C}$ is of course taken to be the one-dimensional space of constants.

THEOREM 2.1. Let $\{X_t\}$ and $\{H_s\}$ be $\mathcal{C}$-ergodic one-parameter groups with $\{X_t\}$ unitary. Suppose H, the infinitesimal generator of $\{H_s\}$, is a root operator for $\{X_t\}$ with positive definite root. Then $\{X_t\}$ is strongly $\mathcal{C}$-mixing.

Proof. Let $\varphi \in D$ and $\xi \in$ domain of H^*. Then, by Theorem 1.1,

$$\lim_{t\to\infty} (X_t\varphi, H^*\xi) = \lim_{t\to\infty} (HX_t\varphi, \xi) = 0.$$

Since, for fixed φ, the vectors $X_t\varphi$ are uniformly bounded,

$$\lim_{t\to\infty} (X_t\varphi, \psi) = 0 \qquad (*)$$

for every ψ in the closure of the range of H^*. But this is precisely the orthogonal complement to the null space of H, namely, $\mathcal{C}^{\perp}$, by the hypothesis of ergodicity. Another density argument shows that (*) holds for arbitrary φ.

This theorem may be used to shorten slightly Hopf's proof in §§10, 11 of [**3**], for the strong mixing of geodesic flows in spaces of constant negative curvature. Sinaĭ has introduced the notion of fields transversal with respect to an automorphism of a measure space and proved the, more interesting from the point of view of dynamical systems, measure theoretic analogue of Theorem 2.1. (cf. his Theorem 7.1 of [**4**].) Of course, Sinaĭ's analysis in terms of K-systems is much deeper and yields more complete results. This note, however, may serve to separate the formal, Lie-algebraic parts of the theory from the measure-theoretic.

REFERENCES

1. Auslander, L. and L. W. Green, G-induced Flows, *American Journal of Mathematics*, vol. **88** (1966), pp. 43-60.
2. Auslander, L., L. W. Green, and F. Hahn, Flows on homogeneous spaces, *Annals of Mathematical Studies No. 53*, Princeton University Press, Princeton, N. J., 1963.

3. Hopf, E., "Statistik der geodätischen Linien in Mannigfaltigkeiten negativer Krummung," Ber. Verh., Sachs. Akad. Wiss., Leipzig, *Math.-Nat. Kl.*, vol. **51** (1939), pp. 261–304.
4. Sinaĭ, J. G., Classical dynamical systems with countable Lebesgue spectrum II, *Izvestia Akad. Nauk SSSR Ser. Mat. 30* (1966), 15–68.

Added in proof: The hypotheses on the domain D of the definition must be strengthened to imply that $\psi(t)$ be strongly differentiable. This is the situation in applications.

Some Aspects of Differential Equations in B-Algebras

EINAR HILLE

In the main I shall deal with differential equations in a complex non-commutative algebra B with unit element e. Coefficients and solutions will be B-valued functions of a complex variable and the problems studied are those which are suggested in a natural manner by the classical theory of differential equations in the complex plane and by the matrix case. Most of the time first order linear equations will be in the focus but some time will be devoted to the second order case and to nonlinear problems, in particular Riccati's equation.

1. THE HOMOGENEOUS LINEAR FIRST ORDER EQUATION

That the equation is homogeneous means that every term contains either a factor $w(z)$ or $w'(z)$, but the coefficients may multiply these factors on the left, on the right or one on either side. In the general case we have something completely unmanageable. We have to restrict ourselves and the most interesting and most promising case is that of

$$w'(z) = F(z)\, w(z) \tag{1.1}$$

where $F(z)$ is a B-valued function holomorphic in a neighborhood of a point $z = z_0$ of the complex plane. The theory of this equation does not differ essentially from that of

$$w'(z) = w(z)\, F(z). \tag{1.2}$$

On the other hand

$$F(z)\, w'(z) = w(z), \tag{1.3}$$

where $F(z)$ is not regular in the algebra, poses entirely new problems. For an example let me mention that if q is a nilpotent element of the algebra, then the equation

$$q\, w'(z) = w(z) \tag{1.4}$$

has $w(z) \equiv 0$ as its only solution and this extends also to certain classes of quasinilpotent elements q.

Let us return to equation (1.1) with an initial condition

$$w(z_0) = w_0, \tag{1.5}$$

a given element of B. The method of successive approximations applies and gives a unique solution $w(z; z_0, w_0)$ which is holomorphic not merely in a neighborhood of $z = z_0$ but actually in the Mittag-Leffler star $A(z_0, F)$ of $F(z)$ with respect to z_0. We have

$$w(z, z_0, w_0) = w(z; z_0, e)\, w_0 \tag{1.6}$$

and the algebraic nature of the solution is determined entirely by that of the initial element w_0.

It is obvious that $w(z; z_0, w_0)$ is a singular element of the algebra for every z in the domain of existence of the solution if w_0 is singular. But here it is "iff." It is clear that $w(z; z_0, e)$ is regular in some neighborhood of $z = z_0$. Actually it is regular everywhere in $A(z_0; F)$. This follows essentially from the relation

$$w(z; z_0, e) = w(z; z_1, e)\, w(z_1; z_0, e), \quad z_1 \in A(z_0; F), \tag{1.7}$$

which follows from (1.6) and serves as the basis for the analytic as well as the algebraic continuation of the solution. We say that *a solution* $w(z; z_0, w_0)$ *is fundamental if it is algebraically regular.* A nasc for this to be the case is that w_0 be regular.

Formula (1.7) gives the analytic continuation of $w(z; z_0, e)$ in $A(z_1; F)$. If $z_2 \in A(z_1; F)$ we can then get the analytic continuation in $A(z_2; F)$ etc. This shows that analytic continuation is possible along any path that does not encounter a singular point of F. If the path is a closed curve, beginning and ending at $z = z_0$, then if we start with the value e we may very well return with a different value. There is an element $m(C)$ of B, determined by the path C such that traversing C in one direction carries

$$w(z; z_0, e) \quad \text{into} \quad w(z_0, e)\, m(C) \tag{1.8}$$

and traversing $-C$ instead carries

$$w(z; z_0, e) \quad \text{into} \quad w(z; z_0, e)[m(C)]^{-1}. \tag{1.9}$$

There substitutions $m(C)$ form a group, the *group of monodromy* of the equation. The dependence of the group on the initial point z_0 is only apparent; changing initial point merely introduces an isomorphic group. The group is finitely generated if F has only a finite number of isolated singular points plus a finite number of singular lines.

Let us return to the notion of "fundamental solution." If $B = M_n$, the algebra of $n \times n$ matrices, a solution matrix is fundamental if and only if the *Wronskian* is $\neq 0$. If

$$W'(z) = F(z)\, W(z), \tag{1.10}$$

the Wronskian is the determinant of $W(z)$ and

$$\det [W(z)] = \det [W_0] \exp \left\{ \int_{z_0}^{z} Tr[F(s)]\, ds \right\}, \tag{1.11}$$

where Tr stands for the trace of the matrix F.

We can generalize this as follows. Suppose that μ is a functional defined on B and having the following properties:

(i) μ is multiplicative and neither identically zero nor identically one.
(ii) μ is continuous and bounded.
(iii) μ is Fréchet analytic at $x = e$.
(iv) μ vanishes on the singular elements of B.

Since $\mu(e) = 1$ it follows that $\mu(a) \neq 0$ if a is regular. We have then

$$\mu[w(z; z_0, w_0)] = \mu(w_0) \exp \left\{ \int_{z_0}^{z} \delta\mu[e, F(s)]\, ds \right\} \tag{1.12}$$

and for any $g \in B$

$$\delta\mu[e,g] = \lim_{\eta \to 0} \frac{1}{\eta} [\mu(e + \eta g) - \mu(e)].$$

In the case $B = M_n$ the Fréchet derivative at E in the direction F is simply the trace of F. Condition (iv) above ensures that the formula is trivially true for singular elements w_0. If this condition does not hold we must restrict ourselves to nonsingular initial values.

If μ is linear as well as multiplicative and if B is commutative then the formula becomes

$$\mu[w(z; z_0, w_0)] = \mu(w_0) \exp \left\{ \int_{z_0}^{z} \mu[F(s)]\, ds \right\}, \tag{1.13}$$

and this holds even if B has no unit element.

The definition of a fundamental solution as one which is algebraically regular lacks meaning in an algebra without unit element. But even in such an algebra there would seem to be solutions which are *more equal* than others, but I am at a loss how to single out such elements. Perhaps the circle product $p \quad q = p + q - pq$ could be used. Another guess, possibly a better one, is to say that *a solution is fundamental if it annihilates no nontrivial multiplicative functional.*

2. APPROACH TO A SINGULAR POINT

The singularities of the solutions are determined by those of F to which the point at infinity may have to be added. In general the singularities of the solutions are much more complicated than those of F. For a study of the behavior of a solution as z tends to a singular point, we fall back on what is known as Gronwall's Lemma:

Let $f(t)$ and $g(t) \in C^+[0, \omega]$, let $K(t) \in C^+(0, \omega] \cap L(0, \omega)$ and let

$$f(t) \leqq g(t) + \int_0^t K(s) f(s)\, ds, \tag{2.1}$$

then

$$f(t) \leqq g(t) + \int_0^t K(s) \exp\left[\int_s^t K(u)\, du\right] g(s)\, ds. \tag{2.2}$$

Suppose now that the given equation is

$$w'(t) = F(t)\, w(t), \tag{2.3}$$

where $F(t)$ is B-valued and continuous in the interval $(0, \tau]$. It is desired to find bounds for $w(t)$ as $t \downarrow 0$. Here the Lemma gives the double inequality

$$\| w(\tau) \| \exp\left\{- \int_t^\tau \| F(s) \|\, ds\right\}$$

$$\leqq \| w(t) \| \leqq \| w(\tau) \| \exp\left\{\int_t^\tau \| F(s) \|\, ds\right\}. \tag{2.4}$$

This shows that the integrability properties of $\| F(t) \|$ are decisive.

Note that the inequalities can be extended to complex variables. Consider the equation

$$w'(z) = F(z)\, w(z) \tag{2.5}$$

where $F(z)$ is holomorphic in a sector

$$\alpha \leqq \arg z \leqq \beta, \qquad 0 < |z| \leq R.$$

Set

$$\max \| F(re^{i\theta}) \| \equiv K(r), \qquad \begin{matrix}\max\\ \min\end{matrix} \| w(Re^{i\theta}) \| = \begin{matrix}M\\ m\end{matrix}.$$

Then the inequality reads

$$m \exp\left\{-\int_r^R K(s)\,ds\right\} \leqq \| w(re^{i\theta}) \| \leqq M \exp\left\{\int_r^R K(s)\,ds\right\}. \tag{2.7}$$

Here there are two alternatives.

(i) $K(s) \in L(0, \omega)$. Then the equation (2.5) has a unique solution which tends to e in the sector as $z \to 0$ and all solutions tend to finite limits, the limit being 0 iff $w(z) \equiv 0$.

(ii) $K(s) \notin L(0, \omega)$. Here there are many possibilities. The most interesting one or at least the one best studied is that where $K(s)$ becomes infinite as an integral power of $1/s$. Again there are two distinct cases.

(iia) $K(s) = a/s$. Here

$$m\left(\frac{r}{R}\right)^a \leqq \| w(r\,e^{io}) \| \leqq M\left(\frac{R}{r}\right)^a. \tag{2.8}$$

This case includes in particular that of a *regular singular point* where

$$F(z) = \frac{1}{z}\{a_0 + a_1 z + \cdots\}, \qquad a_n \in B, \tag{2.9}$$

where the power series converges for $|z| < R$.

(iib) $K(s) = a\,s^{-p-1}$. Here

$$m \exp\left\{\frac{a}{p}[R^{-p} - r^{-p}]\right\} \leqq \| w(r\,e^{io}) \| \leqq M \exp\left\{\frac{a}{p}[r^{-p} - R^{-p}]\right\}. \tag{2.10}$$

This includes in particular an *irregular singular point of rank p*.

3. THE REGULAR SINGULAR CASE

We return to equation (2.9). Here the behavior of the solution is essentially determined by the leading coefficient a_0. In the case of an "Euler equation" with

$$F(z) = a/z$$

a solution would be given by

$$z^a = \exp(a \log z).$$

This suggests the classical approach

$$w(z) = \sum_{m=0}^{\infty} c_m z^{a_0 + me}. \tag{3.1}$$

Here it turns out that the spectral properties of a_0 as an element of B and of the *commutator operator*

$$C_{a_0} x = a_0 x - x a_0 \tag{3.2}$$

are decisive. If we substitute the series (3.1) into the differential equation, we obtain equations of the form

$$a_0 c_0 = c_0 a_0, \tag{3.3}$$

$$m c_m - a_0 c_m + c_m a_0 = \sum_{k=1}^{m} a_k c_{m-k}, \quad m = 1, 2, \ldots, \tag{3.4}$$

to be solved for the c_m's. We can take $c_0 = e$ and knowing c_0 we can solve successively for $c_1, c_2, \ldots$, if, and it is a big IF, no integer belongs to the spectrum of the operator C_{a_0}. Now the spectrum of the operator is contained in the difference set

$$\Delta \equiv \{\gamma \mid \gamma = \alpha - \beta, \quad \alpha \in \sigma(a), \beta \in \sigma(a)\}. \tag{3.5}$$

Thus an integer can belong to $\sigma(C_{a_0})$ only if two spectral values of a_0 differ by an integer. If this does not happen, then we can solve successively for the coefficients and the resulting series converges for $|z| < R$.

If integers should belong to $\sigma(C_a)$ there are two alternatives.

(1) All integers in question are poles of the resolvent of C_{a_0} and are finitely generated as spectral differences. This will happen if, e.g., the spectral values of a_0 which give rise to integral differences are themselves poles of the resolvents of a_0 as a left and right multiplier.

(2) Other singularities than poles are present and/or singularities are not finitely generated.

In case (1) a modification of a method of Frobenius combined with a theorem of Foguel and a representation theorem of the resolvent of the commutator due to Daletsky can be used and leads to solutions involving powers of log z. In case (2) no effective procedure has been found.

At an irregular singular point representations by generalized Laplace integerals are available at least in important special cases. This is an extension of a classical method of G. D. Birkhoff given by J. B. Miller. The case $p = 1$ which is more elementary, had been discussed by the author (unpublished).

4. THE GENERALIZED BESSEL EQUATION

Here is a linear second order problem. Given the equation

$$w''(z) + [e - F(z)]\, w(z) = 0, \tag{4.1}$$

where $F(z)$ is holomorphic outside a circle $|z| = R \geqq 0$ and

$$\int_{z_1}^{z_2} \| F(t) \| \, |dt| \leqq M \tag{4.2}$$

for any choice of two points z_1 and z_2 in $|z| > R$ which can be joined by a straight line segment all points of which are outside the disk. Note that Bessel's equation corresponds to $B = C$ and

$$F(z) = \left(\alpha^2 - \frac{1}{4}\right) z^{-2}.$$

Moreover, an equation of this type arises whenever the transformation of Liouville is applied to an equation of the form

$$[P(t)\, y'(t)] + Q(t)\, y(t) = 0 \tag{4.3}$$

where $P(t)$ and $Q(t)$ are polynomials in t and deg $(P) >$ deg $(Q) - 2$. More general cases also lead to the same normal form so it is one of the most important equations in classical theory.

The problem is to discuss the asymptotic behavior of the solutions of (4.1) outside of the disk. This is a perturbation problem and the unperturbed equation

$$w_0'' + w_0 = 0 \tag{4.4}$$

has the independent solutions

$$e \exp(iz) \text{ and } e \exp(-iz). \tag{4.5}$$

Using Gronwall's Lemma one proves that any solution of (4.1) is bounded in any horizontal strip omitting a disk $|z| \leqq R + \epsilon$. This shows the existence of

$$w(z) + \int_z^{\infty} \sin(t - z)\, F(t)\, w(t)\, dt.$$

Differentiation shows that this function is a solution of (4.4). If this solution is $w_0(z)$ we see that $w(z)$ satisfies the singular Volterra equation

$$w(z) = w_0(z) - \int_z^{\infty} \sin(t - z)\, F(t)\, w(t)\, dt \tag{4.6}$$

where the integral is taken along the horizontal from z to $+\infty + iy$. To this equation we again apply Gronwall's Lemma and obtain

$$\| w(z) - w_0(z) \| \leqq M(b) \left\{ \exp\left[\int_z^{\infty} \| F(s) \| \, ds \right] - 1 \right\} \tag{4.7}$$

where $M(b) = \max \| w_0(z) \|$ in the strip $-b \leqq y \leqq b$. This is for approach to infinity in the right half of the strip. A similar formula holds in the left half but usually with a different solution $w_0(z)$.

The special solutions $E^+(z)$ and $E^-(z)$ which correspond to

$$w_0(z) = e \exp (iz) \text{ and } e \exp (-iz),$$

respectively, are the analogues of Hankel's functions in the theory of the Bessel equation in the strict sense. These solutions have asymptotic representations valid in angles of opening $3\pi - \epsilon$ centered on $\arg z = \frac{1}{2}\pi$ in the first case and on $\arg z = -\frac{1}{2}\pi$ in the second. The representation in the first case is of the form

$$\| E^+(z) \exp (-iz) - e \| \leqq \exp \left[\int_z^\infty \| F(s) \| \, | ds | \right] - 1 \tag{4.8}$$

where the path of integration is a straight line in the (2π)-angle symmetric to the central line. A similar formula holds for $E^-(z)$ in its sector.

The solution $w_0(z)$ in (4.7) is in general of the form

$$w_0(z) = a \exp (iz) + b \exp (-iz), \qquad a, b \in B. \tag{4.9}$$

In the classical case $B = C$ such a solution would be oscillatory in some horizontal strip and from (4.9) one could conclude that $w(z)$ is also oscillatory and its zeros approach those of $w_0(z)$. In the general case this does not make sense but multiplicative functionals may still be oscillatory and there may conceivably be asymptotic relations between zeros. Some examples show that this will indeed happen in the matrix case using the determinant as the functional.

5. EQUATIONS OF HIGHER ORDER. THE RICCATI EQUATION

In the classical theory Riccati's equation

$$w'(z) = A_0(z) + A_1(z) \, w(z) + A_2(z) \, [w(z)]^2 \tag{5.1}$$

plays an outstanding role for two distinct reasons:

(1) The equation is closely related to the linear second-order equation. The logarithmic derivative of a solution of such an equation satisfies a Riccati equation and introducing $y'/y = w$ in (5.1) gives a second order linear equation.

(2) Of all equations of the form

$$w' = P(z, w) \tag{5.2}$$

with P a polynomial in w, the Riccati equation is the only nonlinear case where the critical points are fixed, i.e. given by the coefficients of the equation. Riccati's equation does have movable singularities but they are simple poles. No point can be a branch-point of a solution unless it is a singularity of A_0 to A_2 or a zero of A_2.

Here there is a big question of how much of this remains true in the B-algebra case or even in the matrix case. The first property is sufficiently formal so it remains valid and thanks to this fact a considerable part of the theory of the abstract Riccati equation can be derived from corresponding second-order linear equations which are easier to handle. But property (2) goes by the board at least in the strict sense that it holds for (5.1).

Such evidence as is available to me shows that movable singularities in the Riccati case are probably isolated singularities in the neighborhood of which the solution is single valued and can be expanded in convergent Laurent series where the negative powers of order < -1 have quasinilpotent coefficients. In the higher order case there are movable singularities which are branch points combined with an essential singularity. In the matrix case the quasinilpotents are nilpotents and instead of essential singularities we have poles which may be of any order.

The following simple example is of some interest in itself and may possibly be typical. Take

$$(k-1)\, w'(z) = -[w(z)]^k,\ k > 1. \tag{5.3}$$

We start with the case $k = 2$

$$W'(z) = -[W(z)]^2. \tag{5.4}$$

This is the differential equation satisfied by the resolvent of any element of B, more generally, by any locally bounded solution of the first resolvent equation. No solution of this equation can vanish for a finite value of z unless it vanishes identically. By the theorem of Nagumo any point of the plane can be a singular point of a solution and at such a point there is a convergent Laurent series where the holomorphic as well as the principal parts are solutions in their own rights. If the singular point is at $z = 0$ the principal part has the form

$$W(z) = j z^{-1} + q z^{-2} + \cdots + q^{m-1} z^{-m} + \cdots \tag{5.5}$$

which converges for all $z \neq 0$. Here j is an idempotent, q a quasinilpotent, $jq = qj = q$. In the matrix case, $B = M_n$, we have $q^n = 0$ and we have a pole of an order not exceeding n.

We can reduce the general case (5.3) to the special one (5.4) by setting

$$W = w^{k-1}. \tag{5.6}$$

It follows that (5.3) also has singularities at preassigned points. In particular, there is a solution given by

$$w(z) = (j/z)^{1/(k-1)}\left[\sum_{m=0}^{\infty} (q/z)^m\right]^{1/(k-1)} \tag{5.7}$$

Since the series inside the brackets represent a function holomorphic for $z \neq 0$ and different from zero, the formal expansion of the $(k - 1)$th root converges for all values of $z \neq 0$ and the resulting Laurent series has coefficients which are quasinilpotents. In the matrix case it reduces to a polynomial in $1/z$ of degree $n - 1$ or less. The outside factor contributes an algebraic branch point and is not single-valued. Thus in this case there are movable branch points which in general are combined with essential singular points.

Hopf-von Neumann Algebras*

JOHN ERNEST

1. INTRODUCTION

In this paper we propose to examine the interplay between the theory of locally compact groups and the theory of von Neumann algebras. In the spirit of [**12**] we consider the category of abstract von Neumann algebras where the relevant maps are the normal *-homomorphisms. In a von Neumann algebra, the σ-weak topology is intrinsic, that is to say, the σ-weak topology is independent of any particular concrete realization of the algebra as an algebra of operators acting on a particular Hilbert space. The normal *-homomorphisms are exactly the σ-weak continuous *-homomorphisms. (cf. [**2**].) The relevant maps in the category of locally compact groups are, of course, the continuous homomorphisms. Our main tool in examining the relation between these two categories is the big group algebra introduced in [**5**]. In that paper we exhibit a covariant functor, which associates with each locally compact group G, an abstract von Neumann algebra $\mathfrak{a}(G)$, called the big group algebra of G. This algebra is characterized by the following universal mapping property.

UNIVERSAL PROPERTY. Let G be a locally compact group. The big group algebra of G, denoted $\mathfrak{a}(G)$, is a von Neumann algebra containing G isomorphically and homeomorphically as a unitary group in the σ-weak topology, such that every strongly continuous unitary representation of G has a unique extension to a σ-weak continuous *-representation of $\mathfrak{a}(G)$.

First note that under these conditions G necessarily generates $\mathfrak{a}(G)$ as a von Neumann algebra. The following proof of this fact is due to Professor Falco Lorenz. Let $\mathfrak{a}(G)$ be represented concretely as a weekly closed *-algebra of operators acting on a Hilbert space $\mathcal{H}$. Let $\mathfrak{A}(G)$ denote the von Neumann subalgebra of $\mathfrak{a}(G)$ generated by G. If $\mathfrak{A}(G) \subsetneqq \mathfrak{a}(G)$, then $\mathfrak{a}(G)' \subsetneqq \mathfrak{A}(G)'$. Here $\mathfrak{a}(G)'$ denotes the commutant of $\mathfrak{a}(G)$. Thus there exists a unitary operator U in $\mathfrak{A}(G)'$ which is not in $\mathfrak{a}(G)'$.

*This research has been supported by a National Science Foundation contract.

Thus $A \to A$ and $A \to U A U^*$ are two distinct normal *-representations of $\mathfrak{a}(G)$ which have the same restriction to a strongly continuous unitary representation of G. This contradicts the assumption that every unitary representation of G has a unique extension to a normal *-representation of $\mathfrak{a}(G)$.

It is a simple matter to note that if such a von Neumann algebra exists, then it is completely determined up to a *-isomorphism. Indeed let G be embedded in two such von Neumann algebras $\mathfrak{a}_1$ and $\mathfrak{a}_2$. Let G_1 and G_2 denote the unitary groups in $\mathfrak{a}_1$ and $\mathfrak{a}_2$ which are isomorphic and homeomorphic to G. Let f_1 denote the isomorphism of G_1 onto G_2 and f_2 the inverse isomorphism. They are both strongly continuous unitary representations since the σ-weak and strong topologies are identical on the unitary group. Thus f_1 and f_2 have unique extensions f_1' and f_2' to normal *-representations of $\mathfrak{a}_1$ and $\mathfrak{a}_2$ respectively. Thus $f_2' \circ f_1'$ is a normal *-representation of $\mathfrak{a}_1$ which is an extension of the identity map on G_1. Since the identity map on $\mathfrak{a}_1$ is also such an extension, $f_2' \circ f_1'$ is the identity map on $\mathfrak{a}_1$. Similarly $f_1' \circ f_2'$ is the identity map on $\mathfrak{a}_2$. Thus f_1' is a *-isomorphism of $\mathfrak{a}_1$ onto $\mathfrak{a}_2$.

In section 2 we shall exhibit two ways of establishing the existence of such a universal group algebra. In the previous descriptions of this group algebra ([**5**], [**6**] and [**8**]) we restricted ourselves to separable (i.e., second countable) groups. Our main purpose in the description given in section 2, is to extend those results to nonseparable groups. We also include in section 2 some additional information on the topologies of the big group algebra, as given in [**5**]. Also in [**5**] we established a Banach space isomorphism of the big group algebra $\mathfrak{a}(G)$ with the second conjugate space of the C^*-group algebra $C^*(G)$. ($C^*(G)$ is defined as the completion of $L^1(G)$ with respect to the norm $|||f||| = \operatorname{Sup}_T \|Tf\|$, where the supremum is taken over all nowhere trivial *-representations of $L^1(G)$.) In this paper we establish that the multiplication defined in $\mathfrak{a}(G)$ corresponds exactly to the R. Arens multiplication [**1**] in the second conjugate space.

We note, in an example at the end of the paper, that every separable (nonfinite) compact abelian group has the same big group algebra, namely ℓ_∞. We are therefore led, in section 3, to introduce a new category, the category of Hopf-von Neumann algebras. We can then obtain a full and faithful covariant functor of the category of locally compact groups into the category of Hopf-von Neumann algebras. Thus two big group algebras, $\mathfrak{a}(G_1)$ and $\mathfrak{a}(G_2)$, are isomorphic as Hopf-von Neumann algebras if and only if G_1 is isomorphic to G_2. Further G and $\mathfrak{a}(G)$ have isomorphic automorphism groups. These results follow from a remarkable duality theorem for locally compact groups, obtained by N. Tatsuuma [**23**]. In section 3 we give a formulation of the Tatsuuma duality theorem in terms of Hopf-von Neumann algebras, and then give a proof based on Wendel's theorem [**26**].

2. THE BIG GROUP ALGEBRA FOR NONSEPARABLE GROUPS

We begin with a constructive definition of the big group algebra. Let G be a locally compact group and let $\mathcal{H}$ denote a Hilbert space of sufficiently high dimension that any cyclic representation of G is unitarily equivalent to a unitary representation acting on a closed subspace of $\mathcal{H}$. (For example it is sufficient to take the dimension of $\mathcal{H}$ equal to the cardinality of G, or equal to the cardinality of any set dense in G.) Let G^s denote the set of all strongly continuous unitary representations of G, with representation space some closed subspace of $\mathcal{H}$.

DEFINITION 2.1. Let $\mathfrak{a}(G)$ denote the set of all maps J on G^s, satisfying the following properties:

(1) for each L in G^s, $J(L)$ is a bounded linear operator on $\mathcal{H}(L)$, the representation space of L;

(2) $\sup\{\|J(L)\| : L \in G^s\} < +\infty$;

(3) if $L, M \in G^s$ and $L \leq M$, then $J(L)$ is the restriction of $J(M)$ to $\mathcal{H}(L)$;

(4) If L and M are elements of G^s and U is a linear isometry of $\mathcal{H}(L)$ onto $\mathcal{H}(M)$ such that $L = U^{-1}MU$, then

$$J(L) = UJ(M)U^{-1}.$$

$\mathfrak{a}(G)$ is given a *-algebra structure by defining addition, multiplication and the adjoint operation, pointwise. The supremum in condition (2) gives the norm, which makes $\mathfrak{a}(G)$ into a C^*-algebra. It is not difficult to verify that condition (3) may be replaced by

(3′) if $L \in G^s$, $M \in G^s$ and $\mathcal{H}(L) \perp \mathcal{H}(M)$, then

$$J(L \oplus M) = J(L) \oplus J(M).$$

The weak topology of $\mathfrak{a}(G)$ is defined to be the smallest topology such that the complex functions, $J \to (J(L)\psi, \varphi)$ are continuous, for all L in G^s and for all ψ, φ in the representation space of L. As described in [**5**] and [**6**], there exist natural norm decreasing embeddings of the classical group algebras $L^1(G)$, $C^*(G)$ and $M(G)$, into $\mathfrak{a}(G)$. For example, if ν is a finite complex measure in $M(G)$, then $\hat{\nu}$ is defined in $\mathfrak{a}(G)$ by the requirement that

$$\hat{\nu}(L) = \int_G L_x \, d_\nu$$

for all L in G^s. Further the embedding of $C^*(G)$ into $\mathfrak{a}(G)$ is an isometry.

The locally compact group G is naturally embedded, isomorphically and homeomorphically, as a unitary group in $\mathfrak{a}(G)$, relative to the weak topology of $\mathfrak{a}(G)$. Indeed if $x \in G$, let $\hat{x}(L) = L_x$ for all L in G^s. The proof given in [**5**] that this embedding is a homeomorphism depends on the separability of G. We therefore give here an alternative (and simpler) proof based on the following lemma. (cf. Corollary 10.3, [**20**]). This proof of Lemma 2.2 is due to J. M. G. Fell.

LEMMA 2.2. The left regular representation of a locally compact group is a weak operator topology homeomorphism.

Proof. Let L_{x_ν} denote a net converging to the identity $I = L_e$ of the image group. We wish to show that x_ν converges to e. Proceeding by way of contradiction, we suppose it does not. Then there exists a subnet, say x_n of x_ν, and a compact neighborhood U of e such that $x_n \notin U$, for all n. Choose a compact neighborhood N of e such that $NN^{-1} \subset U$. Then for each x_n we have

$$(L_{x_n}\chi_N, \chi_N) = \int \chi_{x_nN} \cdot \chi_N)d\mu = \mu(x_nN \cap N) = 0$$

for every n. Here χ_N denotes the characteristic function of N. Thus $|((L_{x_n} - I)\chi_N, \chi_N)| = (\chi_N, \chi_N) = \mu(N) > 0$. Thus L_{x_n} does not converge weakly to I, which contradicts our first assumption.

COROLLARY 2.3. The embedding of G in $\mathfrak{a}(G)$ is a homeomorphism relative to the weak topology of $\mathfrak{a}(G)$.

Proof. The embedding is continuous since each representation in G^s is weakly continuous. If $\hat{x}_\nu$ is a net in $\hat{G}$ converging weakly to $\hat{x}$ in $\hat{G}$ then $\hat{x}_\nu(L)$ converges weakly to $\hat{x}(L)$ for every L in G^s. In particular, L_{x_ν} converges to L_x where L is the left regular representation. By Lemma 2.1, the net x_ν converges to x. Here $\hat{G}$ denotes the image group in $\mathfrak{a}(G)$, under the natural embedding of G in $\mathfrak{a}(G)$.

REMARK 2.4. It is interesting to note that none of the four conditions of Definition 2.1 involves continuity. The concrete dual G^s does have a natural topology (cf. [**9**] and [**21**]). In the case where G is a countable discrete group, so that its group C^*-algebra is separable and contains the identity element, some recent results of M. Takesaki [**21**] enables one to identify those elements J in $\mathfrak{a}(G)$ which are *-strong continuous maps on G^s. (The *-strong operator topology on the set of all bounded linear operators on a Hilbert space $\mathcal{H}$ is the locally convex topology induced by the family of semi-norms of the form $T \to \| T\psi \|$ and $T \to \| T^*\psi \|$ where $\psi \in \mathcal{H}$.) Then the set of *-strong continuous maps in $\mathfrak{a}(G)$ is exactly the C^*-group algebra of G, with respect to the natural embedding of $C^*(G)$ in $\mathfrak{a}(G)$. In the spirit of this result, our main concern in the later portion of this paper is the determination of a condition on the maps J, (not a continuity condition) which will identify the group elements in $\mathfrak{a}(G)$.

REMARK 2.5. The different topologies described in §5 of [**5**] can be defined just as easily in the nonseparable case. Thus the σ-weak topology of $\mathfrak{a}(G)$ is the smallest topology such that the functional

$$J \to \sum_{i=1}^{\infty} (J(L^i)\psi_i, \varphi_i)$$

is continuous, for every sequence $\{L^i\}$ in G^s and every pair of sequences of vectors $\{\psi_i\}$, $\{\varphi_i\}$ such that ψ_i and φ_i are in the representation space $\mathcal{H}(L^i)$ of L^i and $\Sigma_i \|\psi_i\|_i^2 < +\infty$ and $\Sigma_i \|\varphi_i\|_i^2 < +\infty$, where $\| \ \|_i$ denotes the norm in $\mathcal{H}(L^i)$.

The strong topology of $\mathfrak{a}(G)$ is the smallest topology such that the functionals $J \to \|J(L)\psi\|$ are continuous, for all L in G^s and ψ in $\mathcal{H}(L)$. The σ-strong topology is the smallest such that the map

$$J \to \left[\sum_{i=1}^{\infty} \|J(L^i)\psi_i\|^2\right]^{1/2}$$

is continuous, for every sequence $\{L^i\}$ in G^s and every sequence of vectors $\{\psi_i\}$ for which $\psi_i \in \mathcal{H}(L^i)$ and $\Sigma_i \|\psi_i\|_i^2 < +\infty$.

In this remark we wish to point out that the weak and σ-weak topologies of $\mathfrak{a}(G)$ are in fact equivalent. Indeed, every functional of the form

$$J \to \sum_{i=1}^{\infty} (J(L^i)\psi_i, \varphi_i)$$

with $\Sigma_i \|\psi_i\|_i^2 < +\infty$ and $\Sigma_i \|\varphi_i\|_i^2 < \infty$, is of the form $J \to (J(L)\psi, \varphi)$ where $L \in G^s$ and $\psi, \varphi \in \mathcal{H}(L)$. Indeed, let

$$L = U\left(\sum_{i=1}^{\infty} \oplus L^i\right) U^{-1},$$

where U is a linear isometry of $\Sigma_i \oplus \mathcal{H}(L^i)$ onto a subspace of $\mathcal{H}$ and let $\varphi = U\{\varphi_i\}$ and $\psi = U\{\psi_i\}$. Thus in particular, a fundamental neighborhood of the origin, for both the weak and the σ-weak topology, is of the form

$$\{J: |(J(L)\psi, \psi)| \leq 1\}$$

where $L \in G^s$ and $\psi \in \mathcal{H}(L)$.

Similarly, the strong and σ-strong topologies for $\mathfrak{a}(G)$ are equivalent. Indeed a fundamental neighborhood of the origin, for both the strong and σ-strong topology, is of the form

$$\{J: \|J(L)\psi\| \leq 1\}$$

where $L \in G^s$ and $\psi \in \mathcal{H}(L)$.

REMARK 2.6. $\mathfrak{a}(G)$ is a von Neumann algebra satisfying the universal mapping property. $\mathfrak{a}(G)$ has a natural representation as a von Neumann algebra. Indeed let

$$\mathcal{H}_s = \sum_{L \in G^s} \oplus \mathcal{H}(L).$$

If $J \in \mathfrak{a}(G)$, let $\varphi(J)$ be the linear operator acting on $\mathcal{H}_s$ defined by

$$\varphi(J)\{\psi_L\} = \{J(L)\psi_L\} \text{ where } \{\psi_L\} \in \mathcal{H}_s$$

Clearly $\|\varphi(J)\| \leq \|J\|$. In fact φ is a *-isomorphism and isometry of $\mathfrak{a}(G)$ into the algebra of all bounded operators on $\mathcal{H}_s$. Remark 2.5 implies that Theorem 6.1 of [**5**] can be strengthened. Thus φ is a strong homeomorphism and a weak homeomorphism. Further $\varphi(\mathfrak{a}(G))$ is a von Neumann algebra whose weak and σ-weak topologies are equivalent and whose strong and σ-strong topologies are equivalent. This is not too surprising as it is not difficult to show that any von Neumann algebra is isomorphic to a von Neumann algebra in which the weak and σ-weak topologies coincide and the strong and σ-strong topologies coincide. Indeed, given any von Neumann algebra $\mathfrak{a}$, the diagonal of the direct product of $\mathfrak{a}$ with itself a countable number of times is the required von Neumann algebra.

Note that section 7 of [**5**] applies immediately to the nonseparable case. Thus $\mathfrak{a}(G)$ is a von Neumann algebra containing G isomorphically and (weakly) homeomorphically as a unitary group which generates $\mathfrak{a}(G)$. It remains to show that this von Neumann algebra does satisfy the universal mapping property of the previous section. Every representation L in G^s may be extended to a normal *-representation L' of $\mathfrak{a}(G)$ by defining $L'(J) = J(L)$ for all J in $\mathfrak{a}(G)$. Note that L' is normal since the map $J \to (L'_J\psi, \psi) = (J(L)\psi, \psi)$ is σ-weak continuous by the definition of the σ-weak topology of $\mathfrak{a}(G)$, (cf. Remark 2.5). Further any strongly continuous unitary representation of G may be extended to $\mathfrak{a}(G)$ since any such representation is equivalent to a direct sum of cyclic representations contained in G^s. Any such extension is unique since the extended representation is σ-weak continuous and linear combinations of elements of G are σ-weak dense in $\mathfrak{a}(G)$.

REMARK 2.7. A second way of exhibit a von Neumann algebra satisfying the universal mapping property of section 1 is to consider the second conjugate space of the group C^*-algebra. Indeed section 3 of [**5**] applies to the nonseparable case to show that $\mathfrak{a}(G)$ may be identified, as a Banach space, with the second conjugate of $C^*(G)$. For notational convenience, let $\mathfrak{A}$ denote the group C^*-algebra $C^*(G)$. We define a map of $\mathfrak{A}^{**}$ into $\mathfrak{a}(G)$ as follows. If $F \in \mathfrak{A}^{**}$, let $\hat{F}$ denote the element of $\mathfrak{a}(G)$ defined by the requirement that for each L in G^s and ψ, φ in $\mathcal{H}(L)$

$$(F(L)\psi, \varphi) = F(f_{L,\psi,\varphi})$$

where $f_{L,\psi,\varphi}$ is that element of $\mathfrak{A}^*$ defined by

$$f_{L,\psi,\varphi}(x) = \int_G x(\xi)(L_\xi\psi, \varphi)d\mu(\xi)$$

for all x in $L^1(G)$. (The function $f_{L,\psi,\varphi}$ is defined for all points in the completion $\mathfrak{A}$ of $L^1(G)$ by continuity.) The proof of Theorem 3.1 of [**5**] is valid in the nonseparable case. Thus the map $F \to \hat{F}$ is a one-to-one linear map of A^{**} onto $\mathfrak{a}(G)$ which, as is pointed out in [**10**], is an isometry. Further since we have noted (cf. Remark 2.5) that the weak and σ-weak topologies of $\mathfrak{a}(G)$ are identical, the map is a homeomorphism relative to the weak* topology of $\mathfrak{A}^{**}$ and the σ-weak topology of $\mathfrak{a}(G)$.

Given this identification of $\mathfrak{A}^{**}$ with $\mathfrak{a}(G)$ as Banach spaces, the question naturally arises as to the relation of the multiplication defined in $\mathfrak{a}(G)$ to the multiplication in $\mathfrak{A}^{**}$ defined by R. Arens [**1**]. Further there is a natural involution in $\mathfrak{A}^{**}$ defined, for F in $\mathfrak{A}^{**}$, by $F^*(f) = \overline{F(f^*)}$ for all f in $\mathfrak{A}^*$, where $f^*(S) = \overline{f(S^*)}$ for all S in $\mathfrak{A}$.

PROPOSITION 2.8. The map Φ: $F \to \hat{F}$ is a *-algebra isomorphism of $\mathfrak{A}^{**}$ onto $\mathfrak{a}(G)$, where the multiplication in $\mathfrak{A}^{**}$ is the Arens multiplication [**1**]. Further the map Φ is an isometry and a homeomorphism relative to the weak*-topology of $\mathfrak{A}^{**}$ and the σ-weak topology of $\mathfrak{a}(G)$.

Proof. All the facts of this theorem have been established in the previous discussion except the fact that Φ preserves multiplication and the involution in $\mathfrak{A}^{**}$. According to Theorem 6 of [**25**] $\mathfrak{A}^{**}$ (with Arens multiplication) is *-algebra isomorphic to a von Neumann algebra, where the weak* topology of $\mathfrak{A}^{**}$ corresponds to the σ-weak topology of the von Neumann algebra. Thus the maps $S \to ST$, $T \to ST$ and $S \to S^*$ are all weak* continuous in $\mathfrak{A}^{**}$, just as the corresponding maps are σ-weak continuous in $\mathfrak{a}(G)$. We know that Φ preserves multiplication on the dense subalgebra $\mathfrak{A}$ of $\mathfrak{A}^{**}$. By weak* continuity of the map $S \to ST$ we have $\Phi(ST) = \Phi(S)\Phi(T)$ for S in $\mathfrak{A}^{**}$ and T in $\mathfrak{A}$. Similarly by weak* continuity of the map $T \to ST$ we have $\Phi(ST) = \Phi(S)\Phi(T)$, for all S,T in $\mathfrak{A}^{**}$. Finally since Φ preserves the involution on $\mathfrak{A}$ and since the involution is weak* continuous, we have that Φ preserves the involution on $\mathfrak{A}^{**}$.

REMARK 2.9. The material of section 2 of [**8**] may be easily extended to the nonseparable case. We recall a few definitions. Two representations L and M of G are said to be *disjoint* if no subrepresentation of L is unitarily equivalent to any subrepresentation of M. We say L

covers M, denoted $L\}M$, if no subrepresentation of M is disjoint from L. We say L is *quasiequivalent* to M, denoted $L \sim M$ if L covers M and M covers L. The collection Q of all quasi-equivalence classes of representations of G forms a complete distributive lattice with respect to the ordering given by the covering relation, which we call the *representation lattice* of G. This lattice is isomorphic to the lattice of all central projections in the big group algebra. (cf. Corollary 2 to Theorem 1 of [**8**].) More explicitly, if $\mathfrak{a}(G)$ is concretely represented as a von Neumann algebra acting on a Hilbert space $\mathfrak{H}$, and if E is a central projection of $\mathfrak{a}(G)$, then the restriction to G, of the induction $\mathfrak{a}(G) \to \mathfrak{a}(G)_E$, gives a strongly continuous unitary representation of G. In this way one obtains a one-to-one correspondence between the lattice of central projections in $\mathfrak{a}(G)$ and a cross-section of the representation lattice. Different concrete realizations of $\mathfrak{a}(G)$ give different cross-sections, but a one-to-one correspondence between the projection lattice and the representation lattice is determined.

REMARK 2.10. It is interesting to note that the central projection lattice admits an additional algebraic structure. Notice that if $L \sim L'$ and $M \sim M'$, where L,L',M,M' are unitary representations of G, then $L \otimes M \sim L' \otimes M'$. Thus the tensor product operation among representations induces a corresponding product $E \circ F$ on the lattice of central projections of $\mathfrak{a}(G)$. We summarize the basic properties of this binary operation.

(i) commutativity.
(ii) associativity.
(iii) $(\vee_\lambda E_\lambda) \circ E = \vee_\lambda (E_\lambda \circ E)$.
(iv) If $E_1 \geq E_2$ and $F_1 \geq F_2$, then $E_1 \circ F_1 \geq E_2 \circ F_2$.
(v) There exists an $\circ$-identity, i.e., a central projection $E_\circ$ such that $E_\circ \circ E = E$ for all central projections E in $\mathfrak{a}(G)$.
(vi) There exists a zero element R such that $R \circ E = R$ for all central projections E in $\mathfrak{a}(G)$.
(vii) If I is the identity of $\mathfrak{a}(G)$, then $I \circ I = I$.

Properties (i) through (iv) follow from easily verifiable properties of tensor products of representations. The $\circ$-identity $E_\circ$ is just the central projection corresponding to the trivial representation of G. The zero element R is just the central projection corresponding to the left (equivalently the right) regular representation of G. This property of the regular representation was proved by Tatsuuma [**23**], but also appears as an exercise in Dixmier [**3**, page 273] who attributes the result to J. M. G. Fell. This result was also obtained by Stinespring [**20**, page 48]. In fact if R is the left regular representation and M is any representation of G, then $R \otimes M \simeq \alpha R \sim R$, where α is the dimension of $\mathfrak{H}(M)$. The appropriate isometry establishing this fact may be defined as follows. Let $\{\varphi_\lambda\}$ denote an orthonormal basis for $\mathcal{H}(M)$. Then for each $f \otimes g$ in $L^2(G) \otimes \mathcal{H}(M)$, let

$$U(f \otimes g) = \{(g, M_{(\cdot)}\varphi_\lambda)f(\cdot)\} \in \bigoplus_\alpha L^2(G)$$

where (,) is the inner product in $\mathcal{H}(M)$ and $\bigoplus_\alpha L^2(G)$ denotes the direct sum of α copies of $L^2(G)$.]

Unfortunately this projection lattice, even with this product $\circ$, does not contain enough information to serve as a dual object. Indeed G. I. Katz has pointed out to the author the example of the two nonabelian finite groups of order eight. Both groups have four one dimensional irreducible representations and one four dimensional irreducible representation. Further one may verify that these two nonisomorphic groups admit isomorphic projection lattices.

3. HOPF–VON NEUMANN ALGEBRAS

In this section we shall examine the duality theorem of N. Tatsuuma [**23**]. We wish, in the spirit of [**17**], to cast the theory in such a form that the dual object has a reasonable algebraic and topological structure. We therefore introduce the concept of Hopf–von Neumann algebra, which is a von Neumann algebra admitting a comultiplication. (cf. [**19**]).

DEFINITION 3.1. A Hopf–von Neumann algebra is a von Neumann algebra $\mathfrak{a}$ that admits an associative comultiplication, i.e., a normal *-isomorphism d of $\mathfrak{a}$ into $\mathfrak{a} \otimes \mathfrak{a}$ such that $(d \otimes i) \circ d = (i \otimes d) \circ d$, where i denotes the identity map on $\mathfrak{a}$.

A Hopf–von Neumann algebra $\mathfrak{a}$ is said to have a co-unit c, if c is a normal complex valued homomorphism on $\mathfrak{a}$ such that

$$(c \otimes i) \circ d = (i \otimes c) \circ d = i$$

where one identifies, in the usual way, $\mathbb{C} \otimes \mathfrak{a}$ and $\mathfrak{a} \otimes \mathbb{C}$ with $\mathfrak{a}$.

A Hopf–von Neumann algebra is said to be *cocommutative* if $d = \Phi d$, where Φ maps $\mathfrak{a} \otimes \mathfrak{a}$ onto $\mathfrak{a} \otimes \mathfrak{a}$ and is defined by $\Phi(S \otimes T) = T \otimes S$ for all S and T in $\mathfrak{a}$.

PROPOSITION 3.2. Let G be a locally compact group. The big group algebra, $\mathfrak{a}(G)$, is a cocommutative Hopf–von Neumann algebra with co-unit.

Proof. Let $\mathfrak{a}(G)$ be realized concretely as the von Neumann algebra generated by the range of the representation φ, which is the direct sum of the representations in G^s. See Remark 2.6. Then we define the comultiplication in $\mathfrak{a}(G)$ to be the unique extension to $\mathfrak{a}(G)$, of the representation $\varphi \otimes \varphi$ of G. Here d is an associative comultiplication since the range of d is contained in $\mathfrak{a}(G) \otimes \mathfrak{a}(G)$ and since $(d \otimes i) \circ d$ and $(i \otimes d) \circ d$ both agree on G, a generating set for $\mathfrak{a}(G)$. To see that d is injective note that φ is quasi-equivalent to $\varphi \otimes \varphi$, since φ contains the trivial representation. Thus (cf. Lemma 4 of [**4**]) the comultiplication is a normal *-isomorphism of $\mathfrak{a}(G)$ onto $\mathfrak{a}(\varphi \otimes \varphi) \subset \mathfrak{a}(\varphi) \otimes \mathfrak{a}(\varphi)$ and where $\mathfrak{a}(\varphi \otimes \varphi)$ denotes the von Neumann algebra generated by the range of $\varphi \otimes \varphi$. The comultiplication d is cocommutative since $(\Phi d)(x) = \Phi(x \otimes x) = x \otimes x = d(x)$ for all x in G, a generating set for $\mathfrak{a}(G)$.

We next observe that $\mathfrak{a}(G)$ admits a co-unit. Let c' denote the trivial map of G into $\mathbb{C}$, i.e., $c'(x) = 1$, for all x in G. Let c denote the unique extension to a normal *-homomorphism of $\mathfrak{a}(G)$ into $\mathbb{C}$. Note that $(c \otimes i) \circ d$ and $(i \otimes c) \circ d$ acts as the identity on G. But the identity map on G has a unique extension to $\mathfrak{a}(G)$, namely the identity map i on $\mathfrak{a}(G)$. Thus $(c \otimes i) \circ d = (i \otimes c) \circ d = i$.

REMARK 3.3. The comultiplication in a Hopf–von Neumann algebra may be used to define the *inner tensor product* of two normal *-representations. If L and M are two such representations of a Hopf–von Neumann algebra $\mathfrak{a}$, then we define

$$L \boxtimes M = (L \otimes M) \circ d$$

where we have chosen $\otimes$ to denote outer tensor product and $\boxtimes$ to denote inner tensor product. We then have that the unique extension of a unitary representation of a locally compact group to a normal *-representation of its big group algebra $\mathfrak{a}(G)$, preserves tensor products. More explicitly, if L and M are unitary representations of G and L' and M' denote the corresponding extensions to *-representations of $\mathfrak{a}(G)$, then the unique extension of $L \otimes M$ to $\mathfrak{a}(G)$ is exactly $L' \boxtimes M'$.

PROPOSITION 3.4. Let G be a locally compact group. Let L denote the left regular representation of G and let $\mathfrak{a}(L)$ denote the von Neumann algebra generated by the range of L. Then $\mathfrak{a}(L)$ is a cocommutative Hopf–von Neumann algebra. Further L contains the one-dimensional trivial representation if and only if $\mathfrak{a}(L)$ admits a co-unit.

Proof. Let E denote the central projection of $\mathfrak{a}(G)$ for which $\mathfrak{a}(G)_E$ is isomorphic to $\mathfrak{a}(L)$ by means of an isomorphism which extends the map $xE \to L_x$, for all x in $G \subset \mathfrak{a}(G)$. (cf. Remark 2.9.) To see that $\mathfrak{a}(G)_E$ is a Hopf-von Neumann algebra, recall that $L \otimes M$ is quasi-equivalent to L, for any unitary representation M of G. (cf. Remark 2.10.) In particular we have $L \sim L \otimes L$. Thus $\mathfrak{a}(L)$ is isomorphic to $\mathfrak{a}(L \otimes L)$ under the mapping determined uniquely by the property that

$$L_x \to L_x \otimes L_x$$

for all x in G. (cf. Lemma 4 of [4].) We thus obtain a normal *-isomorphism d'.

$$d' : \mathfrak{a}(L) \to \mathfrak{a}(L \otimes L) \subset \mathfrak{a}(L) \otimes \mathfrak{a}(L).$$

Further d' is clearly a comultiplication since $(d' \otimes i) \circ d'$ and $(i \otimes d') \circ d'$ both agree on the generating set $\{L_x : x \in G\}$ of $\mathfrak{a}(L)$. In terms of the isomorphic algebra $\mathfrak{a}(G)_E$, the comultiplication is just the map

$$\mathfrak{a}(G)_E \to \mathfrak{a}(G)_E \otimes \mathfrak{a}(G)_E$$

which extends the map $xE \to xE \otimes xE$ for all x in G. Thus the comultiplication in $\mathfrak{a}(L) \simeq \mathfrak{a}(G)_E$ is just that induced by the comultiplication in $\mathfrak{a}(G)$.

This comultiplication is cocommutative since $\Phi d'$ and d' are identical on the generating set $\{xE : x \in G\}$ of $\mathfrak{a}(G)_E$.

Suppose now that L contains the trivial representation of G, $x \to 1 \in \mathbb{C}$ for all x in G. Let F denote the corresponding central projection of $\mathfrak{a}(G)$. Then $F \leq E$, and the map

$$c' : \mathfrak{a}(G)_E \to \mathfrak{a}(G)_F \simeq \mathbb{C}$$

defined by $SE \to SF$ for all SE in $\mathfrak{a}(G)_E$, is a normal *-homomorphism of $\mathfrak{a}(G)_E$ into $\mathbb{C}$. Further c' is a co-unit for $\mathfrak{a}(G)_E$. In fact it is the co-unit induced in $\mathfrak{a}(G)_E$ by the co-unit of $\mathfrak{a}(G)$. Note that c' is a co-unit since $(c' \otimes i) \circ d'$ and $(i \otimes c') \circ d'$ are both the identity on the generating set $\{xE : x \in G\}$ of $\mathfrak{a}(G)_E$.

Conversely, suppose $\mathfrak{a}(G)_E$ admits a co-unit c'. Then c' may be looked upon as a one-dimensional representation of $\mathfrak{a}(G)_E$ that reduces to the one-dimensional trivial representation on the generating set $\{xE : x \in G\}$ of $\mathfrak{a}(G)_E$. Thus there exists a central projection F of $\mathfrak{a}(G)_E$ such that c' is the induction

$$\mathfrak{a}(G)_E \to (\mathfrak{a}(G)_E)_F = \mathfrak{a}(G)_F \simeq \mathbb{C},$$

where $F \leq E$. (cf. Proposition 3 of [8].) Since E is in the center of $\mathfrak{a}(G)$ and F is in the center of $\mathfrak{a}(G)_E$ and $F \leq E$, we may consider F to be a projection in the center of $\mathfrak{a}(G)$. Since the correspondence between the central projection lattice of $\mathfrak{a}(G)$ and the representation lattice of G is a lattice isomorphism, (cf. Remark 2.9) $F \leq E$ implies that the left regular representation covers, and hence contains, the one dimensional trivial representation.

DEFINITION 3.5. If $\mathfrak{a}$ is a Hopf–von Neumann algebra with comultiplication d, the *intrinsic group* of $\mathfrak{a}$ is the group of invertible elements T of $\mathfrak{a}$ for which $d(T) = T \otimes T$.

PROPOSITION 3.6. The elements of the intrinsic group of any Hopf–von Neumann algebra are unitary.

Proof. If T is an element of the intrinsic group, then T^*T and TT^* are also. Thus

$$\| T^*T \| = \| d(T^*T) \| = \| T^*T \otimes T^*T \| = \| T^*T \|^2.$$

Thus $\| T^*T \| = 1$. Similarly $(T^*T)^{-1}$ is contained in the intrinsic group and thus $\| (T^*T)^{-1} \| = 1$. Since T^*T is a positive operator, the spectral theorem implies $T^*T = I$. Similarly $TT^* = I$.

REMARK 3.7. All the operator topologies, weak, σ-weak, strong and σ-strong, of a von Neumann algebra, coincide on the unitary group. Thus the intrinsic group of a Hopf–von Neumann algebra is a topological group in this topology. It is not difficult to show that the intrinsic group of any Hopf–von Neumann algebra $\mathfrak{a}$ forms a linearly independent set in $\mathfrak{a}$. (cf. [**18**].) A very important open question is the determination of those Hopf–von Neumann algebras for which the intrinsic group is a locally compact group. Another major problem is the determination of the conditions under which the intrinsic group generates the algebra.

We are now ready to discuss the Tatsuuma duality theorem. We begin with the Hopf–von Neumann algebra $\mathfrak{a}(L)$, the von Neumann algebra generated by the range of the left regular representation. The following proof based on the work of Wendel [**26**], was developed as a joint effort of the J. L. Kelley seminar at Berkeley (Spring '66) where the author was lecturing on Tatsuuma's duality theory. In particular, J. Feldman and C. Akemann were major contributors.

PROPOSITION 3.8. (Tatsuuma duality theorem). Let G be a locally compact group, L its left regular representation, and $\mathfrak{a}(L)$ the von Neumann algebra generated by the range of L. The intrinsic group of the Hopf–von Neumann algebra $\mathfrak{a}(L)$ is isomorphic and homeomorphic to G.

Proof. Suppose T is in the intrinsic group of $\mathfrak{a}(L)$. We wish to show that T is of the form L_x for some x in G. The first step of our proof is the same as the first step of Tatsuuma's proof [**23**], but we include it here for completeness.

LEMMA 3.9. (N. Tatsuuma). Suppose T is an intrinsic element of $\mathfrak{a}(L)$. For each f in $C_{\infty}(G)$ and each g in $L^2(G)$, we have

$$T(gf) = Tg \cdot Tf.$$

Proof. (cf. Lemma 3 of [**23**].) We remark that $C_{00}(G)$ denotes the algebra of all continuous complex valued functions on G with compact support. Clearly the pointwise product gf is contained in $L^2(G)$. In the verification that $L \otimes L$ is quasi-equivalent to L (cf. Remark 2.10), one introduces a unitary map U of $L^2(G) \otimes L^2(G)$ onto $\bigoplus_{\alpha} L^2(G)$, where α is the dimension of $L^2(G)$, by the requirement that

$$U(f \otimes g) = \{(g, L_{(\cdot)}\varphi_\lambda) f(\cdot)\} \in \bigoplus_{\alpha} L^2(G)$$

where $\{\varphi_\lambda\}$ denotes an orthonormal basis for $L^2(G)$ and $\bigoplus_\alpha L^2(G)$ denotes the direct sum of α copies of $L^2(G)$. With respect to the isometry U, αL is unitary equivalent to $L \otimes L$. One thus obtains a natural isomorphism of $\mathfrak{a}(L) \simeq \mathfrak{a}(\alpha L)$ (cf. Lemma 4 of [**4**]) into $\mathfrak{a}(L) \otimes \mathfrak{a}(L)$. This isomorphism is just the comultiplication in $\mathfrak{a}(L)$, since L_x maps into $L_x \otimes L_x$ for all x in G. Since T is intrinsic, we have

$$U((T \otimes T)(f \otimes g)) = (\bigoplus_\alpha T)\, U(f \otimes g)$$

for all f, g in $L^2(G)$. Thus

$$U(Tf \otimes Tg) = (\bigoplus_{\bar{\alpha}} T)\{(g, L_{(\cdot)}\varphi_\lambda) f(\cdot)\}.$$

Since the basis $\{\varphi_\lambda\}$ is arbitrary we have

$$(T_g, L_{(\cdot)}\psi)\, Tf(\cdot) = T((g, L_{(\cdot)}\psi) f(\cdot)) \tag{1}$$

for all f, g, ψ in $L^2(G)$.

Next note that if $g \in L^2(G)$ and $\psi \in C_\infty(G)$, then

$$(g, L_x\psi) = (g * \psi^\sim)(x) \text{ for all } x \text{ in } G, \text{ where } \psi^\sim(x) = \psi(x^{-1}). \tag{2}$$

Indeed

$$\begin{aligned}(g, L_x\psi) &= \int_G (L_x^* g(y))\overline{\psi(y)}\, d\mu(y) \\ &= \int_G g(xy)\psi^\sim(y^{-1})\, d\mu(y) \\ &= (g * \psi^\sim)(x).\end{aligned}$$

Putting (2) in (1) we obtain

$$(Tg * \psi^\sim)\cdot(Tf) = T((g * \psi^\sim)\cdot f) \tag{3}$$

for all ψ in $C_{00}(G)$ and g, f in $L^2(G)$.

We remark that (3) is to be interpreted as equality of elements of $L^2(G)$ and that the "dot" refers to pointwise multiplication of functions. Further since $C_{00}(G)$ is closed under the $\sim$-operation, we may write (3) more simply in the form

$$(Tg * \psi)\cdot Tf = T((g * \psi)\cdot f) \tag{4}$$

for all ψ in $C_{00}(G)$ and g, f in $L^2(G)$.

Choose an approximate identity $\{\psi_\lambda\}$ from $C_{00}(G)$ such that

$$\lim_\lambda \|g * \psi_\lambda - g\|_2 = 0$$

for all g in $L^2(G)$. Then one may verify that, for f in $C_{00}(G)$

$$\|(g * \psi_\lambda)\cdot f - g\cdot f\|_2 \leq \|f\|_{00}\, \|(g * \psi_\lambda) - g\|_2$$

Thus we have

$$T((g * \psi_\lambda)\cdot f) \to T(g\cdot f) \text{ in } L^2(G).$$

Examining the other side of equality (4) we see that $(Tg * \psi_\lambda)\cdot Tf$ is a convergent net in $L^2(G)$. Since $Tg * \psi_\lambda$ converges to Tg in $L^2(G)$, it is easy to show that $(Tg * \psi_\lambda)\cdot Tf$ must converge to $Tg\cdot Tf$. Thus equation (4) implies

$$T(g\cdot f) = Tg\cdot Tf \qquad \text{a.e.}$$

for all g in $L^2(G)$ and f in $C_{00}(G)$.

LEMMA 3.10. If T is an intrinsic element of $\mathfrak{a}(L)$, then T maps the positive cone of $L^2(G)$ into the positive cone of $L^2(G)$.

Proof. We first note, for any characteristic function χ_E of a compact set E, that $T\chi_E$ is a positive element of $L^2(G)$. In fact N. Tatsuuma has proved [**23**] that $T\chi_E$ is always a characteristic function of a measurable set. For completeness we record Tatsuuma's proof of this fact.

Let ψ_n denote a sequence in $C_{00}(G)$ which converges to χ_E in $L^2(G)$. Then $\psi_n\chi_E$ converges to $\chi_E^2 = \chi_E$ in $L^2(G)$. Indeed

$$\|\chi_E^2 - \psi_n\chi_E\|_2 \le \|\chi_E\|_{\infty}\|\chi_E - \psi_n\|_2.$$

Thus $T(\psi_n\chi_E)$ converges to $T(\chi_E)$ in $L^2(G)$. By Lemma 3.9 one has

$$T(\psi_n\chi_E) = T(\psi_n)T(\chi_E).$$

Thus $T(\psi_n)T(\chi_E)$ is a convergent sequence in $L^2(G)$ and $T(\psi_n)$ converges to $T(\chi_E)$ in $L^2(G)$. Thus $T(\psi_n)T(\chi_E)$ must converge to $[T(\chi_E)]^2$. Hence

$$T(\chi_E) = T(\chi_E^2) = [T(\chi_E)]^2.$$

Thus $T(\chi_E)$ has only values 0 or 1. Hence $T(\chi_E)$ is in the positive cone of $L^2(G)$.

Finite linear combinations of characteristic functions of compact sets are dense in $L^2(G)$. (cf. [**13**], page 242.) Thus positive linear combinations of characteristic functions of compact sets are dense in the positive cone of $L^2(G)$. The lemma now follows since the positive cone of $L^2(G)$ is closed.

Having obtained these two crucial properties of an intrinsic element T, we can now fairly easily obtain the duality theorem (Proposition 3.8) from Wendel's theorem (Theorem 3 of [**26**]).

Using Lemma 3.9 again we have, for f positive in $C_{00}(G)$

$$\|f\|_1 = \int_G (f^{1/2})^2 d\mu = \|f^{1/2}\|_2^2 = \|Tf^{1/2}\|_2^2$$

$$= \int_G |Tf^{1/2}|^2 d\mu = \int_G |Tf|\, d\mu = \|Tf\|_1.$$

Thus T is L^1-norm preserving on the positive elements of $C_{00}(G)$. For f real valued in $C_{00}(G)$ we have $f = f^+ - f^-$ where $f^+ \in C_{00}(G)^+$, $f^- \in C_{00}(G)^+$ and $\|f\|_1 = f^+\|_1 + \|f^-\|_1$. Thus $Tf = Tf^+ - Tf^-$ and Tf is real a.e. since $Tf^+ \geq 0$ and $Tf^- \geq 0$ a.e.. Further $Tf^+ \cdot Tf^- = T(f^+ \cdot f^-) = T(0) = 0$ a.e.. Thus $\|Tf\|_1 = \|Tf^+ - Tf^-\|_1 = \|Tf^+\|_1 + \|Tf^-{}_1\| = \|f^+\|_1 + \|f^-\|_1 = \|f\|$. Thus T is a L^1-norm preserving map of the real valued functions of $C_{00}(G)$ into real $L^1(G)$. Since the real-valued continuous functions with compact support are dense in real $L^1(G)$, T may be extended to a norm-preserving map $\tilde{T}$ of real $L^1(G)$ onto real $L^1(G)$. Since T is an element of $\mathfrak{a}(L)$, the double commutator theorem implies that T must commute with right translations on $C_{00}(G)$ and hence that $\tilde{T}$ commutes with right translations on real $L^1(G)$. By Wendel's theorem (Theorem 3 of [**26**]) $\tilde{T}$ is of the form $\tilde{T} = \lambda L_x$ where λ is a scalar of unit modulus and $\tilde{L}_x$ denotes a left translation of real $L^1(G)$, with respect to x, where x is in G. Since T maps the positive cone of $L^2(G)$ into the positive cone of $L^2(G)$, its restriction to $C_{00}(G)$ preserves positivity of functions and hence $\tilde{T}$ maps the positive cone of $L^1(G)$ into the positive cone of $L^1(G)$. Thus the scalar λ must be 1. Hence T acts as left translation with respect to x on the real continuous functions with compact support. By linearity and continuity we have $T = L_x$ where L_x denotes left translation on $L^2(G)$, with respect to x.

The fact that the intrinsic group is isomorphic and homeomorphic to G follows directly from the fact that the left regular representation is faithful and a σ-weak homeomorphism. (cf. Lemma 2.2.)

REMARK 3.11. It should be pointed out that a result almost equivalent to Proposition 3.7 was obtained earlier by W. F. Stinespring [**20**] for the case where the group G is unimodular. Stinespring's result (Theorem 10.4 of [**20**]), however, required one additional property for the intrinsic elements of $\mathfrak{a}(L)$, and this has been shown to be unnecessary by Tatsuuma's theorem. More explicitly Stinespring assumed that the intrinsic elements satisfied the property $T = \check{T}$. Here $\check{T} = CTC$, where C denotes complex conjugation on $L^2(G)$, i.e., $(Cf)(x) = \overline{f(x)}$ for all f in $L^2(G)$ and x in G.

REMARK 3.12. In [**23**], Tatsuuma assumed the intrinsic elements of $\mathfrak{a}(L)$ were unitary operators. In this description we have assumed only that the intrinsic elements are invertible. (cf. Definition 3.5 and Proposition 3.6). In [**24**] Tatsuuma has further relaxed this hypothesis. Indeed he proves that one need only assume that the intrinsic elements of $\mathfrak{a}(L)$ are nonzero operators T such that $d(T) = T \otimes T$. A similar result was obtained by Stinespring in his work on unimodular groups. See Theorem 10.2 of [**20**].

We next give a formulation of Tatsuuma duality in terms of the big group algebra.

PROPOSITION 3.13. Let G be a locally compact group and let $\mathfrak{a}(G)$ be its big group algebra. The intrinsic group of $\mathfrak{a}(G)$ is isomorphic and homeomorphic to G.

Proof. Let E denote the central projection of $\mathfrak{a}$ such that the map induced on G by the induction $\mathfrak{a} \to \mathfrak{a}_E$ is quasiequivalent to the left regular representation L. Indeed we may assume, without loss of generality, that $\mathfrak{a}$ is concretely represented as a von Neumann algebra acting on a Hilbert space, in such a way that $\mathfrak{a}_E = \mathfrak{a}(L)$ and $xE = L_x$ for all x in G. Let T be an intrinsic element of $\mathfrak{a}$. Then TE is an intrinsic element of $\mathfrak{a}_E = \mathfrak{a}(L)$ since the comultiplication in $\mathfrak{a}_E$ is just that induced by the comultiplication in $\mathfrak{a}$. There thus exists a group element, say x_T in G, such that $TE = L_{x_T} = x_T E$. Thus $(x_T^{-1} T)E = E$, the identity element of $\mathfrak{a}_E$.

Consider now the map

$$\eta\colon \mathfrak{a} \to \mathfrak{a} \otimes \mathfrak{a}_E$$

defined by $\eta = (i \otimes L') \circ d$ where i is the identity map on $\mathfrak{a}$ and L' is the induction $\mathfrak{a} \to \mathfrak{a}_E$. The restriction of η to G is a unitary representation quasi-equivalent to L. (cf. Remark 2.10.) Under the regular representation L, $x_T^{-1} T$ is mapped into the identity operator E in $\mathfrak{a}(L) = \mathfrak{a}_E$. Since $x_T^{-1} T$ is in the intrinsic group of $\mathfrak{a}$ we have that η maps $x_T^{-1} T$ into $x_T^{-1} T \otimes x_T^{-1} TE$. Thus $x_T^{-1} T \otimes x_T^{-1} TE$ must be the identity operator of $\mathfrak{a} \otimes \mathfrak{a}_E$, i.e., $x_T^{-1} T$ must be the identity of $\mathfrak{a}$.

REMARK 3.14. In this remark we wish to show that a more classical version of duality is equivalent to Proposition 3.13. Once again let G be a locally compact group. Let $\mathcal{H}$ be a Hilbert space of sufficiently high dimension that any cyclic representation of G is unitary equivalent to a representation acting on a closed subspace of $\mathcal{H}$. Let G^s denote the set of all strongly continuous unitary representations of G, with representation space some closed subspace of $\mathcal{H}$. Let G^+ denote the set of all maps J on G^s satisfying the following properties:

(i) for each L in G^s, $J(L)$ is a unitary operator on $\mathcal{H}(L)$.

(ii) if $L \in G^s$, $M \in G^s$ and $\mathcal{H}(L) \perp \mathcal{H}(M)$ then $J(L \oplus M) = J(L) \oplus J(M)$.

(iii) if L and M are members of G^s and U is a linear isometry of $\mathcal{H}(L)$ onto $\mathcal{H}(M)$ such that $L = U^{-1}MU$, then $J(L) = UJ(M)U^{-1}$.

(iv) if L and M are in G^s and if U is a linear isometry of $\mathcal{H}(L) \otimes \mathcal{H}(M)$ onto a closed subspace of $\mathcal{H}$, then

$$J(U(L \otimes M)U^{-1}) = U(J(L) \otimes J(M))U^{-1}$$

Give G^+ a multiplicative structure by defining $(JK)(L) = J(L)K(L)$ for all L in G^s. Give G^+ the smallest topology such that the maps $J \to \|J(L)\psi\|$ are continuous, for all L in G^s and ψ in $\mathcal{H}(L)$.

Then G^+ is a topological group isomorphic and homeomorphic to G. Indeed the natural embedding $x \rightarrow \hat{x}$ of G into G^+ defined by $\hat{x}(L) = L_x$ for all L in G^s, is an isomorphism and homeomorphism of G onto G^+.

Notice that any map J satisfying (i), (ii) and (iii) is necessarily an element of $\mathfrak{a}(G)$. (cf. Definition 2.1.) Thus to show this more classical version of duality is equivalent to Proposition 3.13 we must show that a unitary element J of $\mathfrak{a}(G)$ satisfies condition (iv) above, if and only if it is an element of the intrinsic group of $\mathfrak{a}(G)$.

Condition (iv) implies that if L and M are cyclic representations of G and L' and M' their unique extensions to normal *-representations of $\mathfrak{a}(G)$, then

$$(L \otimes M)'_J = L'_J \otimes M'_J.$$

(This follows from the fact that $L'_J = J(L)$ for all L in G^s). Now every representation of G is a direct sum of cyclic representations of G. Further the extension to $\mathfrak{a}(G)$ of a direct sum of representations must be the same as the direct sum of the extensions, since they both agree on G. Finally the tensor product is distributive over direct sums. Hence we have

$$(L \otimes M)'_J = L'_J \otimes M'_J$$

for all representations L and M of G. In particular if $L = M = I$, the universal representation of G consisting of the direct sum of all representations in G^s, then I' is a concrete realization of $\mathfrak{a}(G)$ and $(I \otimes I)'$ is exactly the comultiplication in $\mathfrak{a}(G)$. Thus

$$d(J) = (I \otimes I)'_J = I'_J \otimes I'_J = J \otimes J,$$

since I' is just the identity map on $\mathfrak{a}(G)$. Hence J is a member of the intrinsic group.

Conversely, suppose J is an element of the intrinsic group of $\mathfrak{a}(G)$. Then for any L and M in G^s and any linear isometry U of $\mathcal{H}(L) \otimes \mathcal{H}(M)$ onto a closed subspace of $\mathcal{H}$. We have

$$\begin{aligned} J(U(L \otimes M)U^{-1}) &= [U(L \otimes M)U^{-1}]'_J \\ &= U(L \otimes M)'_J U^{-1} \\ &= U(L' \mathbin{\times\!\!\!\!\times} M')_J U^{-1} \\ &= U((L' \otimes M') \circ d)_J U^{-1} \\ &= U(L'_J \otimes M'_J)U^{-1} \\ &= U(J(L) \otimes J(M))U^{-1}. \end{aligned}$$

Thus J is a unitary element satisfying condition (iv).

REMARK 3.15. In an earlier paper the author stated a weak duality theorem for separable locally compact groups (cf. page 292 of [7]), which is easily shown to be implied by the classical version of duality (Remark 3.14). The reasoning leading to the duality statement in [7] was in error. Tatsuuma's theorem completely remedies this situation. Indeed Tatsuuma's theorem strengthens that statement to say that every locally compact group is equal to its fulfillment $\mathcal{U}$. (We had asserted only that G is embedded in $\mathcal{U}$ and that every unitary representation of G has a unique extension to $\mathcal{U}$). The only correction that need be made in [7] is that line 19, page 292 should read "$\mathcal{U}$ is isomorphic and homeomorphic to a group of unitary operators" instead of "$\mathcal{U}$ is isomorphic and homeomorphic to the group of all unitary operators."

REMARK 3.16. Note that the classical version of Tatsuuma's theorem subsumes the Tannaka theorem for compact groups. Indeed, this is our meaning of the phrase "classical version." If a map J satisfies the given conditions for all finite dimensional representations in G^s, where G is compact, then it has a unique extension to a map on all of G^s, satisfying the given conditions. Thus J must be of the form $\hat{x}$ for some x in G, where $\hat{x}(L) = L_x$ for all L in G^s. This follows from the fact that every representation in G^s is the direct sum of finite-dimensional representations.

REMARK 3.17. The duality theory described in Remark 3.14 suffers from a major defect. The "dual" of a locally compact group is not another locally compact group but a complicated object in quite a different category. G. I. Katz has developed a duality theory that remedies this situation. He introduces the concept of "ring-groups" which is shown to extend the notion of unimodular locally compact groups. This new category contains unimodular groups and the objects dual to them. In this category of ring-groups a true duality is obtained. Since the Tatsuuma duality theorem does not assume unimodularity of the group, it is an interesting question whether Katz's concept of ring-group can be suitably modified so as to be a generalization of locally compact groups which are not necessarily unimodular. See references [**14**], [**15**] and [**16**].

Let $\mathcal{G}$ denote the category of locally compact groups, where the morphisms are the continuous homomorphisms.

Let $\mathfrak{A}$ denote the category of Hopf–von Neumann algebras. A morphism φ of a Hopf–von Neumann algebra $(\mathfrak{a}, d)$ into a Hopf–von Neumann algebra $(\mathfrak{b}, d')$ is a normal *-homomorphism of $\mathfrak{a}$ into $\mathfrak{b}$ which preserves comultiplication, i.e., a normal *-homomorphism for which the following diagram commutes.

$$\begin{array}{ccc} \mathfrak{a} & \xrightarrow{d} & \mathfrak{a} \otimes \mathfrak{a} \\ \varphi \downarrow & & \downarrow \varphi \otimes \varphi \\ \mathfrak{b} & \xrightarrow{d'} & \mathfrak{b} \otimes \mathfrak{b} \end{array}$$

PROPOSITION 3.18. The association of the big group algebra $\mathfrak{a}(G)$ with each G in the category $\mathcal{G}$ is a covariant functor of the category $\mathcal{G}$ into the category $\mathfrak{A}$. This is a full and faithful functor in the sense that there is a one-to-one correspondence between

$$\text{Mor}(G, H) \text{ and } \text{Mor}(\mathfrak{a}(G), \mathfrak{a}(H)).$$

Further the automorphism group of G is isomorphic to the automorphism group of $\mathfrak{a}(G)$. (Aut $G \simeq$ Aut $\mathfrak{a}(G)$.)

Proof. Suppose φ is a morphism of G into H. Consider H as embedded in $\mathfrak{a}(H)$. Then φ has a unique extension to a normal *-representation φ' of $\mathfrak{a}(G)$ into $\mathfrak{a}(H)$. Further $(\varphi' \otimes \varphi') \circ d$ and $d' \circ \varphi'$ are normal *-representations of $\mathfrak{a}(G)$ into $\mathfrak{a}(H) \otimes \mathfrak{a}(H)$ which agree on G and are therefore identical. Thus φ' is a morphism of $\mathfrak{a}(G)$ into $\mathfrak{a}(H)$.

Thus to each $\varphi \in$ Mor (G, H) we have associated a morphism $\varphi' \in$ Mor $(\mathfrak{a}(G), \mathfrak{a}(H))$. This correspondence is surjective. Suppose $\psi \in$ Mor $(\mathfrak{a}(G), \mathfrak{a}(H))$. Let $\psi_\circ$ denote its restriction to G. Suppose $x \in G$. We must show that $\psi_\circ(x) \in H$. By Proposition 3.13 it is sufficient to show that $\psi_\circ(x)$ is in the intrinsic group of $\mathfrak{a}(H)$. But since ψ preserves comultiplication, we have

$$d'(\psi_\circ(x)) = ((\psi \otimes \psi \circ d)(x) = \psi(x) \otimes \psi(x) = \psi_\circ(x) \otimes \psi_\circ(x).$$

Thus $\psi_\circ(x) \in H$ and $\psi_\circ \in \text{Mor}(G, H)$ and $\psi_\circ' = \psi$. The correspondence is one-to-one since each φ in Mor(G, H) has a *unique* extension φ'.

Further if φ is surjective, then φ' is surjective. Indeed if φ maps G onto H, then the range of φ' is a von Neumann algebra containing H and contained in $\mathfrak{a}(H)$. Thus the range of φ' is $\mathfrak{a}(H)$.

We next note that the isomorphisms in Mor(G, H) are in one-to-one correspondence with the isomorphisms of Mor$(\mathfrak{a}(G), \mathfrak{a}(H))$. Indeed, suppose φ is an isomorphism (and homeomorphism) of G onto H. Then φ' is surjective and $(\varphi')(\varphi^{-1})'$ is a normal *-homomorphism of $\mathfrak{a}(G)$ onto $\mathfrak{a}(G)$ which leaves G fixed. Thus $(\varphi')(\varphi^{-1})'$ is the identity map and φ' is an isomorphism. On the other hand, suppose ψ is an isomorphism of $\mathfrak{a}(G)$ onto $\mathfrak{a}(H)$. Since ψ preserves comultiplication, the intrinsic group of $\mathfrak{a}(G)$, i.e., G, is mapped onto the intrinsic group of $\mathfrak{a}(H)$, i.e., H. Thus the restriction to G, of any Hopf-algebra isomorphism of $\mathfrak{a}(G)$ onto $\mathfrak{a}(H)$, is an isomorphism of G onto H.

In particular if $G = H$, we have a one-to-one map of Aut G onto Aut $\mathfrak{a}(G)$. Since $G \to \mathfrak{a}(G)$ is functorial, these two automorphism groups are isomorphic.

We conclude with a simple example.

EXAMPLE 3.19. Let G denote the circle group, i.e., $G = \{\tau : 0 \leq \tau < 2\pi\}$ where the group operation is addition mod 2π. Then

$$\hat{G} = \{\exp in\tau : -\infty < n < +\infty\}$$

and $C^*(G) = C_0(\hat{G}) = c_0$, the space of all complex sequences $\{\alpha_n : -\infty < n < +\infty\}$ such that $\lim_{n\to\infty} \alpha_n = \lim_{n\to-\infty} \alpha_n = 0$. Then $(C^*(G))^* = c_0{}^* = \ell_1$ and $\mathfrak{a}(G) = (C^*(G))^{**} = \ell_\infty$. Further G is embedded in ℓ_∞ in the following way: $\tau \leftrightarrow \{\exp in\tau\}$, where, for each fixed τ in G, the sequence $\{\exp in\tau\}$ is a unitary element of the von Neumann algebra $\ell_\infty = \mathfrak{a}(G)$.

Note that in this example, the big group algebra of any separable compact abelian group is ℓ_∞. Thus to distinguish the big group algebras of distinct compact abelian groups, knowledge of the embedding, or, equivalently, knowledge of the comultiplication, is essential.

REFERENCES

1. Arens, R. F., The adjoint of a bilinear operation, *Proc. Amer. Math. Soc.*, 2 (1951) 839–848.
2. Dixmier, J., Les algèbres d'operateurs dans l'espace hilbertien, Gauthier-Villars, Paris 1957.
3. ———, Les C^*-algèbres et leurs representations, Gauthier-Villars, Paris, 1964.
4. Ernest, J., A decomposition theory for unitary representations of locally compact groups, *Trans. Amer. Math. Soc.*, 104 (1962) 252–277.
5. ———, A new group algebra for locally compact groups I, *Amer. J. Math.*, 86 (1964) 467–492.
6. ———, A new group algebra for locally compact groups II, *Canad. J. Math.*, 17 (1965) 604–615.
7. ———, Notes on the duality theorem of non-commutative, noncompact topological groups, *Tôhoku Math. J.*, 15 (1963) 182–186.
8. ———, The representation lattice of a locally compact group, *Illinois J. Math.*, 10 (1966) 127–135.
9. Fell, J. M. G., C^*-algebras with smooth dual, *Illinois J. Math.* 4 (1960) 221–230.
10. Gardner, L. T., On duality for locally compact groups, preliminary report, abstract 622-18, Notices *Amer. Math. Soc.* 12 (1965) 330.
11. Grothendieck, A., Un résultat sur le dual d'une C^*-algèbre, *J. Mathematique Pures et Appliquees*, 36 (1957) 97–108.
12. Guichardet, A., Sur la categorie des algèbres de von Neumann, *Bull. Sciences Math.*, 2e serie, 90 (1966) 41–64.
13. Halmos, P. R., Measure Theory, D. Van Nostrand, Princeton, 1950.
14. Katz, G. I., Generalization of the group principle of duality, *Doklady Akademii Nauk SSSR* 138 (1961) 275–278. (Translation in *Soviet Mathematics* 2 (1961) 581–584.)
15. ———, Ring-groups and the principle of duality I, Trudy Moskov. *Mat. Obsc.* 12 (1963) 259–301.
16. ———, Ring-groups and the principle of duality II, Trudy Moskov. *Mat. Obsc.* 13 (1965) 84–113.

17. Kelley, J. L., Duality for compact groups, *Proc. Nat. Acad. Sci.*, 49 (1963) 457–458.
18. Larson, R. G., Cocommutative Hopf algebras, to appear.
19. Rieffel, M. A., Burnside's theorem for representations of Hopf algebras, to appear.
20. Stinespring, W. F., Integration theorems for gages and duality for unimodular groups, *Trans. Amer. Math. Soc.*, 90 (1959) 15–56.
21. Takesaki, M., a duality in representation theory of C^*-algebras, Ann. of Math. (2) 85 (1967) 370–382.
22. Tannaka, T., Uber den Dualitatssatz der nichtkommutativen topologischen Gruppen, *Tôhoku Math. Journ.*, 53 (1938), 1–12.
23. Tatsuuma, N., A duality theorem for locally compact groups I, *Proc. Japan Acad.*, 41 (1965) 878–882.
24. ——, A duality theorem for locally compact groups II, *Proc. Japan. Acad.*, 42, (1966) 46–47.
25. Tomita, M., The second dual of a C^*-algebra, (1964) unpublished.
26. Wendel, J. G., Left centralizers and isomorphisms of group algebras. *Pacific J. Math.*, 2 (1952) 251–261.

University of Rochester
Rochester, New York

University of California
Berkeley, California

Tulane University
New Orleans, Louisiana

University of California
Santa Barbara, California

Subspaces and Cocycles

HENRY HELSON

1. INTRODUCTION

This is an account of a certain part of the function theory of compact abelian groups with ordered duals, the part having to do with cocycles as elaborated in [**1**] and [**2**]. Very recently T. Gamelin has written an exceedingly interesting paper on the subject, and with his permission I shall give his main theorem and the ideas behind it.

We consider a subgroup Γ of the discrete real line R_d; its dual K is a quotient group of B, the Bohr compactification of the real line R. Elements of Γ are called λ, τ, and those of K are x, y. χ_λ is the character on K with values $\chi_\lambda(x) = x(\lambda)$. Normalized Haar measure on K is σ. A summable function f on K has Fourier series

$$f(x) \sim \sum_{\lambda} a(\lambda)\, \chi_\lambda(x),$$

where the Fourier coefficients $a(\lambda)$ are defined by

$$a(\lambda) = \int f(x)\, \chi_\lambda(-x) d\sigma(x).$$

H^2 is the subspace of L^2 consisting of all functions whose coefficients $a(\lambda)$ vanish for all $\lambda < 0$; H_0^2 is the slightly smaller space of functions for which also $a(0) = 0$.

A closed subspace $\mathfrak{M}$ of L^2 is called *invariant* if for each f in $\mathfrak{M}$ and $\lambda > 0$ we have $\chi_\lambda f$ in $\mathfrak{M}$. Then the subspaces $\mathfrak{M}_\lambda = \chi_\lambda \cdot \mathfrak{M}$ form a nested family of closed subspaces of L^2. $\mathfrak{M}$ is called *simply invariant* if they are not all identical; in that case they are all distinct, and

$$\bigcap_{\lambda < \infty} \mathfrak{M}_\lambda = \{0\}; \qquad \bigcup_{\lambda > -\infty} \mathfrak{M}_\lambda \text{ is dense in } L^2.$$

We are interested only in simply invariant subspaces $\mathfrak{M}$, and furthermore only in subgroups Γ of R_d that are not simply arithmetic progressions. Thus Γ is order-dense in R_d and we are not talking about the circle group, which is exceptional in some respects and would have to be treated separately.

Denote by P_λ the orthogonal projection of L^2 on $\mathfrak{M}_\lambda$, and complete the definition for all λ in R_d so as to make $(I - P_\lambda)$ a decomposition of the identity. A continuous unitary group is defined in L^2 by setting

$$V_t = -\int_{-\infty}^{\infty} e^{it\lambda}\, dP_\lambda .$$

If $\mathfrak{M}$ is H^2 or H_0^2, V_t is the translation operator T_t:

$$T_t f(x) = f(x + e_t),$$

where e_t is the element of K defined by $e_t(\lambda) = e^{it\lambda}$. The elements e_t form a dense subgroup of K that is the continuous image of the real line under the mapping which carries t to e_t. This subgroup, which we call K_0, is the object in K dual to the order relation given in Γ.

For other simply invariant subspaces $\mathfrak{M}$ the group $\{V_t\}$ is a perturbed version of $\{T_t\}$: $V_t = A_t T_t$, where A_t is multiplication by a measurable function $A_t(x)$ for each t. These functions have the following properties: A_t has modulus one almost everywhere on K for each t; A_t depends continuously on t as a mapping from the line into L^2; and for each real t and u we have almost everywhere

$$A_{t+u} = A_t \cdot T_t A_u .$$

Any family of functions A_t with these properties is called a *cocycle* on K. Indeed except for the notion of continuity this is an instance of the general algebraic notion of one-dimensional cocycle. In connection with Gamelin's theorem we shall have to define another kind of cocycle.

It is important that any cocycle can be presented as a Borel function $A(t, x)$ on $R \times K$ with the property that $A(t, x) = A_t(x)$ for almost all x, except in a null-set of t. Conversely, a Borel function $A(t, x)$ of modulus one almost everywhere on $R \times K$ and satisfying the functional equation (except on a null-set of t, u, x) comes from a cocycle. This fact is easy if Γ is denumerable [**2**], but has been proved in general by Gamelin.

2. ANALYSIS OF COCYCLES

The connection between function theory in the unit circle and the structure of invariant subspaces contained in H^2 on the circle was discovered by Beurling. This connection was exploited by Lowdenslager and myself for the purposes of harmonic analysis on groups K of the type now being discussed. Now the correspondence between simply invariant subspaces and cocycles provides a new analytic tool in the subject. Determining the structure of cocycles on K seems to be a central problem in the harmonic analysis of K.

The correspondence between simply invariant subspaces in L^2 and their cocycles is not quite one–one; H^2 and H_0^2 lead to the same cocycle, for example. More generally for any invariant subspace $\mathfrak{M}$ we can define

$$\mathfrak{M}_+ = \bigcap_{\lambda<0} \mathfrak{M}_\lambda, \qquad \mathfrak{M}_- = \text{closure of} \bigcup_{\lambda>0} \mathfrak{M}_\lambda;$$

the first one contains $\mathfrak{M}$ and the second is contained in $\mathfrak{M}$. It is proved in [**1**] that these invariant subspaces are at most one dimension apart, so that one of them at least coincides with $\mathfrak{M}$. If we consider only the larger one (that is, H^2 in preference to H_0^2) then the correspondence between simply invariant subspaces and cocycles is perfect.

Let E be a measurable function on K with modulus one almost everywhere. Then $E \cdot H^2$ is a simply invariant subspace whose cocycle is

$$A(t,x) = E(x + e_t)^{-1}E(x);$$

cocycles of this form are called *coboundaries*. On the circle it is true that every simply invariant subspace has this form (as proved by Beurling for subspaces contained in H^2); an equivalent statement is that every periodic cocycle is a coboundary. On K it is true more generally that every almost periodic cocycle is a coboundary (or rather, to be precise, differs from a coboundary at most by a cocycle that is constant in x for each t, a trivial cocycle even if not a coboundary). (A vector-valued function on the line is almost periodic if it can be extended to be a continuous function on the Bohr group B.)

Nevertheless cocycles need not be coboundaries, even if we enlarge the group of coboundaries by the other trivial cocycles just mentioned. The formula

$$A(t,x) = \exp(i \int_0^t m(x + e_u)du)$$

defines a cocycle whenever m is a real function on K smooth enough for the integral to make sense. In [**1**] certain cocycles of this form were shown not to be coboundaries, with functions m having absolutely convergent Fourier series. It was necessary to assume for the analysis that Γ possesses an infinite set linearly independent over the rational numbers; the restriction was removed by Kahane, by use of refined and powerful technique.

Since cocycles are not all coboundaries, not every simply invariant subspace $\mathfrak{M}$ of L^2 has the form $E \cdot H^2$ or anything closely related to it. It should be of interest to give representative elements in each cohomology class explicitly. It was proved in [**2**] that each class contains cocycles of the form BC, where B is given by the exponential formula above, with a very smooth function m, and C is a cocycle assuming only the values 1, -1, and having other interesting properties. However, B and C are by no means determined by the cohomology class. It seems very difficult to decide in general whether a given function m leads to a coboundary or not.

3. ANALYTIC COCYCLES

A simply invariant subspace $\mathfrak{M}$ contains H_0^2 if and only if its cocycle A is *analytic* in the following sense: for almost every x in K, $A(t, x)$ is the boundary function (in t) of a function that is analytic and bounded in the upper half-plane. More generally, one subspace contains another if and only if the quotient of their cocycles (in the right order) is analytic.

Let $\mathfrak{M}, \mathfrak{N}$ be simply invariant subspaces with cocycles A, B. We obtain a new simply invariant subspace by closing the linear span of all products fg, where f and g are bounded functions in $\mathfrak{M}$, $\mathfrak{N}$ respectively. Theorem: this subspace has cocycle AB.

These results, with some necessary technical comments, are proved in [**2**]. They contain more information than the corresponding statements about the circle, which are trivial. Both of these theorems have to do with properties of cocycles as functions of t for fixed x. The importance of this point of view was suggested originally by Keith Yale.

The hard problem now is to relate cohomology with analyticity. We should like to know, for example, whether to every $\mathfrak{M}$ we can find a unitary function E such that $E \cdot \mathfrak{M}$ is contained in H^2; this is the same as asking whether every cohomology class contains an analytic cocycle. Nothing is known about this and similar questions.

4. GAMELIN'S WORK

One theorem about the structure of cocycles has been quoted. Gamelin has found another one of entirely different character. Its consequences have not been thoroughly explored yet. I shall merely sketch the idea involved, as I understand it.

Let τ be an arbitrary element of Γ different from 0. Denote by C the closed subgroup of K consisting of all x such that $x(\tau) = 1$. C intersects K_0 in those points e_t with t equal to $2\pi k \tau^{-1}$, for k integral. Similarly, C intersects each coset of K_0 in an arithmetic progression. If C were a cross-section for the cosets of K_0, that is if C intersected each one in a single point, we could easily prove that every cocycle is a coboundary. However no Borel cross-section exists, and C is the next best thing we can find.

Denote by e the element e_t with $t = 2\pi\tau^{-1}$. Since e is in C, translation by e carries C onto itself and preserves the Haar measure σ_0 of C. This homeomorphism induces a unitary mapping T of functions defined on C: $Tf(x) = f(x + e)$. Now a *cocycle* on C is a function $A = A_n(x)$ defined for almost all x in C and with unitary values, for each n, and such that almost everywhere

$$A_{m+n} = A_m \cdot T^m A_n.$$

A coboundary is a cocycle of the form

$$A_m = T^m E^{-1} \cdot E,$$

for some unitary function E on C.

Gamelin's result now has two parts, which I describe informally. First, there is a canonical way of extending a cocycle on C to a cocycle on K, and this procedure establishes an isomorphism of the cohomology groups. Second, every cocycle A on C is determined by the function A_1 on C, by application of the functional equation, and specifically A is a coboundary if and only if A_1 is a function of the form $TE^{-1} \cdot E$ for some unitary function E on C.

The first fact is analogous to a theorem well known in the cohomology theory of finite groups. In our context the extension is made in the following way. For integral k and x in C we define

$$B(2\pi k\tau^{-1}, x) = A_k(x).$$

Still with x in C, define $B(t, x)$ to be constant for t in each interval $2\pi k\tau^{-1} \leq t < 2\pi(k + 1)\tau^{-1}$. Finally, for x in C we set

$$B(t, x + e_u) = B(t + u, x)B(u, x)^{-1}.$$

The definition is unambiguous if we require that $0 \leq u < 2\pi\tau^{-1}$; one must verify that the same formula holds without this restriction.

Obviously the product of two cocycles on C is carried onto the product of their extensions to K. It has to be shown that coboundaries on C, and only coboundaries, have extensions to coboundaries on K; and that every cohomology class on K contains at least one extension.

Once stated the second part of the result hardly requires proof. The characterization of functions that can be represented in the form $TE^{-1} \cdot E$, where E is one kind of function or another and T some given transformation, is an interesting question in a number of contexts, and there is a body of results bearing on the problem. Gamelin has found *real* cocycles that are not coboundaries on C, and by extension on K, by constructing subsets of C with certain properties. This solves a problem raised in [**2**], and these cocycles are of quite a different kind than the ones produced by means of the exponential formula.

5. CONCLUSION

I would like to mention that interesting work based on new ideas has been done recently by M. Nadkarni, and by him in collaboration with Z. Ditzian. It is not easy to summarize so I must merely refer to their forthcoming papers.

REFERENCES

1. Helson, H. and D. Lowdenslager, Invariant subspaces, *Proc. Int. Symp. on Linear Spaces*, Jerusalem, 1961, 251–262.
2. Helson, H., Compact groups with ordered duals, *Proc. London Math Soc.*, (3) 14A (1965) 144–156.

The Ideal Theorem in Certain Banach Algebras of Functions Satisfying Smoothness Conditions

C. HERZ
Cornell University

1. INTRODUCTION

Let $\mathbf{S}(R^n)$ denote the space of infinitely differentiable functions on R^n which tend to zero at infinity together with their derivatives faster than any power of the distance from the origin. Let N be a norm on $\mathbf{S}(R^n)$ with the additional properties that there exist constants a and b such that

$$|f(x)| \leq aN(f), \qquad N(fg) \leq bN(f)N(g)$$

for all $f, g \in \mathbf{S}(R^n)$, $x \in R^n$. We write $\mathbf{N}(R^n)$ to denote the completion of $\mathbf{S}(R^n)$ for the norm N. Then $\mathbf{N}(R^n)$ is a Banach algebra whose structure space is R^n itself.

Given a closed set $E \subset R^n$ put

$\mathbf{I}_0(E)$ = set of infinitely differentiable functions with compact support disjoint from E,

$\mathbf{I}_S(E)$ = set of functions in $\mathbf{S}(R^n)$ which vanish on E,

$\mathbf{I}_N(E)$ = set of functions in $\mathbf{N}(R^n)$ which vanish on E,

The set E is a *set of spectral synthesis* with respect to the algebra $\mathbf{N}(R^n)$ if $\mathbf{I}_N(E) = \bar{\mathbf{I}}_0^N(E)$, the closure in the N-norm.

From the point of view of classical analysis there are distinct ways in which spectral synthesis can fail.

DEFINITION. The set E is a *Schwartz set* for the norm N if $\mathbf{I}_S(E) \not\subset \bar{\mathbf{I}}_0^N(E)$.

DEFINITION. The set E is *rough* relative to the algebra $\mathbf{N}(R^n)$ if $\mathbf{I}_N(E) \not\subset \bar{\mathbf{I}}_S^N(E)$. (Otherwise E is *smooth.*)

The problem of the existence of Schwartz sets is a straight forward one. It is obvious that if the norm N^* is stronger than the norm N then a

Schwartz set for N is *a fortiori* a Schwartz set for N^*. Thus Schwartz sets come into the picture when the norm N is too strong. By contrast, the question of the existence of rough sets is both subtle and profound. Rough sets can occur for two opposing heuristic reasons: the norm N is too weak, $\mathbf{I}_N(E)$ contains too many functions, or the norm N is too strong, $\bar{\mathbf{I}}_S^N(E)$ contains too few functions. This distinction may appear to be purely a matter of idiosyncratic attitude, but we shall soon see that it has some sense.

We need a couple of terms.

DEFINITION. The algebra $\mathbf{N}(R^n)$ is *smooth* if there are no sets rough relative to it. The *ideal theorem* holds for $\mathbf{N}(R^n)$ if each closed set is a set of spectral synthesis with respect to it.

The *Fourier algebra* $\mathbf{A}(R^n)$ is defined by the norm

$$A(f) = \int |\hat{f}(\xi)|\, d\xi, \qquad \hat{f}(\xi) = \int e^{-2\pi i \xi x} f(x)dx.$$

The ideal theorem fails in $\mathbf{A}(R^n)$ for all n, but one should distinguish two statements. L. Schwartz [5] proved: *the sphere $S^{n-1} \subset R^n$ is a Schwartz set for the norm A if $n \geq 3$.* This gives a counterexample to the ideal theorem in $\mathbf{A}(R^n)$ for $n \geq 3$, but spheres are always smooth relative to the algebra $\mathbf{A}(R^n)$. The smoothness question is much more difficult, and Malliavin [4] proved: *the algebra $\mathbf{A}(R^n)$ is not smooth for any n.*

The motivation for this work was the problem of trying to "save" the ideal theorem. One might adopt the attitude that the existence of rough sets relative to $\mathbf{A}(R^n)$ is due to the fact that the A-norm is too strong. This raises the question of how little can one weaken the A-norm and yet get a smooth algebra (the weakest admissible norm gives $\mathbf{C}_0(R^n)$ which is smooth). This is an interesting and important question, but we do not pursue it here. Rather, we shall take the point of view that $\mathbf{A}(R^n)$ fails to be smooth because it contains functions that are not smooth enough. We shall look for subalgebras of $\mathbf{A}(R^n)$ that are smooth. This means taking norms N that are stronger than the A-norm. Before going further we should place some restrictions on the norms under consideration. We wish to keep the Euclidean geometry of R^n in the picture. Hence we shall assume

(i) N is invariant under Euclidean motions, that is, if $g(x) = f(\sigma x + h)$ where σ is an orthogonal transformation and $h \in R^n$, then $N(g) = N(h)$. A second desideratum is that we can restrict our attention to compact sets and this is insured by

(ii) For $0 \leq t \leq 1$, $N(f^t) \leq N(f)$ where $f^t(x) = f(tx)$. Conditions (i) and (ii) are not serious limitations on the algebra $N(R^n)$. The next condition, however, prevents the norm from being very strong

(ii*) For $t > 0$, $\quad N(f^t) = N(f)$.

A norm satisfying (i) and (ii*) will be said to *be strongly homogeneous*, and the algebra $\mathbf{N}(R^n)$ is strongly homogeneous if N is equivalent to a strongly homogeneous norm. The norm A is obviously strongly homogeneous.

We shall start with the problem of finding smooth, strongly-homogeneous, subalgebras of $\mathbf{A}(R^n)$.

For $n \leq 2$ introduce a norm $\tilde{B}$ defined by

$$\tilde{B}(f) = \sup_{t>0} t^{-n/2}\{\int \sup_{|x-y|\leq t} |f(x) - f(y)|^2 dx\}^{1/2}.$$

It is not hard to check that we obtain a strongly homogeneous algebra $\tilde{\mathbf{B}}(R^n)$, but this is not a subalgebra of $\mathbf{A}(R^n)$. Hence we consider $\mathbf{A}(R^n) \cap \tilde{\mathbf{B}}(R^n)$, which is the same as the completion of $\mathbf{S}(R^n)$ for the norm $A + \tilde{B}$. All known spectral synthesis theorems about $\mathbf{A}(R^n)$ which do not restrict the sets in question are included in

THEOREM 1. For $n \leq 2$, the ideal theorem holds in $\mathbf{A}(R^n) \cap \tilde{\mathbf{B}}(R^n)$.

Theorem 1 is easily proved and is probably the best one can do as far as the ideal theorem is concerned. There is, however, a closely related result which leads to some interesting extensions. We define a norm B on $\mathbf{S}(R^n)$, for all n, as follows. For $h \in R^n$ the translation operator is defined by $T(h)f(x) = f(x + h)$ and the kth difference operator by $\Delta^k(h) = \{T(h) - I\}^k$. Put

$$\omega_2(h) = \{\int |\Delta^k(h)f(x)|^2 dx\}^{1/2}$$

where k is the least integer $> n/2$. Let $\bar{\omega}_2(t)$ be the average value of $\omega_2(h)$ on the sphere $|h| = t$, and set

$$B(f) = \int_0^\infty t^{-n/2}\bar{\omega}_2(t)dt/t.$$

It turns out that $\mathbf{B}(R^n)$ is a strongly homogeneous algebra of continuous functions. Moreover, S. Bernstein's theorem on absolutely convergent Fourier series generalize to $\mathbf{B}(R^n) \subset \mathbf{A}(R^n)$. For this reason we call $\mathbf{B}(R^n)$ the *Bernstein algebra*. We have

THEOREM 2. For $n \leq 2$, the ideal theorem holds in $\mathbf{B}(R^n)$.

Now $\mathbf{B}(R^n) \subset \tilde{\mathbf{B}}(R^n)$, so, from the standpoint of harmonic analysis, Theorem 2 gives less than Theorem 1. On the other hand, Theorem 2 is a special case of a far-reaching statement which has nothing to do with harmonic analysis. For $0 < \alpha \leq n$ we shall define a Lipshitz norm Λ^α on $\mathbf{S}(R^n)$, ($\Lambda^\alpha = \Lambda^\alpha_{n/\alpha,1}$ in the notation of [**2**]), which gives rise to a strongly homogeneous algebra $\Lambda^\alpha(R^n)$. The Bernstein algebra is $\mathbf{B}(R^n) = \Lambda^{n/2}(R^n)$ and we have

THEOREM 3. For $0 < \alpha \leq 1$, the ideal theorem holds in $\Lambda^\alpha(R^n)$.

If $\alpha \geq \beta$ then $\Lambda^{\alpha}(R^n) \subset \Lambda^{\beta}(R^n)$, thus Theorem 3 seems to suggest that the ideal theorem holds in $\Lambda^{\alpha}(R^n)$ if the Λ^{α}-norm is not too strong. We may therefore expect that the possible failure of the ideal theorem for $\alpha > 1$ would be due to the existence of Schwartz sets. The question of Schwartz sets can be answered completely.

THEOREM 4. For $\alpha \geq n' = n/(n-1)$, the sphere $S^{n-1} \subset R^n$ is a Schwartz set for the norm Λ^{α}.

In the reverse direction, it can be shown (we shall not do it here) that Schwartz sets do not exist for the norm Λ^{α} if $\alpha < n'$. It is to be expected that the presence or absence of Schwartz sets involves dimensional considerations, but this does not seem relevant to the smoothness question. I should guess that the algebras $\Lambda^{\alpha}(R^n)$ are smooth for all α; the limitation $\alpha \leq 1$ in Theorem 3 is probably a fault of technique. I don't have methods for proving smoothness where the ideal theorem fails, and Theorem 4 shows that $\alpha \leq 1$ is the best possible bound independent of dimension which can occur in Theorem 3.

The case $n = 1$ of Theorem 2 was proved by Beurling [**1**]. His method of "contractions" gives an easy proof of Theorem 3 for $\alpha < 1$. The delicate situation is $\alpha = 1$ in Theorem 3, including the case $n = 2$ of Theorem 2. The contraction method is adapted to norms defined in terms of first differences. For $\alpha \geq 1$ the Λ^{α}-norm apparently depends on second differences.

The case $n = 3$ of Theorem 4 follows from the Schwartz counterexample in $\mathbf{A}(R^3)$, but $\Lambda^2(R^2)$ presents a new phenomenon.

Since $\alpha \leq n$, the 1-dimensional situation is completely covered by Theorem 3. Thus the deep open questions about Lipschitz algebras only occur in several variables. Giving back to the Fourier algebras, we can ask whether Theorems 1 and 2 can be substantially improved. Conjecture: the algebra $\mathbf{A}(R^n) \cap \Lambda^{\alpha}(R^n)$ is not smooth for any $\alpha < n/2$.

2. LIPSCHITZ SPACES AND ALGEBRAS

In [**2**] we considered a family of spaces $\Lambda^{\alpha}_{a,p}(R^n)$ where $-\infty < \alpha \leq \infty$, $1 \leq a \leq \infty, 1 \leq p \leq \infty$. When $\alpha > 0$ these spaces are the completions of $\mathbf{S}(R^n)$ for the norms $\Lambda^{\alpha}_{a,p}$ where

$$\Lambda^{\alpha}_{a,p}(f) = \{ \int (| h |^{-\alpha} \| \Delta^k(h) f \|_a)^p \, đh \}^{1/p}.$$

Here $đh$ is the rotationally invariant measure on $R^n - \{0\}$ such that for a radial function $u(x) = v(|x|)$ we have

$$\int_{R_n - \{0\}} u(h) đh = \int_0^{\infty} v(t) dt/t.$$

To be specific we may fix k as the least integer $> \alpha$, but according to Lemma 1.1 (references are always to [**2**]) we get an equivalent norm for any $k > \alpha$.

We shall be concerned here with the cases $0 < \alpha \leq n$, $a = n/\alpha$, and $p = 1$. To abbreviate we write $\Lambda^\alpha = \Lambda^\alpha_{a,1}$ ($a = n/\alpha$ unless otherwise stated). Thus the norm is

$$\Lambda^\alpha(f) = \int_0^\infty t^{-\alpha}\bar{\omega}_k(t)dt/t$$

where

$$\omega_k(h) = \{\int |\Delta^k(h)f(x)|^\alpha dx\}^{1/2},$$

$$\bar{\omega}_k(t) = \text{average value of } \omega_k(h) \text{ on the sphere } |h| = t.$$

As general matters of notation, $*$ denotes convolution on R^n,

$$f*g(x) = \int f(x-y)g(y)dy;$$

a' is the conjugate index of a, that is, $1/a + 1/a' = 1$; and f_t denotes the function $f_t(x) = t^{-n}f(t^{-1}x)$.

The fundamental result about the spaces $\Lambda^\alpha(R^n)$ is

THEOREM 2 of [**2**]. Given $k > \alpha$ there exists a radial function $\kappa \in S(R^n)$ such that for all $f \in \Lambda^\alpha(R^n)$ we have an absolutely convergent integral representation

$$f(x) = \int\int \kappa_{|h|}(x-y)\Delta^k(h)f(y)dy\bar{d}h.$$

This fundamental formula may be rewritten as

$$f = \int_0^\infty t^\alpha \kappa_t * u(\cdot;t)dt/t$$

where $u(x;t)$ is the average value of $|h|^{-\alpha}\Delta^k(h)f(x)$ on the sphere $|h| = t$. What is essential is not the exact form of u, but only the fact that

$$\int_0^\infty \|u(\cdot;t)\|_a dt/t = \Lambda^\alpha(f).$$

Theorem 2 has two important consequences which we state as propositions.

PROPOSITION 1. $\Lambda^\alpha(R^n)$ is a strongly homogeneous algebra of continuous functions on R^n.

Proof. The representation formula for $f \in \Lambda^\alpha(R^n)$ gives

$$\|f\|_\infty \leq \int_0^\infty t^\alpha \|\kappa_t\|_{a'} \|u(\cdot;t)\|_a dt/t.$$

Since $\|\kappa_t\|_{a'} = t^{-n/a}\|\kappa\|_{a'}$, we get $\|f\|_\infty \leq \|\kappa\|_{a'}\Lambda^\alpha(f)$. To show that Λ^α is an algebra norm we use the fact that the norm is defined up to equivalence using kth order differences for any $k > \alpha$. There is a Leibnitz formula

$$\Delta^k(h)(fg) = \sum_{i=0}^{k} \binom{k}{i} \Delta^i(h) f \cdot \Delta^{k-i}(h) T^i(h) g,$$

and on taking L_a-norms one has

$$\|\Delta^k(h)(fg)\|_a \leq \sum_{0 \leq i < k/2} \binom{k}{i} 2i \|f\|_\infty \|\Delta^{k-i}(h) g\|_a$$

$$+ \sum_{k/2 \leq i \leq k} \binom{k}{i} \|\Delta^i(h) f\|_a 2^{k-1} \|g\|_\infty.$$

If $k > 2\alpha$ then all the differences $\Delta^j(h)$ which occurs have $j > \alpha$. Hence

$$\Lambda^\alpha(fg) \leq \text{const } \|f\|_\infty \Lambda^\alpha(g) + \text{const } \Lambda^\alpha(f) \|g\|_\infty$$
$$\leq \text{const } \Lambda^\alpha(f)\, \Lambda^\alpha(g).$$

The norm Λ^α is obviously invariant under Euclidean motions. The fact that $\Lambda^\alpha(f^t) = \Lambda^\alpha(f)$ is easily checked; $\alpha = n/a$ is the essential point here.

Closely related to the Λ^α-norm is $\tilde{\Lambda}^\alpha$ defined by

$$\tilde{\Lambda}^\alpha(f) = \sup_{t>0} t^{-\alpha} \tilde{\omega}_j(t)$$

where

$$\tilde{\omega}_j(t) = \{\int \sup_{|h| \leq t} |\Delta^j(h) f(x)|^a dx\}^{1/a}.$$

Here j is the least integer $\geq \alpha$, and it is of vital importance that we don't need $j > \alpha$ when α is an integer. Thus for all α with $0 < \alpha \leq 1$

$$\tilde{\Lambda}^\alpha(f) = \sup_{t>0} t^{-\alpha}\{\int \sup_{|x-y| \leq t} |f(x) - f(y)|^a dx\}^{1/a}.$$

Also $\tilde{B} = \tilde{\Lambda}^{n/2}$. The proof of Theorem 3 depends on the cases $0 < \alpha \leq 1$ of

PROPOSITION 2. There exists a constant c depending only on α and n such that for all $f \in \Lambda^\alpha(R^n)$,

$$\tilde{\Lambda}^\alpha(f) \leq c\, \Lambda^\alpha(f).$$

The proof of Proposition 2 is quite delicate but not particularly interesting. Hence we shall put it at the end in §5 although logically it belongs at this place. Proposition 2 is the main idea in this paper.

A simpler but related result is this. Let D^α be a derivative of order α (any version of functional derivative will do when α is not an integer). The kernel k can be so chosen that $D^\alpha \kappa \in S(R^n)$. The representation formula gives

$$D^\alpha f = \int_0^\infty (D^\alpha \kappa)_t * u(\cdot; t) dt/t$$

and hence

$$\| D^\alpha f \|_a \leq \int_0^\infty \| (D^\alpha \kappa)_t \|_1 \| u(\cdot; t) \|_a dt/t = \| D^\alpha \kappa \|_1 \Lambda^\alpha(f).$$

Thus the derivatives of order α of elements of $\Lambda^\alpha(R^n)$ belong to $\mathbf{L}_a(R^n)$.

3. LIPSCHITZ ALGEBRAS AND FOURIER TRANSFORMS

Let ϕ denote the class of functions $\varphi \in \mathbf{L}_1(R^n)$ such that $\varphi(\xi)$ is a decreasing function of $|\xi|$. Put $(\mathbf{L}_1)^\circ$ for the space of functions g such that there exists $\varphi \in \Phi$ with $|g| \leq \varphi$ almost everywhere. We obtain a convolution subalgebra of $\mathbf{L}_1(R^n)$, but $(\mathbf{L}_1)^\circ$ excludes functions which are "very lacunary." Write $(\mathbf{L}_1)^1 = \mathbf{L}_1(R^n)$, and for $0 < \sigma < 1$ we have an increasing family of intermediate spaces $(\mathbf{L}_1)^\sigma$ where $g \in (\mathbf{L}_1)^\sigma$ iff there exists $\varphi \in \Phi$ such that

$$\int |g(\xi)|^{1/\sigma} \varphi^{1-1/\sigma}(\xi) d\xi < \infty.$$

Intuitively speaking, the greater σ, the more lacunary functions admitted in $(\mathbf{L}_1)^\sigma$.

THEOREM 1 of [**2**]. Let α and σ be related by $\alpha = (1 - \sigma)n$. For $1/2 \leq \sigma \leq 1$ the Fourier transform maps $(\mathbf{L}_1)^\sigma$ continuously into $\Lambda^\alpha(R^n)$. For $n/2 \leq \alpha \leq n$ the Fourier transform maps $\Lambda^\alpha(R^n)$ continuously into $(\mathbf{L}_1)^\sigma$.

When $\alpha = n/2$, $\sigma = 1/2$ we can go both ways. Thus

COROLLARY. The spaces $\mathbf{B}(R^n)$ and $(\mathbf{L}_1)^{1/2}$ are Fourier transforms of each other, that is, $f \in \mathbf{B}(R^n)$ iff there exists $\varphi \in \Phi$ such that $\int |\hat{f}(\xi)|^2 \varphi^{-1}(\xi) d\xi < \infty$. (This statement is due to Beurling [**1**] when $n = 1$.)

All that really concerns us is the well-known Bernstein theorem, $\mathbf{B}(R^n) \subset \mathbf{A}(R^n)$, and hence $\Lambda^\alpha(R^n) \subset \mathbf{A}(R^n)$ for $\alpha \geq n/2$, but the stronger result says that $\mathbf{B}(R^n)$ does not contain very lacunary Fourier transforms. This is perhaps a "reason" for suspecting that $\mathbf{B}(R^n)$ is smooth.

When $0 < \alpha < n/2$, $\Lambda^\alpha(R^n)$ is not contained in $\mathbf{A}(R^n)$. On the other hand, when $\alpha > n/2$, $\Lambda^\alpha(R^n)$ does not contain all the Fourier transforms of elements of $(\mathbf{L}_1)^\circ$. Therefore, except for the Bernstein algebras, the $\Lambda^\alpha(R^n)$ do not have a simple description in terms of Fourier transforms. In addition, our theorems do not tell very much about ideal theory in the convolution algebras $(\mathbf{L}_1)^\sigma$ for $\sigma \neq 1/2$.

4. PROOF OF THEOREMS 1 AND 3

The technique of [**3**] can be formulated very generally. Suppose N is a homogeneous norm of $\mathbf{S}(R^n)$, that is, N is continuous in the topology of $S(R^n)$, there exist constants a and b such that

$$|f(x)| \leq aN(f), \qquad N(fg) \leq b\,N(f)N(g)$$

$$N(T(h)f) = N(f), \text{ and } N(f^t) \leq N(f) \text{ for } 0 \leq t < 1.$$

(The Euclidean invariance of N is unimportant here.) Choose once and for all u, $k \in \mathbf{D}(R^n)$, the infinitely differentiable functions with compact support, having the properties

$$u = 1 \text{ on a neighborhood of } 0,$$

$$\int k(x)dx = 1, k \geq 0, \operatorname{supp} k \subset \{x: |x| < 1\}.$$

Write u^ϵ, k_ϵ for the functions $u^\epsilon(x) = u(\epsilon x)$, $k_\epsilon(x) = \epsilon^{-n}k(\epsilon^{-1}x)$.

The algebra $\mathbf{N}(R^n)$ is the completion of $\mathbf{S}(R^n)$ for the N-norm. Two basic facts are

LEMMA 1. For each $f \in \mathbf{N}(R^n)$, $\lim_{\epsilon \to 0} N(u^\epsilon f - f) = 0$.

LEMMA 2. For each $f \in \mathbf{N}(R^n)$, $\lim_{\epsilon \to 0} N(k_\epsilon * f - f) = 0$.

Proofs. We have $N(u^\epsilon f) \leq bN(u^\epsilon)N(f) \leq bN(u)N(f)$ for $0 < \epsilon < 1$. Hence multiplication by u^ϵ is a linear operation on $\mathbf{N}(R^n)$ uniformly bounded in $\epsilon < 1$. Also

$$N(k_\epsilon * f) = N\{\int T(h)f\,k_\epsilon(h)dh\} \leq N(f)\,\|k_\epsilon\|_1 \leq N(f)\,\|k\|_1;$$

so convolution by k_ϵ is a linear operation uniformly bounded in ϵ. Since $\mathbf{D}(R^n)$ is dense in $\mathbf{N}(R^n)$ and both

$$\lim_{\epsilon \to 0} u^\epsilon f = f, \ \lim_{\epsilon \to 0} k_\epsilon * f = f$$

in the topology of $\mathbf{D}(R^n)$, the assertions are established.

It follows from Lemma 1 that we can confine our attention to functions of compact support in $\mathbf{N}(R^n)$. Suppose that E is a given compact set in R^n, $f \in \mathbf{I}_N(E)$ has compact support, and $0 < \epsilon < 1$. Say that φ

is (f, E, ϵ)-admissible if

$$\varphi \text{ is a summable function of compact support}$$

$$\varphi(x) = f(x) \text{ whenever } d(x, E) \leq \epsilon$$

where d denotes the distance. Write

$$f = (f - k_\epsilon * f) + k_\epsilon * (f - \varphi) + k_\epsilon * \varphi.$$

By Lemma 2, $N(f - k_\epsilon * f) = o(1)$, a quantity which tends to 0 as $\epsilon \to 0$. At the same time, if φ is (f, E, ϵ)-admissible then $k_\epsilon * (f - \varphi) \in \mathbf{I}_o(E)$. Hence we have proved

LEMMA 3. Let E be a compact set and $f \in \mathbf{N}(R^n)$ a function of compact support. A necessary and sufficient condition that $f \in \bar{\mathbf{I}}_o^N(E)$ is that there exist a family $\{\varphi\}$ of (f, E, ϵ)-admissible functions such that $N(k_\epsilon * \varphi) = o(1)$.

It is in fact necessary that one be able to choose $\{\varphi\}$ such that $N(\varphi) = o(1)$, but it may be difficult to find such a family. Our procedure is to choose the (f, E, ϵ)-admissible functions in a very crude fashion. Let $y = y(x; \epsilon)$ be a measurable mapping defined for $d(x, E) \leq \epsilon$ with the properties

$$y(x) \in E, y(x) = x \text{ if } x \in E, \ |x - y(x)| < 2\epsilon.$$

(The existence of such a mapping is trivial.) For all $f \in \mathbf{N}(R^n)$ we define $L_\epsilon^E f$ by

$$L_\epsilon^E f(x) = f(x) - f[y(x; \epsilon)] \text{ if } d(x, E) \leq \epsilon$$

$$= 0 \quad \text{otherwise.}$$

LEMMA 4. The compact set E is a set of spectral synthesis relative to $\mathbf{N}(R^n)$ if there exists a constant c such that for each $f \in \mathbf{S}(R^n)$

$$N(k_\epsilon * L_\epsilon^E f) \leq c\, N(f) \text{ and } N(k_\epsilon * L_\epsilon^E f) = o(1).$$

Proof. Since $f \to k_\epsilon * L_\epsilon^E f$ is a linear transformation, and $\mathbf{S}(R^n)$ is dense in $\mathbf{N}(R^n)$, we conclude that $N(k_\epsilon * L_\epsilon^E f) = o(1)$ for each $f \in \mathbf{N}(R^n)$. If $f \in \mathbf{I}_N(E)$, then $\varphi = L_\epsilon^E f$ is an (f, E, ϵ)-admissible function. The statement now follows from Lemma 3.

To apply Lemma 4 we shall need

LEMMA 5. Suppose $0 < \alpha \leq 1$ and E is compact. Then for $a = \alpha/n$ and each $f \in \mathbf{S}(R^n)$ we have

$$\| L_\epsilon^E f \|_a \leq 2\epsilon^\alpha \tilde{\Lambda}^\alpha(f) \text{ and } \| L_\epsilon^E f \|_a = o(\epsilon^\alpha).$$

Proof. Put $E(\epsilon) = \{x : 0 < d(x, E) \leq \epsilon\}$, and

$$f^*(x; t) = \sup_{|x-y| \leq t} |f(x) - f(y)|.$$

Then

$$\| L_\epsilon^E f\|_a^a = \int_{E(\epsilon)} |f(x) - f[y(x;\epsilon)]|^a dx \leq \int_{E(\epsilon)} \{f^*(x;2\epsilon)\}^a dx.$$

This gives $\| L_\epsilon^E f\|_a \leq \tilde{\Lambda}^\alpha(f)(2\epsilon)^\alpha$, but also, since $f^*(x;2\epsilon) = O(\epsilon)$ for $f \in \mathbf{S}(R^n)$ we get

$$\| L_\epsilon^E f\|_a^a = O(\epsilon^a) \,|\, E(\epsilon) \,|$$

where $|E(\epsilon)|$, the measure of $E(\epsilon)$, tends to O with ϵ. Therefore

$$\| L_\epsilon^E f\|_a = o(\epsilon) = o(\epsilon^\alpha) \text{ for } \alpha \leq 1.$$

PROOF OF THEOREM 3. The Λ^α-norm of the convolution $k * g$ may be estimated by

$$\Lambda^\alpha(k * g) = \int |h|^{-\alpha} \| \Delta^k(h)k * g\|_a \, d\!\!\!{}^-h$$
$$\leq \int |h|^{-\alpha} \| \Delta^k(h)k\|_1 \, d\!\!\!{}^-h \cdot \|g\|_a = \Lambda_{1,1}^\alpha(k) \cdot \|g\|_a.$$

The effect of dilations is easily computed, $\Lambda_{1,1}^\alpha(k_\epsilon) = \epsilon^{-\alpha}\Lambda_{1,1}^\alpha(k)$. We get

$$\Lambda^\alpha(k_\epsilon * L_\epsilon^E f) \leq \epsilon^{-\alpha} \Lambda_{1,1}^\alpha(k) \| L_\epsilon^E f\|_a.$$

Theorem 3 is a consequence of Lemma 4, Lemma 5, and Proposition 2.

PROOF OF THEOREM 1. The A-norm of the convolution $k * g$ may be estimated by $A(k * g) \leq \|k\|_2 \|g\|_2$. Hence

$$A(k_\epsilon * L_\epsilon^E f) \leq \|k_\epsilon\|_2 \| L_\epsilon^E f\|_2 = \epsilon^{-n/2} \|k\|_2 \| L_\epsilon^E f\|_2.$$

Lemma 5 with $\alpha = n/2$ gives the required estimates for the A-norm for use in Lemma 4. The estimates for the $\tilde{B}$-norm are obtained from $\tilde{\Lambda}^\alpha(k_\epsilon * g) \leq \text{const. } \epsilon^{-2} \|g\|_a$. The proof of this estimate involves exactly the same ideas as the proof of Proposition 2 in §6, and we omit the details.

The contraction method of Beurling [**1**] uses a different choice of $\{\varphi\}$ in Lemma 3. Given $\delta > 0$ define $K_\delta f(x) = f(x)$ if $|f(x)| \leq \delta$, $=$ $\delta f(x)/|f(x)|$ if $|f(x)| > \delta$. Since f is uniformly continuous on a neighborhood of E, there is a function $\delta(\epsilon)$ tending to 0 with ϵ such that $K_\delta f$ is (f, E, ϵ)-admissible whenever $\delta \leq \delta(\epsilon)$. If one can prove that $\lim_{\delta \to 0} N(K_\delta f) = 0$ for each $f \in \mathbf{N}(R^n)$ having compact support, then Lemma 3 can be applied immediately. In case $N = \Lambda^\alpha$ with $0 < \alpha < 1$, Beurling's method gives a simpler proof of Theorem 3.

5. PROOF OF THEOREM 4

The dual space of $\Lambda^\alpha(R^n)$ is a certain space of tempered distributions. Define a function φ on R^n by $\varphi(x) = 1$ for $|x| \leq 1$ and $\varphi(x) = 0$ for

$|x| > 1$. Write Lap to denote the Laplace operator, and consider Lap φ as a distribution.

The fact we need is

LEMMA 6. If $\alpha \geq n'$ then Lap φ represents an element of the dual space of $\Lambda^{\alpha}(R^n)$.

Proof. By definition, for $f \in \mathbf{S}(R^n)$ we have

$$\int f(\text{Lap}\ \varphi)\, dx = \int (\text{Lap} f)\ \varphi\, dx.$$

In the notation of [**2**], $\Lambda^{\alpha}(R^n) = \Lambda^{\alpha}_{a,1}(R^n)$ where $a = n/\alpha$ and Proposition 6.1 gives the fact that Lap $\Lambda^{\alpha}_{a,1}(R^n) = \Lambda^{\alpha-2}_{a,1}(R^n)$. Thus we have only to prove that φ represents an element of the dual space of $\Lambda^{\alpha-2}_{a,1}(R^n)$. It follows from Proposition 7.1 that this is true iff $\Lambda^{2-\alpha}_{a',\infty}(\varphi) < \infty$. When $0 < \beta < 1$ the $\Lambda^{\beta}_{b,\infty}$-norm is defined by

$$\Lambda^{\beta}_{b,\infty}(\varphi) = \sup_h |h|^{-\beta} \| \Delta(h)\varphi \|_b.$$

For the function φ in question, $\| \Delta(h)\varphi \|_b = 0(|h|^{1/\beta})$ as $|h| \to 0$, and we find that $\Lambda^{\beta}_{b,\infty}(\varphi) < \infty$ iff $\beta \leq 1/b$. To prove the Lemma it suffices to consider only $\alpha = n'$. Then $a = n - 1$, and

$$2 - \alpha = (n-2)/(n-1), \quad a' = (n-1)/(n-2);$$

so $\Lambda^{2-\alpha}_{a',\infty}(\varphi) < \infty$. The proof breaks down in the exceptional case $n = 2$, $\alpha = 2$. Here we have already seen that

$$\text{Lap}\ \Lambda^2(R^2) \subset \mathbf{L}_1(R^2),$$

and, since $\varphi \in L_\infty(R^2)$, the statement still holds.

To prove Theorem 4 one has only to observe that for $f \in \mathbf{S}(R^n)$ we have

$$\int f(\text{Lap}\ \varphi)\, dx = \int (\text{Lap} f)\ \varphi\, dx = \int_{|x| \leq 1} \text{Lap} f(x)\, dx$$

$$= \int_{S^{n-1}} (\partial f/\partial r)\, d\sigma$$

where $d\sigma$ is the surface measure on the sphere. If $u \in \mathbf{S}(R^n)$ is any function such that $u(x) = 1$ for $x \in S^{n-1}$ then for $f(x) = (1 - |x|^2)u(x)$ we have $f \in \mathbf{I}_S(S^{n-1})$ but $\int f(\text{Lap}\ \varphi)\, dx \neq 0$. Since $\int g(\text{Lap}\ \varphi)\, dx = 0$ for all $g \in \mathbf{I}_o(S^{n-1})$, it follows from Lemma 6 that $f \notin \bar{\mathbf{I}}^N_o(S^{n-1})$.

6. PROOF OF PROPOSITION 2

The representation formula for elements of $\Lambda^{\alpha}(R^n)$ gives

$$\Delta^j(h) f(x) = \int \int t^{\alpha} \Delta^j(h) \kappa_t(y) u(x - y; t)\, dy\, dt/t$$

$$\equiv \int \int U(h, t, x, y) dy dt/t$$

where $\int \| u(\cdot; t) \|_a dt/t = \Lambda^\alpha(f)$. On writing

$$f^*(x; \epsilon) = \sup_{|h| \leq \epsilon} | \Delta^j(h) f(x) |,$$

we get

$$f^*(x; \epsilon) \leq \sup_{|h| \leq \epsilon} \int \int | U(h, t, x, y) | dy dt/t$$

$$\leq v(x; \epsilon) + w(x) \epsilon^\alpha$$

where

$$v(x; \epsilon) = \sup_{|h| \leq \epsilon} \int \int_{|y| \leq 2j\epsilon} | U(h, t, x, y) | dy dt/t$$

and

$$w(x) = \sup_h \int \int_{|y| > 2j|h|} | h |^{-\alpha} | U(h, t, x, y) | dy dt/t.$$

Since $\tilde{\Lambda}^\alpha(f) = \sup_\epsilon \epsilon^{-\alpha} \| f^*(\cdot; \epsilon) \|_a$, Proposition 2 is a consequence of the next two statements.

LEMMA 7. $\| w \|_a \leq \text{const.}\ \Lambda^\alpha(f)$.

LEMMA 8. $\| v(\cdot; \epsilon) \|_a \leq \text{const.}\ \Lambda^\alpha(f)\, \epsilon^\alpha$.

Proof of Lemma 7. If $|h| \leq |y|/2j$ and $j \geq \alpha$ then $| \Delta^j(h) \kappa(y) | \leq \lambda(y) | h |^\alpha$ where $\lambda(y)$ is some fixed numerical function of the bounds for the derivatives of order $\leq j$ of the function κ in the annulus $|y|/2 \leq |x| \leq 3|y|/2$. Since $\kappa \in \mathbf{S}(R^n)$, it follows that $\lambda \in \mathbf{L}_1(R^n)$. One easily sees that as long as $|h| \leq |y|/2j$,

$$| \Delta^j(h) \kappa_t(y) | \leq t^{-\alpha} \lambda_t(y) | h |^\alpha.$$

Therefore

$$w(x) \leq \int \int \lambda_t(y) | u(x - y; t) | dt/t.$$

This gives

$$\| w \|_a \leq \int \| \lambda_t \|_1 \| u(\cdot; t) \|_a dt/t \leq \| \lambda \|_1 \Lambda^\alpha(f).$$

Proof of Lemma 8. By the Hölder inequality applied to

$$U(h, t, x, y) = | u(x - y; t) \psi^{-1/a'}(t) | \cdot | t^\alpha \Delta^j(h) \kappa_t(y) \psi^{1/a'}(t) |$$

we have

$$v^a(x; \epsilon) \leq \gamma^{a-1}(\epsilon) \int \int_{|y| \leq 2j\epsilon} | u(x - y; t) |^a \psi^{1-a}(t) dy dt/t$$

where

$$\gamma(\epsilon) = \sup_{|h| \leq \epsilon} \left\{ \int \int | t^\alpha \Delta^j(h) \kappa_t(y) |^{a'} \psi(t) dy dt/t \right\}^{1/a'}.$$

Here ψ is any function we wish, and we take $\psi(t) = \|u(\cdot;t)\|_a$. The estimate on $\gamma(\epsilon)$ is

$$\gamma(\epsilon) \leq \sup_{|h|\leq\epsilon} \int \|t^\alpha \Delta^j(h)\kappa_t\|_{a'} \psi(t)\, dt/t$$

$$\leq 2^j \int \|t^\alpha \kappa_t\|_{a'} \psi(t)\, dt/t = 2^j \|\kappa\|_{a'} \Lambda^\alpha(f).$$

Hence

$$\nu^a(x;\epsilon) \leq (2^j\|\kappa\|_{a'}\Lambda^\alpha(f))^{a-1} \int\int_{|y|\leq 2j\epsilon} |u(x-y;t)|^a \psi^{1-a}(t)dy\, dt/t.$$

Integrating over x we get

$$\|\nu(\cdot;\epsilon)\|_a^a \leq (2^j\|\kappa\|_{a'}\Lambda^\alpha(f))^{a-1} \int\int_{|y|\leq 2j\epsilon} \psi(t)dy\, dt/t$$

$$= (2^j\|\kappa\|_{a'}\Lambda^\alpha(f))^{a-1}\, b_n(2j\epsilon)^n\, \Lambda^\alpha(f)$$

where $b_n(2j\epsilon)^n$ is the volume of the ball of radius $2j\epsilon$. The end formula is

$$\|\nu(\cdot;\epsilon\|_a \leq \text{const } \Lambda^\alpha(f)\, \epsilon^{n/a}.$$

BIBLIOGRAPHY

1. Beurling, A., Analysis of some convolution algebras, *Annales de l'Institut Fourier* 14 (1964), Fasc. 2, 1–32.
2. Herz, C., Lipschitz spaces and Bernstein's theorem on absolutely convergent Fourier transforms, to appear.
3. Herz, C., Synthèse harmonique de distributions dans le plan, *C. R. Acad. Sci.* Paris 260 (1965), 4887–4890.
4. Malliavin, P., Impossibilité de la synthèse spectrale sur les groupes non compacts, *Publ. Math. Inst. Hautes Etudes Sci.* Paris (1959), 61–68.
5. Schwartz, L., Sur une propriété de synthèse spectrale dans les groupes non compacts, *C. R. Acad. Sci.* Paris 227 (1948), 424–426.

Positive Definite Operator-Valued Kernels and Unitary Representations[1]

R. A. KUNZE

1. INTRODUCTION

The simple connection between positive definite functions on groups and unitary representations with cyclic vectors has been well known since the early papers of Gelfand-Raikov [**2**] and Godement [**3**]. This theory was subsequently generalized by S. Ito [**8**] and M. G. Krein [**10**] to positive definite kernels on homogeneous spaces invariant under the action of a group. As indicated by Gelfand [**1**] the results are of particular interest in the context of spherical functions on symmetric Riemannian spaces.

Let G be a connected semisimple Lie group with finite center and K a maximal compact subgroup of G. A complex-valued function p defined on G is called a spherical function if $p(k_1\ x\ k_2) = p(x)$ for all k_1, k_2 in K and x in G. A nonzero spherical function p is said to be *elementary* if it is continuous and if

$$\int_K p(xky)dk = p(x)\,p(y)$$

for all x, y in G. An elementary positive definite spherical function p determines a strongly continuous unitary representation T of G which is not only cyclic but actually irreducible (see e.g. Helgason [7]); moreover, T is of class 1. If T is any continuous unitary representation of G, T is said to be of class 1 if T has a cyclic vector φ such that $T(k)\varphi = \varphi$ for all k in K and if any other vector invariant under the restriction of T to K is a scalar multiple of φ. It turns out that every representation of class 1 is determined by an elementary positive definite spherical function p and that p is unique up to a scalar factor.

The class 1 representation T associated with such a p may be realized in a number of ways. The usual construction involves a space of functions

[1]Research supported by NSF Grant No. GP-3874.

on G, but in the present context it is more convenient for our purpose to describe T as follows:

Let S be the homogeneous space $K\backslash G$ of right cosets of K in G. For z, w in S, set $Q(z, w) = p(xy^{-1})$ where $x \in z$ and $y \in w$. Then Q is a well defined continuous function on $S \times S$ which is positive definite and invariant under right translations. The space H° of all functions on S, expressible as finite sums of the form

$$f(z) = \sum_j c_j Q(z, w_j)$$

is invariant under the right translations $T(a)$: $f(z) \to f(za)(a \in G)$, and each operator $T(a)$ is unitary relative to the inner product on H° defined in the standard way [**10**] by Q.

Unfortunately, the method sketched above applies only to the class 1 representations which form a rather small and relatively special subclass of the known irreducible representations of G. Therefore, it is natural to ask whether one can describe a wider class by a more general but similar method.

There is a very interesting series of unitary representations, called the discrete series, whose general theory is due to Harish-Chandra [**5, 6**], which may be exhibited when every maximal compact subgroup of each simple component of G has a nondiscrete center. As shown by Langlands [**11**] these representations can be realized concretely in Hilbert spaces of holomorphic vector-valued functions on bounded symmetric domains; they arise naturally in connection with various questions concerning automorphic forms. The special case of $Sp(n, R)$ acting in the Siegel upper half plane is considered in great detail by Godement in [**4**].

From the work of Langlands and Godement, it is obvious that one should study positive definite operator valued kernels Q, and that it is appropriate to replace the invariance condition by the condition that Q transform suitably under the action of G. In the present paper, we prove a number of general results in this setting, applicable to arbitrary locally compact groups. Subsequently we shall consider the more detailed questions one may ask concerning semisimple Lie groups.

The paper is organized as follows. In Section 2, the known results about kernel function spaces in which the kernel function is operator valued are reviewed along the lines sketched by Korányi in [**9**]. Then in Section 3 we consider a locally compact group G acting in a space S. The basic problem is that of studying unitary representations of G in which the Hilbert space is a kernel function space on S and the representation is a multiplier representation. We show that with every positive definite operator valued kernel which transforms under the action of G according to a given multiplier there is associated a unitary representation of G on the corresponding kernel function space. This generalizes part of the aforementioned work of Ito and Krein. In Section 4, we show that the multiplier representations considered in Section 3 can also be formulated (within unitary equivalence) in terms of kernel function spaces on G given by kernels with certain transformation properties. We then give a characterization of all such representations by suitably generalizing the notion of a cyclic representation.

2. OPERATOR VALUED KERNEL FUNCTIONS

Let S be a locally compact Hausdorff space and L a given complex Hilbert space. The first problem we shall consider is that of characterizing certain Hilbert spaces of functions on S with values in L.

Let H be a complex Hilbert space of continuous functions from S to L with the property that for each point z in S, the linear map

$$E_z: f \to f(z) \qquad (f \in H)$$

is continuous from H to L and has dense range. Then E_z has a continuous nonsingular adjoint $E_z^*: L \to H$ such that

$$(E_z f \mid \varphi) = (f \mid E_z^* \varphi)$$

for all f in H and φ in L. A function f in H is orthogonal to $E_z^*(H)$ if and only if $f(z) = 0$. Hence H is generated by the subspaces $E_z^*(L)$. Therefore the functions f expressible as finite sums

$$f = \sum_j E_{w_j}^*(\varphi_j)$$

with w_j in S and φ_j in L form a dense linear submanifold H° of H. For any such f

$$\|f\|^2 = \sum_{ij} (E_{w_i} E_{w_j}^* \varphi_j \mid \varphi_i).$$

Since $\|f\| \geq 0$, it follows that the operator valued kernel

$$Q(z, w) = E_z E_w^*$$

has the property that

$$\sum_{ij} (Q(w_i, w_j)\varphi_j \mid \varphi_i) \geq 0$$

for all $w_1, \ldots, w_n$ in S and $\varphi_1, \ldots, \varphi_n$ in L. In particular, as E_w^* is non-singular

$$(Q(w, w)\varphi \mid \varphi) > 0$$

for all $\varphi \neq 0$. Moreover, it is easy to verify that Q is continuous as a function on $S \times S$ to the space $B(L)$ of bounded linear operators on L in the strong operator topology.

DEFINITIONS. We shall call a continuous function $Q: S \times S \to B(L)$ a *kernel* and say that Q is *positive definite* if $Q(w, w) > 0$ for all w in S and

$$\sum_{ij} (Q(w_i, w_j)\varphi_j \mid \varphi_i) \geq 0 \tag{2.1}$$

for all $w_1, \ldots, w_n$ in S and all $\varphi_1, \ldots, \varphi_n$ in L. For any such Q we denote the set of all functions $f: S \to L$ of the form

$$f(z) = Q(z, w)\varphi \qquad (w \in S, \varphi \in L)$$

by H_Q^{00}. The vector space spanned algebraically by H_Q^{00} will be denoted by H_Q^0.

THEOREM 1. For any positive definite kernel $Q: S \times S \to B(L)$ there is a unique Hilbert space H_Q of continuous functions $f: S \to L$ with the following properties.

(a) H_Q° is a dense linear submanifold of H_Q.

(b) For each z in S, the linear map

$$E_z: f \to f(z)$$

is continuous from H_Q to L.

(c) $$Q(z, w) = E_z E_w^*$$

for all z, w in S.

We give a brief sketch of the proof. Using (2.1) one may show there is a well-defined (and obviously unique) inner product on $H^\circ = H_Q^\circ$ such that

$$(Q(\cdot, w)\varphi \mid Q(\cdot, z)\psi) = (Q(z, w)\varphi \mid \psi) \tag{2.2}$$

for all z, w in S and φ, ψ in L. Although this inner product is not apriori strictly positive, the Schwarz inequality shows that for any f in H°

$$\| f(z) \| \leq \| Q(z, z) \|^{1/2} \| f \| \tag{2.3}$$

for all z in S. Therefore $f = 0$ when $\|f\| = 0$. From the continuity of Q and the uniform boundedness principle one sees that the function

$$(z, w) \to \| Q(z, w) \|$$

is bounded on compact subsets of $S \times S$. It follows from this and (2.3) that for any compact subset K of S, there exists a constant C_K such that

$$\sup_{z \in K} \|f(z)\| \leq C_K \|f\| \tag{2.4}$$

for all f in H°. Thus every Cauchy sequence in H° converges pointwise and uniformly over compact sets. From this it is easy to see that H° has a unique completion $H = H_Q$ with the properties stated in the theorem.

3. MULTIPLIER REPRESENTATIONS ON H_Q

As in Section 2, let S be a locally compact space and L a complex Hilbert space. In addition, let G be a locally compact topological transformation group on S with G acting on the right and $Q: S \times S \to B(L)$ a given positive definite kernel. We are concerned here with the problem of constructing and characterizing certain unitary representations of G in the Hilbert space H_Q. To explain the problem it is necessary to introduce some terminology.

DEFINITION. We shall call a continuous function $M: S \times G \to B(L)$ a *multiplier* if $M(z, e) = I$ and

$$M(z, ab) = M(z, a)\, M(za, b) \tag{3.1}$$

for all z in S and all a, b in G where za denotes the image of z under a and e is the identity of G.

We note here that if M is a multiplier, then $M(z, a)$ is always invertible, that is, has a continuous 2-sided inverse. For it is easy to see from (3.1) that

$$M(z, a)^{-1} = M(za, a^{-1}). \tag{3.2}$$

We are interested in the unitary representations T of G on H_Q with the property that

$$T(a) f(z) = M(z, a) f(za)$$

where M is some fixed multiplier. Given any such representation T, it is evident that

$$E_z T(a) = M(z, a)\, E_{za}.$$

From this it follows that

$$T(a)^* E_z^* = E_{za}^* M^*(z, a)$$

where $M^*(z, a)$ denotes the adjoint of $M(z, a)$. Replacing z by w in the second equation and multiplying by the first, we find that

$$Q(z, w) = M(z, a)\, Q(za, wa)\, M^*(w, a).$$

This indicates the relevance of the following terminology.

DEFINITION. We say that a kernel $Q: S \times S \rightarrow B(L)$ is a *G-kernel with multiplier* $M: S \times G \rightarrow B(L)$ if

$$Q(z, w) = M(z, a)\, Q(za, wa)\, M^*(w, a) \tag{3.3}$$

for all z, w in S and all a in G.

THEOREM 2. For any positive definite G-kernel Q with multiplier M, the equation

$$T(a) f(z) = M(z, a) f(za)$$

defines a strongly continuous unitary representation T of G on H_Q.

The following observation will be useful in the proof.

LEMMA. If f is a continuous function from S to L, the equation

$$g(z, a) = M(z, a) f(za)$$

defines a continuous function on $S \times G$.

Proof. Let K be a compact subset of $S \times G$. Then from the continuity of M and the uniform boundedness principle it follows that

$$\sup_{(z,a) \in K} \| M(z, a) \| < \infty.$$

From this, the fact that $S \times G$ is locally compact, and the inequality

$$\| g(z, a) - g(w, b) \|$$

$$\leq \| M(z, a) \| \cdot \| f(za) - f(wb) \| + \| M(z, a) f(wb) - M(w, b) f(wb) \|$$

it is easy to see that g is continuous on $S \times G$.

PROOF OF THE THEOREM. Let C be the vector space of all continuous functions from S to L. For each a in G, let $R(a)$ denote the linear transformation on C defined by

$$R(a) f(z) = M(z, a) f(za).$$

By the lemma $R(a)$ maps C into C, and by (3.1), $R(ab) = R(a)R(b)$ for all a, b in G; moreover, $R(e) = I$, as $M(z, e) = I$ for all z in S.

Now observe that from the boundedness of the operators $M(z, a)$, it follows that whenever $f_1, f_2, \ldots$ is a sequence in C which converges pointwise to a function f in C, then $R(a) f_n \rightarrow R(a) f$ pointwise for every a in G.

Next we shall show that the set $H^{00} = H_Q^{00}$ is mapped into itself by each of the operators $R(a)$. For this note that (3.3) is equivalent to the equation

$$E_z E_w^* = M(z,a)\, E_{za} E_{wa}^* M^*(w,a) \tag{3.4}$$

If we replace a by a^{-1}, z by za, and use (3.2), we then find that

$$M(z,a)\, E_{za} E_w^* = E_z E_{wa^{-1}}^* M^*(w, a^{-1}).$$

Thus for a in G, w in S, and φ in L

$$R(a)\, E_w^* \varphi = E_{wa^{-1}}^* M^*(w, a^{-1})\, \varphi. \tag{3.5}$$

This proves our assertion. By linearity $H^\circ = H_Q^\circ$ is also invariant under each of the operators $R(a)$. Moreover,

$$\begin{aligned}(R(a)E_w^*\varphi \mid R(a)E_z^*\psi) &= (E_{wa^{-1}}^* M^*(w,a^{-1})\varphi \mid E_{za^{-1}}^* M^*(z,a^{-1})\psi) \\ &= (M(z,a^{-1})E_{za^{-1}} E_{wa^{-1}}^* M^*(w,a^{-1})\varphi \mid \psi) \\ &= (E_z E_w^* \varphi \mid \psi) \\ &= (E_w^* \varphi \mid E_z^* \psi)\end{aligned}$$

by (3.4) and (3.5). Thus

$$(R(a)f \mid R(a)g) = (f \mid g) \tag{3.6}$$

for all f and g in H°.

This being the case, it is easy to see that $R(a)$ is an isometric mapping of $H = H_Q$ into itself. For suppose $f \in H$, and let $\{f_n\}$ be any sequence in H° such that $\|f - f_n\| \to 0$. Then it follows from (2.4) that $f_n \to f$ pointwise, as well. Thus $R(a)f$ is the pointwise limit of the sequence $\{R(a)f_n\}$. On the other hand, by (3.6)

$$\|R(a)f_n - R(a)f_m\| = \|f_n - f_m\|,$$

Thus there exists a function g in H such that $\|g - R(a)f_n\| \to 0$. Since this implies the pointwise convergence of $\{R(a)f_n\}$ to g, it results that $R(a)f = g$. Moreover, $\|R(a)f_n\| = \|f_n\|$, and taking limits, we see that $\|R(a)f\| = \|f\|$.

Let $T(a)$ denote the restriction of $R(a)$ to H. Then $T(a)$ is a unitary operator on H, and $T: a \to T(a)$ $(a \in G)$ is a unitary representation of G in H.

It remains to prove that T is strongly continuous. It follows directly from the lemma that for any f in H, $a \to (T(a)f \mid g)$ is a continuous function on G for all g in H^{00}. By linearity the same is obviously true for g in H°. Since H° is dense in H, it follows easily that T is weakly continuous, and being unitary, T is also strongly continuous. This completes the proof.

The representation T described above will sometimes be denoted by $T(\cdot, Q, M)$.

We conclude this section with the following elementary result.

THEOREM 3. Let Q be a positive definite G-kernel with multiplier M and A an arbitrary bounded linear operator on L with a bounded inverse. Then the equation

$$Q_A(z, w) = A^*Q(z, w)A$$

defines a positive definite G-kernel with multiplier

$$M_A(z, a) = A^*M(z, a)A^{*-1}$$

and $T(\cdot, Q_A, M_A)$ is unitarily equivalent to $T(\cdot, Q, M)$.

Proof. It is obvious that Q_A is a positive definite kernel on $S \times S$. Moreover, the equation

$$(Vf)(z) = A^*(f(z))$$

defines a unitary map V of H_Q on H_{Q_A}. To see this, first note that

$$VQ(\cdot, w)\varphi = Q_A(\cdot, w)A^{-1}\varphi \tag{3.7}$$

for any w in S and φ in L. Thus we have

$$\begin{aligned}(VE_w^*\varphi \mid VE_z^*\psi) &= (Q_A(z, w)A^{-1}\varphi \mid A^{-1}\psi)\\ &= (Q(z, w)\varphi \mid \psi)\\ &= (E_w^*\varphi \mid E_z^*\psi)\end{aligned}$$

by (2.2). From this it follows that V maps H_Q° isometrically into $H_{Q_A}^\circ$. Now let f be an arbitrary member of H_Q and $f_1, f_2, \ldots$ a sequence of functions in H_Q° such that $\|f - f_n\| \to 0$. Then

$$\|Vf_n - Vf_m\| = \|f_n - f_m\|$$

so that the sequence $Vf_1, Vf_2, \ldots$ converges in norm and pointwise to some g in H_{Q_A}. On the other hand $Vf_1, Vf_2, \ldots$ converges pointwise to Vf; hence $Vf = g$, and we also have $\|Vf\| = \|f\|$. From (3.7) it is clear that V maps H_Q^{00} onto $H_{Q_A}^{00}$. Therefore V is an isometric linear mapping of H_Q onto H_{Q_A}. Finally, for any a in G and f in H_Q

$$\begin{aligned}VT(a, Q, M)f(z) &= A^*M(z, a)f(za)\\ &= A^*M(z, a)A^{*-1}\cdot A^*f(za).\end{aligned}$$

Thus $VT(a, Q, M) = T(a, Q_A, M_A)V$.

4. THE HOMOGENEOUS CASE

In this section we maintain our previous assumptions concerning S, L, and G, and study the situation in which S is homogeneous under G. By this we mean only that G acts transitively on S.

The following definition will be useful in formulating our first result.

DEFINITION. If K is a subgroup of G and U a unitary representation of K on L, we shall say that a kernel $Q'\colon G \times G \to L$ is of *type U* if

$$Q'(k_1 x, k_2 y) = U(k_1) Q'(x, y) U(k_2)^* \tag{4.1}$$

for all k_1, k_2 in K and all x, y in G.

THEOREM 4. Let S be homogeneous under G, $Q\colon S \times S \to L$ a positive definite G-kernel with multiplier M, and z_0 a point in S for which $Q(z_0, z_0) = I$. Let K be the subgroup of G leaving z_0 fixed and set

$$U(k) = M^*(z_0, k^{-1}) \tag{4.2}$$

for k in K. Then U is a continuous unitary representation of K on L, and there exists a positive definite G-invariant kernel Q' of type U such that the representation $T(\cdot, Q, M)$ of G on H_Q is unitarily equivalent to the representation $T(\cdot, Q')$ on $H_{Q'}$.

REMARK. The equation (4.2) always defines a representation U of K. The unitarity of U follows from the normalization $Q(z_0, z_0) = I$. If $Q(z_0 . z_0) \neq I$ but $Q(z_0, z_0)$ is invertible, then we may always replace Q by Q_A and M by M_A, as in Theorem 3, where $A = Q(z_0, z_0)^{-1/2}$ without essentially altering the situation. Finally, we note that if L is finite dimensional, then $Q(z, z)$ is invertible for all z.

Proof of the Theorem. For each w in S there exists an element a in G such that $wa = z_0$; hence

$$\begin{aligned} Q(z, w) &= M(z, a) Q(za, z_0) M^*(w, a) \\ &= M(z, a) Q(za, z_0) M^*(z_0 a^{-1}, a). \end{aligned}$$

Setting $P(z) = Q(z, z_0)$, $U(a) = M^*(z_0, a^{-1})$ and using (3.2), we find that

$$Q(z, w) = M(z, a)\, P(za)\, U(a)^{-1} \tag{4.3}$$

for any z provided $wa = z_0$. In particular

$$P(z) = M(z, k)\, P(zk)\, U(k)^{-1} \tag{4.4}$$

for all z in S and k in K.

Next observe that by (3.1)

$$U(ak) = U(a) U(k) \tag{4.5}$$

for any a in G and any k in K. It follows that $k \to U(k)$ is a strongly continuous representation of K on L. Therefore $U(k^{-1}) = U(k)^{-1}$, and setting $z = z_0$ in (4.4), we see that $U(k)$ is unitary for each k in K.

From (3.1) and (3.2) it is easy to see that for any a, b in G

$$M(z_0b, a) = (U^*(b^{-1}))^{-1}U^*(a^{-1}b^{-1}). \tag{4.6}$$

Thus (4.4) can be written in the form

$$P(z_0b) = (U^*(b^{-1}))^{-1}U^*(k^{-1}b^{-1})P(z_0bk)U(k)^{-1}$$

and transposing terms, we obtain the equation

$$U^*(b^{-1})P(z_0b)U(k) = U^*(k^{-1}b^{-1})P(z_0bk). \tag{4.7}$$

This suggests that we consider the function $P'\colon G \to L$ defined for x in G by

$$P'(x) = U^*(x^{-1})P(z_0x). \tag{4.8}$$

It follows immediately from (4.5) and (4.7) that

$$P'(k_1\ x\ k_2) = U(k_1)P'(x)U(k_2) \tag{4.9}$$

for all k_1, k_2 in K and any x in G. Therefore, the equation

$$Q'(x, y) = P'(xy^{-1}) \tag{4.10}$$

defines a kernel of type U on $G \times G$.

The relation between Q and Q' is easily determined. By (4.3) and (4.6)

$$Q(z_0x, z_0y) = (U^*(x^{-1}))^{-1}U^*(yx^{-1})P(z_0xy^{-1})(U(y^{-1}))^{-1}. \tag{4.11}$$

Since $Q'(x, y) = U^*(yx^{-1})P'(z_0xy^{-1})$, it follows that

$$Q'(x, y) = U^*(x^{-1})Q(z_0x, z_0y)U(y^{-1}) \tag{4.12}$$

for all x, y in G. Therefore, Q' is obviously positive definite and $Q'(e, e) = I$. Moreover, Q' is invariant under G in the sense that $Q'(x, y) = Q'(xa, ya)$ for all a in G. Thus the equation

$$T(a, Q')g(x) = g(xa)$$

defines a unitary representation of G on H_Q.

Now much as in the proof of Theorem 3, one may show that the equation

$$(Vf)(x) = U^*(x^{-1})f(z_0x) \qquad (x \in G)$$

defines a unitary map of H_Q onto $H_{Q'}$. Granting this, we then have

$$VT(a, Q, M)f(x) = U^*(x^{-1})M(z_0x, a)f(z_0xa).$$

By (4.6), $U^*(x^{-1})M(z_0x, a) = U^*(a^{-1}x^{-1})$, and therefore $VT(a, Q, M) = T(a, Q')V$. This completes the proof.

We turn now to the problem of characterizing the representations described in the foregoing. For this purpose the following definitions are relevant.

DEFINITIONS. We shall call a continuous function $P: G \to B(L)$ for which $P(e) = I$ and $Q(x, y) = P(xy^{-1})$ is positive definite a *normalized positive definite function on G*. For any such P we shall ordinarily denote the Hilbert space H_Q by H_P and the representation $T(\cdot, Q)$ by $T(\cdot, P)$. If K is a closed subgroup of G and U a continuous unitary representation of G on L, we shall say that a continuous function $P: G \to B(L)$ is of *type U* if

$$P(k_1\ x\ k_2) = U(k_1)P(x)U(k_2) \tag{4.13}$$

for all k_1, k_2 in K and x in G.

Now suppose $P: G \to B(L)$ is a normalized positive definite function. Then the associated kernel has the representation

$$P(xy^{-1}) = E_xE_y^*$$

and E_e^* is an isometric mapping of L onto a closed subspace L' of H_P. The subspace L' has the property that H_P is generated by elements of the form $T(a, P)f$ with a in G and f in L'. For these elements make up the set H_P^{00}. In addition, if P is of type U, U being a unitary representation of a closed subgroup K on L, then

$$T(k, P)E_e^*\varphi = E_e^*\ U(k)\varphi$$

for all φ in L and k in K. Thus L' is invariant under the restriction of $T(\cdot, P)$ to K and the subrepresentation of $k \to T(k, P)$ defined by L' is equivalent to U.

As we shall show, these properties characterize the representations $T(\cdot, P)$.

DEFINITIONS. Let T be a continuous unitary representation of G on a Hilbert space H. We shall say that a subset Z of H is *cyclic for T* if H is generated by vectors of the form $T(a)f$ with a in G and f in Z. If K is a closed subgroup of G and U a continuous unitary representation of K on L, we shall say that *T is of type U* if there exists a closed subspace L' of H which is cyclic for T and invariant under the restriction of T to K such that U is unitarily equivalent to the subrepresentation of $k \to T(k)$ defined by L'.

THEOREM 5. Let G be a locally compact group, K a closed subgroup, and U a continuous unitary representation of K on L. Then for any representation T *of type U* there exists a normalized positive definite function $P: G \to B(L)$ of type U such that T is unitarily equivalent to $T(\cdot, P)$.

Proof. Let T be of type U and L' a closed subspace of the representation space H exhibiting the fact that T is of type U. Let $U'(k)$ be the restriction of $T(k)$ to L' and A a unitary transformation mapping L onto L' such that $U'(k) = A\,U(k)A^{-1}$ for all k in K. Define $P: G \to B(L)$ by the condition that

$$(P(x)\varphi \mid \psi) = (T(x)A\varphi \mid A\psi) \tag{4.14}$$

for all φ, ψ in L. Then $P(e) = I$, and for any $x_1, \ldots, x_n$ in G and any $\varphi_1, \ldots, \varphi_n$ in L

$$\sum_{ij} (P(x_i x_j^{-1})\varphi_j \mid \varphi_i) = \sum_{ij} (T(x_j^{-1})A\varphi_j \mid T(x_i^{-1})A\varphi_i)$$

$$= \|\sum_j T(x_j^{-1})A\varphi_j\|^2 \geq 0.$$

Since it is also true that

$$P(x) = A^{-1}\,E\,T(x)\,E\,A \tag{4.15}$$

where E is the orthogonal projection of H onto L', it follows that P is strongly continuous and hence that P is a normalized positive definite function. Using (4.14) or (4.15) one easily sees that P is of type U, i.e., that (4.13) holds.

Now we shall prove that T and $T(\cdot, P)$ are unitarily equivalent. For this write $P(xy^{-1}) = E_x E_y^*$ and define $W: L' \to H_P$ by

$$Wf = E_e^* A^{-1} f.$$

Then $T(a, P)\,Wf = E_{a^{-1}}^* A^{-1} f$, so that

$$\begin{aligned}(T(a, P)Wf \mid Wg) &= (E_{a^{-1}}^* A^{-1} f \mid E_e^* A^{-1} g)\\ &= (P(a)A^{-1}f \mid A^{-1}g)\\ &= (T(a)f \mid g)\end{aligned}$$

for all f and g in L'. Let $H°$ be the set of all elements f in H expressible as finite sums of the form

$$f = \sum_j T(a_j)f_j$$

with a_j in G and f_j in L'. For any such f

$$\|f\|^2 = \sum_{ij} (T(a_j^{-1}a_i)f_i \mid f_j)$$

$$= \sum_{ij} (T(a_j^{-1} a_i, P) W f_i \mid W f_j)$$

$$= \|\sum_j T(a_j, P) W f_j\|^2.$$

Therefore, we may extend W to H° by requiring that

$$W\left(\sum_j T(a_j) f_j\right) = \sum_j T(a_j, P) W f_j \tag{4.16}$$

and W as so extended is an isometric linear map of H° onto H_P°. From this it follows that W extends to a unitary transformation of H onto H_P. It follows immediately from (3.16) that $W\ T(a) f = T(a, P) W f$ for all f in H°. Since H° is dense in H, this implies

$$W\,T(a) = T(a, P)\,W \qquad (a \in G)$$

and proves that T and $T(\cdot, P)$ are unitarily equivalent.

REFERENCES

1. Gelfand, I. M., Spherical functions on Riemmannian spaces, *Doklady Akad. Nauk SSSR* (N. S.) 70 (1950), 5-8 *Amer. Math. Soc. Transl.* Series 2, Vol 37.
2. Gelfand, I. M. and D. A. Raĭkov, Irreducible unitary representations of locally bicompact groups, *Mat Sb.* (N. S.) 13 (55) (1943), 301–316.
3. Godement, R., Les fonctions de type positive et la theorie des groupes, *Trans. Amer. Math. Soc.* 63 (1948), 1–84.
4. ———, Seminaire Henri Cartan, E. N. S. 10e annee: 1957/58, *Fonctions Automorphes*, Vol 1 exposes 5, 6.
5. Harish-Chandra, Representations of semi-simple Lie groups V, *Amer. J. Math.* 78 (1956), 1–41.
6. ———, Representations of semi-simple Lie groups VI, *Amer. J. Math.* 78 (1956), 564–628.
7. Helgason, S., Differential Geometry and Symmetrio Spaces, Academic Press, New York and London, 1962.
8. Ito, S., Positive definite functions on homogeneous spaces, *Proc. Japan Acad.* 26(1950) 17–28.
9. Korányi, A., On a theorem of Lowner and its connections with resolvents of self adjoint transformations, *Acta Sci. Math.* Szeged 17 (1956), 63–70.
10. Krein, M. G., Hermitian positive kernels in homogeneous spaces I and II, *Amer. Math. Soc. Transl.* Series 2 Vol 34, Providence, R. I.
11. Langlands, R. P., The dimension of spaces of automorphic forms, *Amer. J. Math.*, 85 (1963), 99–125.